£3/4/
u/kl

ACTIVATION ANALYSIS
HANDBOOK

ACTIVATION ANALYSIS HANDBOOK

R. C. Koch

Nuclear Science and Engineering Corporation
Pittsburgh, Pennsylvania

ACADEMIC PRESS • NEW YORK AND LONDON • 1960

ACADEMIC PRESS INC.
111 FIFTH AVENUE
NEW YORK 3, N. Y.

United Kingdom Edition
Published by
ACADEMIC PRESS INC. (London) LTD.
17 OLD QUEEN STREET, LONDON S. W. 1

Library of Congress Catalog Card Number 60-14271

PRINTED IN THE UNITED STATES OF AMERICA

FOREWORD

It may be said that a reactor or a cyclotron has a touch like that of the legendary King Midas—everything brought into it becomes radioactive. Indeed, the golden possibilities that streams of nuclear particles offer for chemical analysis were realized almost as soon as the types of radioactivity that they produce were understood. The concept of activation analysis is a simple one, and the possibilities of its application are great. However, the complexity of the problem is also very great.

In the modern day, the number of activities that can be produced in simple nuclear reactions is enormous. The 81 naturally occurring elements from hydrogen through bismuth have in the aggregate 270 stable nuclear forms or nuclides and 11 long-lived ones. Including isomeric pairs, there are about 220 different radionuclides formed by the (n, γ) or (d, p) reaction, about 280 are known for the (n, p) reaction, and over a hundred each for the (p, n), (d, xn), (d, α), (α, xn), (α, pxn), (γ, n), (γ, p), and similar reactions that can be considered for activation analysis.

Thus, for the maximum use of this book, Dr. Koch had to acquaint persons who are not professional analysts with the potentialities of the method and with the main technical requirements for sample preparation, irradiation, monitoring, and radiometric assay. In addition, he had to present the nuclear chemistry considerations that can be exploited in activation analysis so that the analyst who is not a nuclear specialist can make a choice of the type of irradiation and can identify and handle the possible nuclear interferences. A glossary of 41 technical terms and analytic descriptions of nuclear reactions of interest are appended for both of these types of user.

The descriptive material in this book represents a scholarly and timely contribution to applied nuclear chemistry not duplicated in the existing reviews of activation analysis. The focus of attention is, for maximum generality, on the trace constituent, but the considerations that apply to the matrix material are given in discussion, and, of course, the nuclear data in the tables apply to it.

The bulk of this book is provided by the tabulations of nuclear reactions that have been used for activation analysis, together with other reactions that may be useful to the analyst or that may provide interference with reactions that are being considered. The pages of Table III present the elements, in order of atomic number. The left page presents data for neutron reactions (thermal neutrons, reactor neutrons, and fast neutrons). The right page gives analogous data for charged particle reactions. The organization of Table III and its conventions are illustrated in principle in Table II.

The data for slow neutron activation have been more widely exploited, and this is reflected in the greater number of literature analyses cited, and the greater detail with which Dr. Koch reports the nuclear properties of the (n, γ) reactions for each element. A special feature of the tables is the sections, for each element, which evaluate possible interfering primary, secondary, and second-order reactions, and possible self-shielding problems. At the bottom of each page is a list of sensitivities that would be achieved for selected reactions using the natural element under specified irradiation conditions.

The present tabulation goes beyond its predecessors in the amount of information tabulated in one place for neutron reactions on each element and the analytical implications of the data.

The parallel presentation of data for charged particle reactions is particularly useful, since much less has been done to exploit these analytically, and comparison with neutron reactions is generally illuminating.

References to data available through the middle of 1959 for excitation functions for charged particle reactions in the energy region up to about 30 Mev are included, with descriptions of those reactions that have thus far been exploited analytically. For the other reactions which could be developed for analysis, cross-sections at a typical useful energy are cited, together with an estimate of the sensitivity to be expected in analysis. The discussion of interferences includes the possibilities of formation of the radionuclide of interest by reactions of elements of neighboring atomic numbers and by reactions of secondary neutrons in the target.

This book should find an important place on the desk of every analyst who has access to neutrons, high energy photons, or charged particles. With the availability of service irradiations of targets that are then shipped to the analytical laboratory, activation analysis can be used in every laboratory facing difficult problems of analysis of minor constituents, since most of the elements have activation products with long enough half-lives to permit assays hours to days after irradiation. The requirements of the electronics and nucleonics age for high purity and for control of minor constituents have also made possible the flexible and sensitive activation methods of determining concentrations. This book should contribute substantially to their development and application.

The basis for this book was a detailed survey of possibilities for activation analysis sponsored by the Air Force Cambridge Research Center of the Air Research and Development Command, Lexington, Massachusetts. I should like to express on behalf of the scientific community sincere appreciation for their cooperation and generosity in the prompt release of this work for publication.

CHARLES D. CORYELL

Cambridge, Massachusetts
July, 1960

PREFACE

During the last decade, activation analysis has been established as a sensitive tool for analysis of trace elements in many materials. The literature contains examples of the development of activation analysis techniques and of successful application of the techniques to solutions of problems in specific scientific disciplines. However, this information is found in a wide variety of sources. Analysts have long recognized a need for its collation and compilation into a single source so that the many phases of theoretical and applied activation analysis would be available in a convenient form for the practicing analyst and for other scientists who can effectively utilize activation analysis in their programs. The Activation Analysis Handbook is intended to serve as a reference source for experimental data and methods to be used by all scientists interested in the use or potential use of activation analysis as an analytical tool.

The original edition of the Activation Analysis Handbook, prepared under the sponsorship of the Air Force Cambridge Research Center of the Air Research and Development Command, contained literature available prior to October, 1958. Data for experimental methods and for nuclear reactions applicable to these methods were tabulated for each element. Since these two bodies of data are common to the trace elements to be analyzed rather than to the matrix materials, the tables were so oriented. However, typical examples of analyses in various matrices and of potential experimental problems which might be encountered in the analysis of a trace element in the presence of other elements are included in the tables. Analytical sensitivities achievable for each element using selected activation reactions under standard experimental conditions are also presented.

The introductory discussion is intended to serve both the scientist or engineer, who may recognize the need for an analytical or experimental method to assist in the solution of a research or engineering problem, and the analyst, who is responsible for providing such analyses. To acquaint the first group of readers with the potential applicability of activation analysis to their fields of interest, a description of its general theoretical and experimental considerations, including references to selected review articles, is presented. A more detailed discussion of specific aspects follows which, it is hoped, will help the analyst to select appropriate activation and analytical methods for a particular application. Sources of general radiochemistry methods for many elements have been noted in the text. However, since specific analytical or radioactivity measurement procedures must be devised for the particular analytical problem, and since detailed procedures for nearly every element are given in the sources listed in the tables, no attempt has been made to present such information in this book.

The present edition of the handbook incorporates a thorough revision of the tables and the bibliography of the original edition. The Addendum to the Bibliography represents the reported data reaching the author in the interval between completion of the original edition and September, 1959.

The author wishes to express his gratitude to the many members of the staff of Nuclear Science and Engineering Corporation who aided in the preparation of this handbook. Special acknowledgment is due to Dr. Paul Kruger and Professor Charles D. Coryell for their critical reviews of the text, to G. L. Grandy, I. J. Gruverman, and C. R. Wilson, for their assistance in compiling the data, and to Mrs. R. White, Mrs. W. Kruger, and J. K. Schivley for their aid in preparing the manuscript. The author also wishes to acknowledge the cooperation and helpful comments of Mr. Clarence Turner and Mr. J. Paul Cali of the Air Force Cambridge Research Center, under whose auspices the original edition of this handbook was prepared.

R. C. KOCH

August, 1960

CONTENTS

FOREWORD   v

PREFACE   vii

CHAPTER 1   INTRODUCTION   1

     Purpose and Scope   1

     History and Growth of Activation Analysis   2

     Activation Analysis: The General Technique   3

CHAPTER 2   ACTIVATION ANALYSIS: THEORETICAL CONSIDERATIONS   5

     Basic Concepts   5

     Sources of Nuclear Data   7

     Sources of Experimental Methods   7

     Selection of Activation Reactions   8

         1. *General Considerations*   8

         2. *Suitability of Activation Products*   8

         3. *Sensitivity Estimates*   8

         4. *Interfering Reactions*   9

         5. *Competing Reactions*   10

         6. *Experimental Feasibility*   10

CHAPTER 3   ACTIVATION ANALYSIS: EXPERIMENTAL METHODS   11

Irradiation Facilities   11

    1. Sources of Neutrons   11

    2. Sources of Charged Particles and Photons   11

    3. Selection of an Irradiation Facility   12

Preparation and Encapsulation of Samples   12

    1. Neutron Irradiations   12

    2. Charged Particle Irradiations   13

    3. Photon Irradiations   13

    4. Comparator or Monitor Samples   13

Irradiations   14

Post-Irradiation Assays   14

Evaluation of the Data   14

CHAPTER 4   THE TABULATION   16

Introduction   16

Directory to the Tabulation   18

Table I: The Elements and Their Atomic Numbers   21

Table II: The Key to the Tabulation   24

Table III: A Tabulation of Nuclear Data and Experimental
        Methods for Activation Analysis   28

GLOSSARY   195

Part I: Definitions   195

Part II: Examples of Nuclear Reactions   196

BIBLIOGRAPHY   199

ADDENDUM TO THE BIBLIOGRAPHY   210

INDEX   213

CHAPTER I

INTRODUCTION

PURPOSE AND SCOPE

Activation analysis has assumed an important role in the determination of trace constituents in a wide variety of materials. As a result of rapid technological advances continued demand is expected for materials having high purity or rigid trace constituent specifications. These specifications may require analytical methods with sensitivities beyond those of most classical methods. For example, it is generally known that the transistor industry requires semiconductors with controlled concentrations of trace impurities, and that the reactor industry requires production of hafnium-free zirconium. The production of such materials demands stringent production quality control methods. It is expected that the principles of activation analysis will be applied to the development of new methods for such quality control and process automation. In addition, basic research and development programs in most branches of science and engineering will require both destructive and nondestructive analytical methods of high sensitivity. Activation analysis can be applied to many of these analytical problems. It also has potential for further development to meet the more stringent analytical requirements which are anticipated in the future.

Activation analysis may be defined as a method of measuring concentrations of constituents in a given sample by measuring the characteristic radiations emitted by the radioactive nuclides resulting from selected nuclear transformations. The unique combination of chemical and nuclear properties of each activation product provides a specific method for its identification and measurement. Of the several possible transformations, one can be chosen based on certain factors. For example, for any given problem, a specific method can be selected based on the properties of the matrix, trace elements, the activation products of interest, the sensitivity required in the analysis, the presence of interfering reactions, the location of a suitable irradiation facility, and cost.

Although the experimental data required for comparing alternate methods are frequently available, they are scattered widely throughout the technical literature. This handbook has been prepared to collate and compile this information in a convenient reference form. Since there exist many published review articles for neutron activation analysis, it is not the purpose of this handbook to give a comprehensive review of all the available activation analysis data. Its purpose is to present a tabulation of the published data pertinent to activation analysis. In particular, this tabulation includes for each element: (1) data for activation analyses utilizing thermal and fast neutrons, charged particles, and photons; (2) nuclear data for these reactions; (3) nuclear data for other reactions potentially useful for activation analysis; (4) nuclear data for possible interfering reactions; (5) evaluations of these reactions; (6) sensitivities for the more important neutron and charged particle activation reactions for each element; and (7) complete bibliographical referencing for all of the data presented.

It is anticipated that the compilation of these data, together with a comprehensive bibliography, will enable the analyst to choose the optimum set of nuclear parameters and will guide him to detailed data for specific assay problems. In addition, it is hoped that this tabulation provides sufficient information to the nonanalyst for proper evaluation of the applicability of activation analysis to his specific laboratory or production problem.

HISTORY AND GROWTH OF ACTIVATION ANALYSIS

After the discovery of induced, or artificial radioactivity by Curie and Joliot in 1933, its application to the solution of analytical problems was readily recognized. In 1936, Hevesy and Levi (H30) used thermal neutron activation to determine the concentration of dysprosium in impure yttrium. Subsequently, the same workers (H31) also detected traces of europium in gadolinium. In 1938, Seaborg and Livingood (S16) demonstrated that charged particle activation could be applied to analytical problems by determining trace quantities of gallium in high purity iron. These pioneers stimulated substantial interest in this new technique. By 1952, several review papers (B36, B45, E1, G17, G18, L4, L5, S58, T9, T18) had appeared which outlined the basic principles of the method and presented applications and experimental data, including both theoretical and experimental analytical sensitivities. Also, Taylor and Havens (T7, T8) discussed the early applications of neutron spectroscopy to chemical analysis. In 1952, Rodden (R10) presented a comprehensive review of the applications of nuclear chemistry, including activation analysis, to analytical problems, and summarized the techniques and sensitivities achieved at that time. Kohn (K25) summarized the applications of radioactivity techniques, including activation analysis, to metallurgical problems.

The increasing application of radionuclides and nuclear chemistry to analytical problems led to a rapid growth of activation analysis as an established laboratory technique by the time of the 1955 International Conference on the Peaceful Uses of Atomic Energy. This growth is evident from the decreasing intervals at which review articles were published during this period, both in the United States (B42, G19, L6, L7, L8, L9, M42), Canada (J11), Europe (H23, J1, L11, S29, S33, W14), and Japan (S3). Papers discussing applications of special analytical techniques, such as ion exchange (B41, C32), gamma spectrometry (C27, M48), and nuclear emulsion detectors (M17, M18), to activation analysis also appeared, along with a detailed discussion of its limitations and sources of errors (P10). The use of low-level neutron sources for activation analysis (M33) and comparisons of this technique with spectrophotometry and other analytical methods were made (M30, M34, S30). Applications of activation analysis to the study of such diverse fields as archeology (A10, S10), biological systems (H4), dating of minerals (H28, M43), and determination of film exposure (B18, B19) were also reported.

In the period since the first Geneva Conference, Leddicotte (L1, L10, L21) has continued to review periodically recent developments in the field, as have workers in the United Kingdom and elsewhere. Cabell and Smales (C2) discuss the application of various radiochemistry methods to analytical chemistry, and Loveridge and Smales (L19), the application to biochemistry. Borg (B62), Lenihan and Smith (L23), and Druyan et al. (D16), review the applications of activation analysis in biological and medical research. Smales et al. (S71, S72), Reed (R19), and Winchester (W22) describe its geochemical applications, and Jervis and Mackintosh (J15) summarize its uses in reactor technology. Jenkins and Smales (J10) and Miller (M54) present reviews of its fundamental concepts, techniques, and applications. Other current articles by Taylor and Havens (T10), De (D5), Fouarge (F18), Schindewolf (S11), and Atkins and Smales (A23) summarize many pertinent data and applications of the technique. Merz and Herr (M53) demonstrate the use of activation analysis for determining isotopic abundances in selected elements. Fink (F6) discusses the effects of interfering nuclear reactions on the validity of activation analysis data, and Plumb (P9) discusses techniques for qualitative activation analysis. Examples of basic studies of selected analytical procedures are discussed by Brooksbank (B40, B66) and Miller (M54). Examples of analysis schemes for separating many elements from a single matrix by Kant et al. (K2), Thompson et al. (T16), Blanchard et al. (B60), and Albert (A4), and examples of the use of gamma spectrometry by Morrison and Cosgrove (C33, M47, M49), Salmon (S69), and Iredale (I1) have appeared. Gaittet and Albert (G28) present a complete routine system of control activation analysis for high purity iron and aluminum. The utilization of linear accelerators as irradiation facilities for thermal and fast neutron induced activation and photon induced activation has been discussed by Burrill and Gale (B51), Turner (T20), and MacGregor (M1), respectively. Odeblad (O2) and Gill (G30) present the basic physical principles of the use of charged particle induced reactions for activation analysis. Mazari *et al.* (M51) describe a method of using proton scattering for analysis of selected elements.

The application of neutron activation analysis techniques to measurements of physical properties of materials, such as particle sizes (A2, A15, B11, B56, L21), the segregation of trace impurities or additives in a metal (E7, L2, P8), the homogeneity of charcoal (B23), and the analysis of surfaces (R15), has been reported. Also, activation analysis has been used to determine the efficiency of special purification steps for high purity metals (A4, C12, G28).

There are three additional review articles to be noted for their bibliographical summaries of the literature related to activation analysis. Two systematic literature reviews by Meinke (M31, M32) containing a total of 1872 references cover the application of nucleonics techniques to analytical chemistry and industrial problems. Pertinent literature concerning chemical and instrumental methods, new apparatus, and nuclear data sources are included.

Concurrent with the preparation of this handbook, Gibbons *et al.* (G5) have prepared a "Bibliography of Radioactivation Analysis," consisting of 261 references. This bibliography is indexed in such a manner that it exhibits separately (1) reviews and papers of general interest, (2) the matrices in which specific elements have been determined, and (3) the elements which have been determined in specific matrices. Although the bibliography in this handbook generally encompasses the scope of that of Gibbons *et al.* the special index and cross-reference system which they present is unique.

ACTIVATION ANALYSIS: THE GENERAL TECHNIQUE

The selection of activation analysis as the appropriate technique for solution of an analytical problem may be based on its sensitivity, speed, economy, convenience, or on the absence of other suitable methods. Sufficient qualitative and quantitative experimental data exist which make this selection possible for most cases.

At this point it is deemed desirable to review the mechanisms involved in activation analysis. A more complete discussion of them will be presented in subsequent sections. In general, these mechanisms consist of the following sequence of considerations and operations for a given analytical problem: (1) the selection of the optimum nuclear reaction; (2) the choice of a suitable irradiation facility; (3) the preparation of samples for irradiation; (4) the irradiation; (5) the post-irradiation assays; and (6) the evaluation of the experimental data.

The selection of an appropriate nuclear reaction for activation analysis is usually based on the physical, chemical, and nuclear properties of the matrix and trace elements, and of their activation products. These properties determine the sensitivity with which a given trace element can be measured, the importance of possible interfering reactions or competing activation products, the extent to which post-irradiation assay techniques must be provided, and the practicability of providing a sample suitable for irradiation. Other considerations such as the proximity to an irradiation facility or economic factors may also be important.

The selection of an irradiation facility is based primarily on the type of nuclear particle required. In the event that neutron activation is the selected method, a wide selection of nuclear reactors, linear accelerators, cyclotrons, and low intensity neutron sources is available for service irradiations (A16). The selection of a particular facility may also be based on the flux intensity required to achieve the desired sensitivity, the energy of the neutrons required, the physical properties of the specimens, the location of the facility, or the cost of the irradiation. For charged particle or photon activation, similar considerations prevail except that the availability of the desired irradiation conditions (*e.g.*, type of particle, beam energy, and intensity) will frequently limit the selection to one or two facilities.

The physical, chemical, and nuclear properties of the constituents of a sample and the properties of their activation products dictate the pre-irradiation treatment of the sample. Some facilities will not permit irradiation of powders, liquids, volatiles, or easily decomposed solids. Nuclear considerations may limit the mass of some samples both in neutron and charged particle irradiations. In addition, at each facility, special irradiation capsules or special restrictions, such as forced cooling, may be required, thus limiting the size of the sample. Chemical decontamination of the surfaces of solids is frequently desirable, although extended purification steps are normally not required. However, any chemical or physical treatment of the sample prior to irradiation must be carried out in a manner which will avoid contamination.

Two general irradiation and analytical techniques apply to both neutron and charged particle activation analysis. These are commonly referred to as the absolute assay technique and the comparative assay technique.

The absolute assay technique requires that the activation be carried out in a neutron flux or particle beam of known intensity, that the pertinent nuclear date be known accurately, and that the radiometric assay be quantitative; *i.e.*, the measurement of the absolute disintegration rates of the activation products with suitably calibrated instruments is required. If this method is selected, the use of beam or flux monitors is recommended.

The comparative assay, or comparator technique utilizes standard samples of the trace elements which are irradiated simultaneously with the samples and assayed in the same manner. Since this technique requires relative measurements only and eliminates the need for certain accurate nuclear data, it usually yields more accurate analytical results with greater convenience than the absolute assay technique.

Hence, the comparative assay technique is more frequently used. If it is selected, suitable comparator samples must be prepared and encapsulated with the samples.

The optimum length and intensity of the irradiation are normally determined by the required sensitivity and the half-lives of the trace element activation products. However, the relative activation of the major constituents of the sample or the presence of interfering reactions may limit either the length or the intensity of the irradiation, and thus may modify the specification of the irradiation conditions for a given analytical problem.

The post-irradiation assays must be adapted to each combination of matrix and trace element. In general, chemical separations of the trace elements from the matrix and from each other are required. The extent of the separation procedures depends on the relative activation of the several constituents, the chemical properties of the activation products, and the half-lives of the species to be assayed. In cases where the major constituents are only slightly activated, gross beta or gamma counting or gamma spectrometry may suffice.

The evaluation of the experimental data allows the analyst to assign a reliability to the assay. Such an evaluation should take into consideration errors due to two general sources, analytical and nuclear. A detailed discussion of these sources of errors is given in the following chapters.

CHAPTER 2

ACTIVATION ANALYSIS • THEORETICAL CONSIDERATIONS

BASIC CONCEPTS

The technique of activation analysis is based on the formation of radioactive nuclides as a net result of reactions between nuclear particles and the isotopes of the trace elements of interest. These isotopes are transformed into different isotopes of either the same or different elements. There are many nuclear reactions which, in principle, can be utilized for this purpose. However, only some of these reactions are of practical interest. In the great majority of cases, two-particle reactions are utilized; one particle being a reactant, and the other being a product. The particles which are available in sufficient intensity for general use as reactants are neutrons, protons, deuterons, tritons, alpha particles, and photons (or electrons). Examples of typical nuclear reactions of interest are summarized in Part II of the Glossary.

Prior to discussing in detail the considerations pertinent to the selection of specific activation analysis methods, the mathematical relationship between the activation processes and the analytical sensitivities will be reviewed. Rigorous treatment of the general rate equations governing the nuclear transformations and the decay of the activation products has been presented by Rubinson (R16) and by Lewis (L13). In summary, the rate of formation of a particular activation product, R_F, in a given sample is proportional to the intensity of the flux or beam of incident particles, to the concentration of the target nuclide in the sample, and to the cross-section for the nuclear reaction. Thus, for the case of neutron irradiations

$$R_F = \phi n \sigma = \frac{\phi m N° f \sigma}{A} \tag{1}$$

where

n = the number of target atoms
ϕ = the neutron flux (n/cm²-sec)
m = the mass of the trace element in the specimen (gm)
A = the atomic weight of the trace element (gm/gm-atom)
f = the fractional isotopic abundance of the target nuclide
$N°$ = Avogadro's number (atoms/gm-atom)
σ = the reaction cross-section (cm²/atom).

The decay rate, D, expressed in atomic disintegrations per second, of the product radionuclide in the specimen is given by

$$D = \lambda N \tag{2}$$

where

N = the number of atoms of the nuclide in the specimen
λ = the decay constant of the nuclide (sec⁻¹).

Therefore, the rate of change of the quantity of the activation product in the sample during the irradiation is given by

$$\frac{dN}{dt} = R_F - D = \frac{\phi m N° f \sigma}{A} - N\lambda \tag{3}$$

It can be shown (e.g., F15) that the disintegration rate of the radionuclide in the specimen after an arbitrary irradiation time, t, is

$$D(t) = \frac{\phi m N° f \sigma (1 - e^{-\lambda t})}{A} \tag{4}$$

For sufficiently long irradiation times, $e^{-\lambda t}$ approaches zero, and we have

$$D^\infty = \frac{\phi m N° f \sigma}{A} \tag{5}$$

Therefore, Eq. (4) becomes the familiar expression

$$D(t) = D^{\infty}(1 - e^{-\lambda t}). \qquad (6)$$

Equation (4) can be used to estimate the activation levels for the various elements in the sample under varying conditions of flux, irradiation time, and sample size. Equation (4) can also be transformed into the following convenient form for calculating the sensitivity for detection of an element under a specified set of irradiation and detection conditions,

$$m = \frac{AD(t)}{\phi N^{\circ}f\sigma(1 - e^{-\lambda t})} \qquad (7)$$

where m is expressed in grams, and $D(t)$ is the minimum detectable disintegration rate for the activation product corrected for losses due to post-irradiation decay or assay.

A similar set of equations can be derived for charged particle induced reactions. In the simple case of a monoenergetic beam for which no significant energy degradation occurs within the target specimen, we have, by analogy to (4),

$$D(t) = bn'\sigma(1 - e^{-\lambda t})$$
$$= \frac{bm'N^{\circ}f\sigma(1 - e^{-\lambda t})}{A} \qquad (8)$$

where

b = the intensity of the particle beam striking the target sample (sec^{-1})

m' = grams of the trace element per square centimeter of matrix

n' = atoms of the target nuclide per square centimeter of matrix

and all other symbols have the same designation as in Eq. (4). Equation (8) reduces to (6) in a manner analogous to that for Eq. (4).

By transforming, we have

$$m' = \frac{AD(t)}{bN^{\circ}f\sigma(1 - e^{-\lambda t})} \qquad (9)$$

Since charged particle beam intensities are frequently expressed in terms of the beam current, J, we have

$$b = kJ = 6.2 \times 10^{12}J \qquad (10)$$

where J is expressed in microamperes. Hence, Eq. (8) becomes

$$D(t) = \frac{Jm'N^{\circ}f\sigma(1 - e^{-\lambda t})}{A}$$
$$\times 6.2 \times 10^{12} \qquad (11)$$

and Eq. (9) becomes

$$m' = \frac{1.6 \times 10^{-13}\,AD(t)}{JN^{\circ}f\sigma(1 - e^{-\lambda t})} \qquad (12)$$

While these expressions are useful for demonstrating the method of calculating activity levels and sensitivities, they are overly simplified for many applications in which neutrons, charged particles, or photons, having wide spectra of energy are utilized, or where the energies of charged particles are degraded in the sample. More exact equations can be derived for these cases in which the weighted mean of the product of the flux and cross-section over the entire energy spectrum is used. Hughes (H46) discusses an example of this technique for neutrons.

Equations (1) through (12) can be utilized for preliminary evaluation of activation analysis as a general method and also for the selection of activation reactions for specific applications. To complete this evaluation for a given activation analysis problem, nuclear data and experimental methods for the elements of interest are desired. Since these data are scattered throughout the literature, a major purpose of this handbook is their collation into a single source.

The types of nuclear data required include a compilation of the nuclear reactions useful for activation analysis, the cross-sections, excitation functions, and isotopic abundances of the stable nuclides, and the half-lives and decay schemes of the radioactive products. Other pertinent information includes a compilation of those reactions which may produce competing radionuclides, the cross-sections or excitation functions for reactions in elements other than the one of interest which may interfere with the analysis by producing the activation product of interest, and the radiation characteristics of the products of the competing reactions.

The information desired for the experimental methods includes examples of reactions which have been used successfully for activation analysis, the sensitivities achieved, the experimental techniques employed for sample preparation and for chemical and instrumental assays, and the evaluation of errors from experimentation or from interfering nuclear phenomena.

SOURCES OF NUCLEAR DATA

Many compilations have been prepared for various types of nuclear data pertinent to activation analysis. Most of these compilations are listed in "A Directory to Nuclear Data Tabulations" (G7). The 1956 revision of the "Chart of the Nuclides" (S53) is a convenient source of data for the isotopic abundances and the thermal neutron cross-sections of stable nuclides, and the half-lives of radioactive nuclides. A trilinear chart (S63) presents similar data in a slightly different format. Strominger, Hollander, and Seaborg (S57) have tabulated the experimental data for nuclear properties of both stable and radioactive nuclides. The Nuclear Data Group at the National Research Council (W6) provides current additions and revisions to the data for half-lives, decay schemes, cross-sections, and other nuclear properties. Salmon (S69) has tabulated similar data for nuclides produced by thermal neutron activation. The Brookhaven National Laboratory group has prepared a 1958 revision (H49) of previous compilations (H47, H48) of neutron cross-sections and resonance parameters. These latter compilations include both graphical and tabular presentations of the data. In addition, Howerston (H54) presents detailed neutron cross-sections of each element at energies up to 14 Mev. Macklin *et al.* (M7, M50) and Booth *et al.* (B61) have measured the activation cross-sections of numerous nuclides for the 25-kev neutrons from an antimony-beryllium source, and Lyon and Macklin (L25) have made similar measurements for 195-kev neutrons. Resonance integrals for a number of the elements are included in papers by Macklin and Pomerance (M9), Klimentov and Gryazev (K23), and Davis and Hauser (D4). The latter paper also presents data for elemental macroscopic cross-sections and for other neutron parameters.

To a review of the application of gamma spectroscopy in activation analysis, Salmon (S69) has appended tabulations of thermal neutron activation products according to half-life, gamma energy, and particle energy. Typical spectra of many of these nuclides are also shown.

Other available data for neutron reactions include presentations of thermal neutron activation cross-sections and the half-lives of the activation products (M35, M52) in a format useful for preparing estimates of sensitivities for different reactions; cross-sections for fast neutron induced reactions occurring in a thermal reactor and their application to activation analysis (M37); cross-sections of about sixty elements for neutron capture in a reactor having an average neutron energy of about 1.5 Mev (R11); and thermal neutron activation products tabulated according to half-life (G2, S69).

Tabulated data for charged particle reactions are less extensive. Jarmie and Seagraves (J8) present charged particle excitation functions for light elements, and Meinke *et al.* (A13, M36) have prepared bibliographies for charged particle excitation functions. Martin *el al.* (M15) have estimated yields for more than 100 nuclides resulting from proton induced reactions in cyclotron irradiations.

Other tabulations which present general data in convenient forms include lists of known radioactive nuclides in order of half-life (C17), of known beta emitters according to half-life and beta energy (H5), and of known gamma emitters according to the energy of their radiations (S45). Also, Freiling (F14) has prepared a nomogram for estimating activities produced in various materials during irradiation by various types of nuclear particles.

SOURCES OF EXPERIMENTAL METHODS

Many review articles containing activation analysis data have been cited in the introductory section of this handbook. These papers are useful as sources of general information and as bibliography sources for specific applications. The bibliographies illustrate the many applications in which activation analyses have been utilized and the diverse sources of detailed information on the subject. In order to complete the collation of the information necessary for evaluating proposed applications of activation analysis, the information given in these review articles has been augmented here with additional data obtained from a comprehensive literature survey.

This survey brings together the operational data which have been reported for activation analyses. It includes, for each element, the reactions which have been used, a brief description of the matrix, sensitivity, and flux or beam intensity, where available, and any new or unusual experimental techniques. The thresholds, cross-sections, and excitation functions for these reactions, where available, are presented in conjunction with the operational data. Where many papers are available for a given reaction, only representative examples have been described. However, all references pertinent to each element have been tabulated. It is hoped that the combination of this information with the tabulated nuclear data will greatly enhance the selection of the most appropriate nuclear reaction, irradiation facility, and experimental techniques for any activation analysis program.

SELECTION OF ACTIVATION REACTIONS

1. General Considerations

The selection of an appropriate activation reaction for a specific application is generally based on the nuclear properties of the matrix and of the trace elements of interest and on a review of available results of experimental activation analyses. However, the chemical and physical properties of the matrix and trace elements are also important. The tabulation of data in this handbook, together with the specific literature sources cited for the given application, will often serve as a sufficient source of information upon which to base this selection. If the properties of the matrix are especially troublesome, the cross-referenced index prepared by Gibbons *et al*. (G5) may provide a convenient directory to appropriate sources of information concerning that matrix.

The principal technical considerations in the selection of suitable nuclear reactions are that they (1) produce radionuclides which are retained in the sample and have appropriate half-life and decay characteristics for accurate measurements, (2) have optimum or sufficient sensitivities, (3) have no interfering reactions producing or consuming the desired activation product, (4) have no reactions producing competing radioactive isotopes of the same element as the activation product, and (5) that the requisite irradiation and post-irradiation assays are feasible.

2. Suitability of Activation Products

The suitability of an activation product is dependent on most of the other factors. It is important that the trace element activation products have chemical or physical properties which insure that they are retained in the sample. Adequate containment must be provided if it is necessary to utilize activation products which are volatile or which may form volatile compounds with other constituents in the sample. Also, the half-life of the activation product must be consistent with the time required for transportation from the irradiation facility and for performance of the post-irradiation assay. The suitability of other decay characteristics depends on the type of radioactivity measuring equipment available to the analyst and on the relative activation of other isotopes of the same element. In certain cases, the activation product may decay to a radioactive daughter which has more favorable decay properties. Finally, the need for a rapid, routine analytical procedure may dictate the use of a nuclear reaction which yields an activation product with a convenient half-life that is either easily separable from the matrix, or which requires no chemical separation or no complicated radioactivity measurements after irradiation. Thus, the choice of reaction may be partially dependent on the analytical requirements, partially on the availability or the proximity of a suitable irradiation facility, and partially on economic or administrative considerations.

3. Sensitivity Estimates

The sensitivity of an analytical procedure can be estimated from Eq. (7) for neutron activation or from Eq. (12) for activation by other particles. However, for short-lived activation products, delays due to transportation or extended chemical separations may result in reduced practical sensitivities. The sensitivity is also dependent upon the type of instrumentation used in the assay. Nuclear factors, such as interfering reactions or the macroscopic cross-section of the matrix, may limit the duration or intensity of the irradiation or the size of the sample, and thus further reduce the sensitivity. The dimensions of the irradiation location or of the largest irradiation capsule may also limit the size of the sample.

4. Interfering Reactions

a. Definitions. The effects of interfering nuclear reactions are dependent upon the composition of the matrix and the nuclear properties of its constituents. These reactions can be classified as primary, secondary, and second-order reactions. Primary reactions are defined as those reactions induced in the original constituents of the sample by the principal irradiating particles. Secondary reactions are reactions induced by particles created by nuclear reactions in the sample or in its environment. For example, in proton irradiations, many neutrons are created by (p, n) reactions in the sample. These neutrons may in turn react with constituents in the sample. Since these particles are not readily distinguished from beam contamination, the definition of secondary reactions may be extended to include reactions due to any particle other than the principal one. Second-order reactions are defined as those reactions induced in transformation products in the sample by the principal irradiating particles.

b. Primary reactions. Interfering primary reactions are those primary reactions induced in sample constituents which yield the same nuclide as the principal activation reaction. Interference may proceed either directly or through an activation reaction followed by beta decay of the primary activation product. For thermal neutron activation, the principal sources of interference with the (n, γ) reaction in an element of atomic number Z are fast neutron induced (n, p) and (n, α) reactions in elements having atomic number $Z + 1$ and $Z + 2$, respectively. The same reactions, induced in the next adjoining elements, may also interfere if they produce nuclides which decay through positron emission or electron capture to the activation product of interest. Furthermore, in certain regions of the periodic table, interference may occur as the result of fission of heavy elements.

The extent to which the fast neutron induced reactions interfere with thermal neutron activation analysis depends on the relative concentrations of the target nuclides in the matrix, the ratio of their cross-sections, and the ratio of the fast to thermal neutron fluxes. In general, these interfering reactions will be important only if they occur in principal components of the matrix or if the trace element to be assayed is present in extremely low concentrations, because the effective fluxes and cross-sections for fast neutron reactions are usually much less than those for thermal neutrons. However, since the relative intensities and energy distributions of fast neutrons vary from reactor to reactor and even with location within a single reactor, the extent of interference varies. Fink (F6) discusses several specific cases illustrating these effects.

Self-shielding effects, in which the high macroscopic cross-section of the matrix or of a comparator sample results in activation gradients, may also be considered primary interferences. However, these effects are discussed elsewhere.

c. Secondary reactions. Secondary reactions are seldom significant in reactor irradiations because the photons and charged particles created by reactor neutrons have either too low an energy or too low an abundance to be significant. However, in charged particle or photon irradiations secondary reactions may be important, especially if the trace and matrix elements have adjacent atomic numbers. The importance of secondary reactions depends upon the composition and size of the sample, the energy of the incident particles, and the ratio of the cross-sections for the primary and secondary reactions. Koch (K24) discusses methods for estimating the contributions of secondary reactions and for correcting for them.

d. Second-order reactions. Two types of second-order reactions occur: those which enhance the production of an activation product, and those which decrease its concentration. Reactions of the first type usually occur when a major constituent of the sample and the trace element have adjacent atomic numbers. In this case, activation products of the major constituent may decay to the stable isotope of the trace element, adding to its concentration. Continued irradiation will then enhance the production of the trace element activation product. An example of this type of interference occurs in the determination of phosphorus in silicon using the reaction $P^{31}(n, \gamma)P^{32}$. The second-order phenomenon,

$$\mathrm{Si}^{30}(n, \gamma)\mathrm{Si}^{31} \xrightarrow{\beta^-} P^{31}(n, \gamma)P^{32}$$

becomes important as the concentration of "bred" P^{31} increases during the irradiation. A

9

mathematical treatment of this system is presented by Kant *et al.* (K2). Other examples of this type are cited by Fink (F6).

The degree to which such reactions interfere depends on the concentrations of the two elements, their activation cross-sections, and the half-life of the intermediate radioactive nuclide. In order to avoid appreciable interference of this type, it is often necessary to limit the intensity or the duration of the irradiation. Thus, the interfering reaction may limit the sensitivity of the analysis.

Second-order reactions may also occur in the activation product itself if its cross-section is sufficiently large. In this case, there is little if any error introduced into the analysis if the comparator method is used, since the second-order reaction also occurs in the comparator. However, if the absolute assay method is used, this effect must be considered. Mathematical treatments for this type of reaction are presented by Rubinson (R16) and by Lewis (L13). For purposes of estimating the importance of such an interference in a given application, the fractional error, ε, introduced into the observed activity of the activation product is approximated by Eq. (13).

$$\varepsilon \cong \frac{\phi \sigma_2}{\lambda_1} \qquad (13)$$

where

ϕ = the neutron flux (n/cm^2-sec)
σ_2 = the cross-section for the second-order reaction (cm^2/atom)
λ_1 = the decay constant for the primary activation product (sec^{-1}).

Equation (15) can also be used for calculating the maximum permissible flux for such an irradiation by assigning the desired upper limit to ε.

Specific elements which may have important second-order reactions are noted in the tabulation for neutron activation techniques. This type of interference is not expected with fast neutrons, charged particles, or photons, since their interaction cross-sections are too small.

5. Competing Reactions

The presence of competing reactions can be determined readily by reference to the nuclear data for the trace element and its neighbors. These reactions usually will occur when the trace element has several stable isotopes of which more than one can be activated. Reactions of the same type as those described as primary or second-order interfering reactions may also be present yielding competing nuclides which are isotopic with the activation product of interest. Competing reactions are equally probable in all types of activation techniques. Since the degree to which the activation products of competing reactions interfere in the assay varies with the type of radiation and the radioactivity measuring equipment, estimates of their effects for given activation methods have not been included in this compilation.

6. Experimental Feasibility

The feasibility of performing the requisite irradiation depends on the physical, chemical, and nuclear properties of the matrix and, to a lesser extent, on those of the trace elements. Some samples may not be permitted in some irradiation facilities because of high macroscopic cross-sections, dimensional considerations, or because they are combustible, volatile, or liquid. Hence, preparation of an irradiation specimen appropriate to the experiment may not be possible.

The feasibility of performing the post-irradiation assay depends on the chemical and decay characteristics of the activation products of both matrix and trace elements and on the radioactivity measuring equipment available. Finally, the need for a routine analytical technique may eliminate those activation reactions which do not yield activation products with convenient half-lives or which require difficult or extended assay procedures.

Many reactions may be rejected on the basis of the foregoing specifications. However, other nontechnical considerations, such as the availability or location of a suitable irradiation facility or the cost of its use, may also affect the final selection of the activation reaction.

CHAPTER 3

ACTIVATION ANALYSIS • EXPERIMENTAL METHODS

IRRADIATION FACILITIES

1. Sources of Neutrons

If neutron activation is the method selected, as is usually the case, a wide variety of neutron sources is available. These sources include reactors, cyclotrons, linear accelerators, and low-level neutron sources (*e.g.*, Sb-Be, Ra-Be). The facility selection can then be based on the neutron energy or flux required, or on the availability, cost, or convenience of a particular facility. A tabulation of neutron irradiation facilities, and of their availability, characteristics, and security regulations, is available (A16). Of the neutron sources, the largest, highest intensity, most widely used type is the thermal reactor. Hughes (H45) has presented a description of the reactor as a source of neutrons and a discussion of the general properties of neutron fluxes and energy distributions. Charpie *et al.* (C10) have given a review of existing reactor facilities, and Chastain (C11) has compiled complete technical descriptions of about thirty reactors, including their experimental facilities. Hess (H29) has compared the neutron energy characteristics of Po-Li, Po-Be, Po-B, Po-BF$_3$, Ra-Be, and Pu-Be sources. Meinke and Anderson (M33, M34) have discussed the use of a Ra-Be source for activation analysis, and De and Meinke (D6) have reviewed the characteristics of an Sb-Be source and its potential applicability to activation analysis. They point out that Sb-Be is less expensive than the other sources and is unrestricted in use, but its relatively short half-life requires periodic reactivation. Further references containing detailed information on these various sources are listed by these authors (D6).

Cyclotrons and linear accelerators are also utilized as neutron sources. Here, neutrons are usually products of charged particle induced reactions in selected materials. Thermal neutrons can be obtained by surrounding the neutron emitter with a suitable moderating material, such as water or paraffin (B51). Frequently, the appropriate irradiation technique can provide monoenergetic neutron beams of a selected energy. Several authors (B33, F11, T4) have reviewed the techniques for production, measurement, and utilization of fast neutrons. Several other descriptions of the use of specific proton induced reactions (B5, G6, G21) and alpha induced reactions (B16) as neutron sources are available. Specific applications of linear accelerators in neutron activation analysis are outlined by Turner (T20), Atchison and Beamer (A18), and Burrill and Gale (B51). References to detailed methods for specific elements are presented in the tabulation.

2. Sources of Charged Particles and Photons

If charged particle or photon activation is under consideration, a more critical evaluation of the available facilities may be required to ascertain which betatron, cyclotron, or linear accelerator provides the required irradiation conditions. Cyclotrons and linear accelerators are the principal facilities for charged particle irradiations, while electron linear accelerators and betatrons are sources of photons. A tabulation of some gamma irradiation facilities is available (A16).

Livingston and Boch (L17) have described one cyclotron which is available for service irradiations, and Martin *et al.* (M15) discuss experimental techniques, targets, reaction yields, and other factors pertinent to cyclotron irradiations. The recent use of cyclotrons for specific activation analyses is described in a number of articles (*e.g.*, F8, G30, P12, S61, S62) which are referenced in the tabulation under the pertinent elements. Also, several papers (G9, O1, O3, O4) describe the use of the 5.3-Mev alpha particles from large Po^{210} sources for activation analysis for a number of light elements.

The most convenient source of photons for activation analysis is probably the electron linear accelerator. The photons comprise the bremsstrahlung produced during acceleration of these fast electrons in the coulombic fields of atomic nuclei. A review of the potential application of this type of photon source to activation analysis is presented by MacGregor (M1).

A unique analytical method for deuterium has been described (F2) utilizing the gamma radiation from a one-curie source of Na^{24} and the detection of prompt neutrons from the resulting (γ, n) reaction in H^2.

3. *Selection of an Irradiation Facility*

The interdependence of the suitability of an irradiation facility and of a specific nuclear reaction and the properties of the matrix and trace elements of interest has already been noted. When a certain type of activation is selected, the choice of facility is partially defined, especially if a specific nuclear reaction at a particular energy is required. This consideration is especially true for charged particle induced reactions. The location of a given facility or the intensity of its neutron flux or particle beam may also be the decisive factor. In addition, it should be noted that each irradiation facility has its own procedures concerning availability for service irradiations, and its own regulations governing the types of materials which may be irradiated and the dimensions of irradiation samples. For example, many irradiation facilities may not permit irradiation of combustible materials, volatiles, liquids, powders, or solids having low melting points, while others may permit some of these to be irradiated after suitable encapsulation. Therefore, the selection of the irradiation facility may be dependent upon the feasibility of preparing the sample in acceptable form or in suitable encapsulation. Since regulations vary

at different irradiation facilities, the analyst will be well advised to contact appropriate operations personnel at the facilities under consideration for detailed information.

PREPARATION AND ENCAPSULATION OF SAMPLES

1. *Neutron Irradiations*

a. Physical preparation. The physical preparation of samples for irradiation will depend on the physical, chemical, and nuclear properties of the matrix and the trace elements, and of their activation products, on the physical and nuclear environment in the irradiation facility, and especially on the type of irradiation to be performed. Chemical preparation will usually be performed at the discretion of the analyst, and encapsulation procedures will normally be specified by the operator of the irradiation facility.

For neutron irradiations, the dimensions of the sample will normally be limited by (1) the size of the available irradiation space, (2) the nuclear properties of the sample or of its activation products, (3) the quantity of sample required to obtain the necessary sensitivity, or (4) the quantity available for analysis. Of these factors, item (2) is probably the most important. The limiting nuclear considerations may be the intensity of activation of the sample, which may present a radiation hazard in the laboratory, or the self-shielding within the sample due to its high macroscopic cross-section. If the cross-section for either thermal or resonance neutrons is sufficiently high, the sample may become black or opaque to the incident neutrons, causing an activation gradient within the sample. Such gradients can introduce appreciable errors in the experimental data (P10).

For the irradiation of powders, liquids, volatiles, and other substances which may undergo physical changes due to thermal or radiolytic conditions, special containment is usually required. The minimum requirements for such containment may be specified by the operators of the irradiation facility.

If analysis of liquid samples is required, it is usually desirable to evaporate them to dryness or to a reduced volume. For all volatile samples, or for samples whose activation

12

products are volatile, care must be taken to prevent loss of volatile matter. Hermetically sealed containers are recommended for such irradiations even if they are not required at the irradiation facility. For special cases, auxiliary cooling of the sample may be required.

b. Chemical preparation. The chemical preparation of the sample will depend primarily on its properties and history. Chemical purification or concentration of the sample prior to irradiation is seldom required and is not recommended, since trace impurities can be readily introduced in such treatments. However, surface decontamination of solid samples prior to irradiation is desirable, especially if mechanical treatments, such as cutting or forming, have been performed previously. However, care must be taken not to introduce new contaminants during etching which might interfere with the analysis. In certain cases, it may be more appropriate to etch surfaces after irradiation to avoid activation of traces of etchant left on the surface.

After decontamination, a known weight of the sample is taken for irradiation. It is usually packaged in a clean container which is not appreciably activated, such as quartz or pure aluminum. This container is then enclosed in a standard irradiation capsule which is usually supplied by the irradiation facility.

2. Charged Particle Irradiations

The discussion of the factors pertinent to neutron irradiations applies to irradiations with charged particles. In this case, however, in addition to item (1), the dimensions of the irradiation beam, other considerations such as energy degradation of the beam and heat dissipation in the sample must be taken into account. The methods of meeting target requirements depend on the particular irradiation arrangement at each accelerator. Some problems and techniques in cyclotron target preparation are discussed by McDonell and Newton (M20).

Some methods available for minimizing energy degradation and excessive temperature in the sample during cyclotron irradiations are (1) preparing the samples as thin targets, (2) rotating the samples through the beam, or (3) mounting the samples tangentially to the beam. For irradiations with monoenergetic charged particles, the use of external cyclotron

beams or linear accelerator beams may be preferable.

Since heat dissipation is an important factor in most charged particle irradiations, materials which have low melting points, poor thermal conductivity, or high volatility are often not amenable to irradiation. Their irradiation may be prohibited in internal cyclotron irradiations. If sealed containers are provided for the irradiation, the mass of the container may be sufficient to prevent proper activation of its contents. It is evident, therefore, that non-volatile rigid samples are most amenable to charged particle irradiations.

3. Photon Irradiations

The considerations for photon irradiations are substantially identical to those for neutrons and charged particles. The limiting factor in this case is generally the relatively low cross-sections of nuclides for photon interactions and the correspondingly larger sample size required to achieve a given level of sensitivity.

4. Comparator or Monitor Samples

Discussion of the two general techniques for quantitative activation analysis has been given on page 4. Prior to encapsulation of the sample, comparator samples for each trace element of interest or flux or beam monitors for the irradiation must be prepared. Comparator samples are known quantities of the element or of one of its compounds. It is extremely important that the comparators be irradiated simultaneously with the samples. A sufficient number of comparators should be included to determine any flux gradients along the length of the irradiation sample. It is also important that no significant self-shielding should occur in the comparator. For example, gold, which has a peak cross-section for resonance neutrons ($\sim$5 ev) of about 3×10^4 barns, must be reduced in thickness to about 500 Å to attain 99% transparency, or it must be diluted with a material of low cross-section. Mahlman and Leddicotte (M10) discuss these problems as they pertain to activation analysis for uranium, and they describe some useful techniques for surmounting them.

If the absolute assay method is required, flux or beam monitors suitable to the particular irradiation should be provided. Foil activation techniques are available for both neutron and charged particle irradiations. If foil techniques are used for neutron irradiations, care must be exercised to avoid self-shielding or flux perturbation by the foil. For charged particle irradiations, care must be exercised to avoid excessive energy degradation in the foils. Foils are not generally used as photon flux monitors. For photon irradiations, chemical or colorimetric dosimeters are available. At some irradiation facilities, instrumental monitoring methods may be available. Further information concerning irradiation monitoring methods can usually be obtained at the irradiation facility.

IRRADIATIONS

The specification of the intensity and duration of the irradiation will normally be based on the sensitivity requirements for the analysis. For short-lived activation products, the sensitivity is proportional to the intensity of the irradiation. For activation products with longer half-lives (*e.g.*, > 30 days), the sensitivity is dependent upon both the intensity and duration of the irradiation. It is usually not feasible or desirable to irradiate to equilibrium, or saturation activation in these cases. Therefore, there is a choice of irradiation conditions, the choice being among several equivalent combinations of intensity and duration. The selection of the optimum irradiation conditions is usually based on the half-lives of the major activation products in the sample. For example, if these half-lives are relatively short with respect to those of the trace element activation product, it is advantageous to irradiate the sample longer at a lower flux to minimize the gross activation. For the opposite case, a shorter irradiation at higher fluxes may be preferable.

The presence of interfering secondary or second-order reactions may also limit the duration or intensity of the irradiation. Other limiting factors are the thermal and irradiation stability of the sample, its thermal conductivity, the cost of the irradiation, and the operating cycles at the irradiation facility.

POST-IRRADIATION ASSAYS

In general, the post-irradiation assay technique for a given trace element must be adapted to facilitate its separation from a specific matrix. It must also be consistent with a possible need for rapid assays because of short half-lives. Two methods of separation are generally used: (1) specific separation of the element of interest followed by a suitable measurement of its characteristic radiations, or (2), in those cases where the radiation from the sought element is sufficiently different from the others present, direct measurement of its radioactivity.

Where many similar analyses are to be performed, it may be desirable to develop a rapid chemical separation or to provide for partial purification of the trace element in conjunction with gamma spectrometry measurements. In special cases, where the primary constituents of the matrix are only slightly activated, gross beta or gamma counting or gamma spectrometry may suffice. The type of detection equipment available may dictate the choice of assay method. It is also required that the radioactivity measuring equipment be suitable for the measurement of the particular radiations with the desired precision and sensitivity. For example, very low activities, unfavorable decay characteristics, or the presence of competing radionuclides may result in poor precision or accuracy. Furthermore, the presence of several of these factors may indicate that a search for a more suitable activation reaction is desirable.

Although no generalized analytical procedures are applicable, a number of recent papers have described analysis schemes for a number of trace elements in a matrix after a single irradiation (A4, A17, B41, B44, B58, C6, C32, G28, K2, S31, T16). Other workers have described the use of gamma spectrometry, either directly on the sample or in combination with limited chemical separations (C33, I1, M48, M49). Compilations of radiochemical procedures in use at various laboratories are also available (*e.g.*, K21, M29).

EVALUATION OF THE DATA

The evaluation of the experimental data consists primarily of an analysis of the experimental errors involved. There are two general types of experimental errors; those due to analytical procedures and those due to nuclear phenomena. An excellent discussion of most of these errors is presented by Plumb and Lewis (P10).

The analytical sources of error include: (1) failure to remove surface contaminants from the sample, (2) introduction of contaminants during sample preparation, or during the addition of carriers or other reagents, (3) faulty preparation of the comparator samples, (4) incomplete exchange between the carrier and the trace element activation product, (5) insufficient decontamination in the chemical procedures, and (6) insufficient precision or accuracy in the radioactivity assay.

Most of these errors can be kept to a minimum by maintaining high standards for laboratory techniques and for control of radioactive contamination. These sources of error are normally within the control of the analyst except that, as ultimate sensitivity is approached, the magnitude of the errors increases rapidly. This increase is due to the increased difficulties in measuring minimum detectable levels of radioactivity accurately.

The nuclear sources of error include (1) self-shielding for thermal or resonance neutrons in the sample or in the comparator or monitor samples, (2) failure to detect flux gradients in the irradiation sample, (3) interference from competing reactions, (4) interference from primary, secondary, or second-order reactions, and (5) interference from charged particle energy degradation during the irradiation. The tabulation presented in the following chapter provides an evaluation of the interfering nuclear phenomena for most reactions pertinent to activation analysis.

It is hoped that the foregoing discussion will be helpful to many analysts in the planning, performance, and evaluation of activation analysis programs, and that the tabulation which is presented in the following section will provide a source of pertinent information in a form which is both useful and convenient.

CHAPTER 4

THE TABULATION

INTRODUCTION

The principal purpose of the tabulation in Table III is the collation of the nuclear data and the experimental methods for activation analysis and their presentation in a form convenient for reference purposes. The several types of data and information and their significance have been discussed in previous sections.

The collation of the data has been performed, element by element, with respect to the trace elements to be assayed. To avoid needless duplication, no attempt has been made to collate or to cross-reference the information with respect to matrix elements. An excellent bibliography of this type (G5) is available from the British Information Service.*

The tabulation consists of five categories of information: (1) nuclear data, (2) experimental methods, (3) evaluation of nuclear reactions, (4) standard sensitivities, and (5) references.

The pertinent nuclear data have been separated into those pertaining to neutron activation and those pertaining to other methods of activation. The data for neutron activation include, for each element, the stable isotopes, their relative abundances, their cross-sections for capture of thermal, epithermal, and reactor spectrum neutrons, the half-lives of their activation products, the cross-sections for second-order capture in the activation products, and the half-lives of the second-order activation products. In addition, cross-sections are included for other reactions [e.g., (n, p), (n, α)] which may be induced in some elements with reactor neutrons. Finally, summaries of decay characteristics of the more important activation products are presented. Nuclear reactions

induced by fast neutrons, charged particles, or photons have also been used for activation analysis. These reactions, and others which are potentially useful for activation analysis, are tabulated for each element in conjunction with their thresholds, cross-sections, and excitation functions, where such data are available. However, since several compilations of excitation functions for reactor neutron reactions are available (H47, H48, H49, H54), these data have generally been excluded from the tabulation. In addition, reactions for which no data are available, or which have no apparent potential application for activation analysis, are not included in the tabulation. Charged particle reactions having thresholds greater than approximately 25 Mev have, therefore, been excluded because their cross-sections are relatively smaller, the beam intensities at these energies are usually rather small, and the number of potential interfering or competing reactions is usually larger than for reactions which proceed at lower energies.

The presentation of experimental methods consists primarily of selected examples of the use of particular nuclear reactions for the analysis of the element in a specific matrix. The tabulated information includes the matrix, sensitivity, flux intensity, and special irradiation or assay methods. Where a sufficient number of papers is available for neutron activation analysis of an element, only representative references are given in the table. The selection of the representative references was based on the general applicability of the method described, the detail with which it is presented, the illustration of a special irradiation or assay technique, or the sensitivity achieved. However, the selection or omission of any particular reference is in no way to be construed as an evalua-

*Address: 30 Rockefeller Plaza, New York, N. Y.

tion of the quality of the reported results or of their significance for their specific application. References not selected as examples are included under the caption "Others."

Evaluations, performed for an individual activation reaction, were based on a search for those primary, secondary, or second-order reactions which might interfere with its use for activation analysis. Self-shielding has also been considered in the evaluation, and its significance has been noted in the tabulation for those elements which have cross-sections greater than twenty barns. Since this is an arbitrarily chosen value, it should not be construed that this effect is negligible for elements of lower cross-section. Special care must be taken for many of these elements when high precision is required. Since the degree to which the activation products of competing reactions affect the analytical data is dependent upon the particular radioactivity measuring technique used, no attempt has been made to evaluate their effects quantitatively.

Standard analytical sensitivities have been calculated for many thermal neutron reactions and for representative charged particle reactions. The standard sensitivity for a neutron reaction is defined here as the mass, in micrograms, of the trace element which yields 1000 dpm of activation product after irradiation in a flux of $10^{14} n/cm^2$-sec to saturation or for a maximum period of thirty days. For charged particle reactions, the standard sensitivity is defined as the quantity of the trace element, in micrograms per square centimeter of matrix, which yields 1000 dpm of activation product after irradiation in a 10-μamp beam to saturation or for a maximum period of eight hours.

For the purpose of calculating standard sensitivities for neutron reactions, Eq. (7) was converted to the simplified form (14) by insertion of the standard values for flux ($10^{14} n/cm^2$-sec) and disintegration rate (1000 dpm).

$$s = \frac{2.8 A \times 10^{-5}}{p \sigma_b (1 - e^{-\lambda t})} \quad (14)$$

where

s = the standard sensitivity (μg)
A = the atomic weight of the trace element (gm/gm-atom)
p = the percent isotopic abundance of the target nuclide
σ_b = the reaction cross-section, barns/atom

As an example, the standard sensitivity is calculated for the reaction $Sr^{88}(n, \gamma)Sr^{89}$, for which

$A = 87.6$ 　　　　 $\sigma_b = 5 \times 10^{-3} b$
$p = 82.65$ 　　　　 $\lambda = 1.36 \times 10^{-2} day^{-1}$
　　　　　　　　　 $t = 30$ days

$$s(Sr) = \frac{2.8 \times 10^{-5} \times 87.6}{82.65 \times 5 \times 10^{-3}(1 - e^{-0.407})}$$

$$= 2 \times 10^{-2} \mu g \quad (14a)$$

Similarly, standard sensitivities for charged particle reactions were calculated by insertion of the standard values for beam current (10μamp) and disintegration rate (1000 dpm) into Eq. (12) to give (15)

$$s'(E) = \frac{4.4 A \times 10^{-5}}{p \sigma_b(E)(1 - e^{-\lambda t})} \quad (15)$$

where $s'(E)$ is the standard sensitivity, and all other quantities have the same designation as in Eq. (14). For these calculations, the maximum known cross-sections were used, and it was assumed that the beam is monoenergetic and that the effective target thickness is small. Thus, the sensitivity, $s'(E)$, is expressed in micrograms per square centimeter detectable at the specified particle energy, E. For example, the standard sensitivity is calculated for the reaction $Mg^{26}(d, \alpha)Na^{24}$, for which

$\sigma_b(E) = 0.09 b$ 　　　 $E = 8.5$ Mev
$p = 11.29$ 　　　　　 $t = 8$ hr
$A = 24.3$ 　　　　　 $\lambda = 0.0462$ hr^{-1}

$$s'(E) = \frac{4.4 \times 10^{-5} \times 24.3}{11.29 \times 0.09 \times (1 - e^{-0.369})}$$

$$= 4 \times 10^{-5} \mu g/cm^2 \text{ at } 8.5 \text{ Mev} \quad (15a)$$

A complete reference code is provided for all data included in the tabulation, except where a full set of data, such as isotopic abundances, is derived from one source. The references, coded with a letter and number, are given in the bibliography where they are presented alphabetically by the name of the first author. If there are several articles by the same author, they are listed in chronological order. The bibliography originally covered the period prior to October, 1958. However, the Addendum to the Bibliography extends this coverage to articles available prior to September, 1959. A continuous coding system is used for both sections of the bibliography.

17

DIRECTORY TO THE TABULATION

The tabulation of data for activation analysis is presented in Table III. To facilitate the use of this tabulation, two preliminary tables have been included. Table I contains a list of the elements with their chemical symbols and atomic numbers. Table II, the Key to the Tabulation, presents the general arrangement of data in the Tabulation. The Tabulation is arranged by element in the order of increasing atomic number. All elements are included up to an atomic number of 94 (plutonium). The information for each element is presented on facing pages. With reference to Table II, it can be seen that the information for neutron activation is given on the left-hand page, and the information for charged particle and photon activation, on the right-hand page.

The information on each page has been divided into three sections. The first section contains the nuclear data and activation analysis methods; the second section contains the evaluation of nuclear reactions for activation analysis; and the third section contains the standard sensitivities for selected reactions. In the Key to the Tabulation, these sections are designated as A-1, B-1, C-1, A-2, B-2, and C-2, where the letters refer to the section, and the numbers refer to the information for neutrons and for charged particles or photons, respectively.

Section A-1, Nuclear Data and Analysis Methods for Neutron Activation, is divided into three sub-sections separated by broken lines: A-1a, Reactor Neutron Reaction Data; A-1b, Neutron Activation Analysis Methods; and A-1c, Data for Other Neutron Reactions.

Sub-section A-1a contains eight columns of nuclear data. Column one lists the stable isotopes and the naturally occurring radioactive isotopes with their half-lives. Column two lists the relative abundances of these isotopes (in percent). Column three lists the absorption and activation cross-sections for thermal neutrons, or for reactor spectrum (pile) neutrons, for each stable isotope. It also lists cross-sections for other neutron induced reactions which occur with reactor neutrons and resonance integrals for absorption or activation reactions. The data in columns one through three are from Hughes and Schwartz

(H49), except where specific notations occur in the tables.

Column four identifies the activation products corresponding to the cross-sections in column three. If an (n, γ) reaction is involved, only the half-life of the product is given. However, for other reactions, the product nuclide is completely identified. Columns five and six list the principal radiations of the activation products and their percent occurrence. Column five presents data for decay through beta emission or electron capture (EC), while column six contains the corresponding data for gamma emission and isomeric transitions (IT). Only those radiations of major importance or abundance are tabulated. The data include the energies of these radiations with their occurrence, in percent. For those nuclides with complicated decay schemes, the symbol "M" in the table indicates that a multiplicity of radiations exists. Where no beta or gamma radiation is present, its absence is indicated in the appropriate column. The data given in columns four, five, and six are from Strominger et al. (S57).

Columns seven and eight list values for second-order reaction cross-sections and for the half-lives of the resulting activation products, respectively. The values in column seven are from reference H49, while those in column eight are from reference S57.

Sub-section A-1b describes selected activation analysis methods utilizing the various neutron reactions, along with the corresponding references, and lists references to other data for these reactions. Thresholds, cross-sections, and excitation functions for these reactions are included.

Sub-section A-1c is composed of available nuclear data for neutron reactions potentially useful for activation analysis, but for which no analytical information has been found.

Section A-2, Nuclear Data and Analysis Methods for Charged Particle and Photon Activation, is divided into two sub-sections: A-2a, Charged Particle and Photon Activation Analysis Methods, and A-2b, Data for Other Charged Particle or Photon Reactions.

Sub-section A-2a contains descriptions of analytical methods using charged particle or photon activation and the thresholds, excitation functions, and cross-section data for these reactions. Sub-section A-2b contains thresholds,

18

excitation functions, and cross-section data for charged particle or photon reactions potentially useful for activation analysis, but for which no analytical information has been found.

Sections B-1 and B-2 contain statements evaluating the nuclear reactions with respect to interfering nuclear phenomena which may occur during activation analysis irradiations utilizing neutrons and charged particles or photons, respectively.

Sections C-1 and C-2 list sensitivities for determination of the element using the selected reactions under a standard set of irradiation and measurement conditions, as defined on page 17.

TABLE I
The Elements and Their Atomic Numbers

ELEMENT	SYMBOL	ATOMIC NUMBER	ELEMENT	SYMBOL	ATOMIC NUMBER
Actinium	Ac	89	Neon	Ne	10
Aluminum	Al	13	Neptunium	Np	93
Antimony	Sb	51	Nickel	Ni	28
Argon	A	18	Niobium	Nb	41
Arsenic	As	33	Nitrogen	N	7
Astatine	At	85	Osmium	Os	76
Barium	Ba	56	Oxygen	O	8
Beryllium	Be	4	Palladium	Pd	46
Bismuth	Bi	83	Phosphorus	P	15
Boron	B	5	Platinum	Pt	78
Bromine	Br	35	Plutonium	Pu	94
Cadmium	Cd	48	Polonium	Po	84
Calcium	Ca	20	Potassium	K	19
Carbon	C	6	Praseodymium	Pr	59
Cerium	Ce	58	Promethium	Pm	61
Cesium	Cs	55	Protactinium	Pa	91
Chlorine	Cl	17	Radium	Ra	88
Chromium	Cr	24	Radon	Rn	86
Cobalt	Co	27	Rhenium	Re	75
Copper	Cu	29	Rhodium	Rh	45
Dysprosium	Dy	66	Rubidium	Rb	37
Erbium	Er	68	Ruthenium	Ru	44
Europium	Eu	63	Samarium	Sm	62
Fluorine	F	9	Scandium	Sc	21
Francium	Fr	87	Selenium	Se	34
Gadolinium	Gd	64	Silicon	Si	14
Gallium	Ga	31	Silver	Ag	47
Germanium	Ge	32	Sodium	Na	11
Gold	Au	79	Strontium	Sr	38
Hafnium	Hf	72	Sulfur	S	16
Helium	He	2	Tantalum	Ta	73
Holmium	Ho	67	Technetium	Tc	43
Hydrogen	H	1	Tellurium	Te	52
Indium	In	49	Terbium	Tb	65
Iodine	I	53	Thallium	Tl	81
Iridium	Ir	77	Thorium	Th	90
Iron	Fe	26	Thulium	Tm	69
Krypton	Kr	36	Tin	Sn	50
Lanthanum	La	57	Titanium	Ti	22
Lead	Pb	82	Tungsten	W	74
Lithium	Li	3	Uranium	U	92
Lutecium	Lu	71	Vanadium	V	23
Magnesium	Mg	12	Xenon	Xe	54
Manganese	Mn	25	Ytterbium	Yb	70
Mercury	Hg	80	Yttrium	Y	39
Molybdenum	Mo	42	Zinc	Zn	30
Neodymium	Nd	60	Zirconium	Zr	40

TABLE II

The Key to the Tabulation

Section A-1: Nuclear Data and Analysis Methods for Neutron Activation

Sub-Section A-1a: Reactor Neutron Reaction Data

Isotope	Abundance (percent)	Cross-section (barns)	Half-life of Activation Product	Principal Beta Radiations	Principal Gamma Radiations	Second-order Cross-section (barns)	Half-life of Second-order Product
I^1	f	σa = activation σ	t	Mev (%) EC (%) = electron capture	M = multiple gammas		
I^2 (T = half-life of I^2)	f	σ = absorption σ	t s = stable	none	IT(%) = isomeric transition		
I^3	f	$\sigma^* a$ = activation σ with pile neutrons	t	Mev (%)	Mev (%)	σ'	t'
		$(n,p)\sigma^* a$ = σ for (n,p) reaction with pile neutrons	product nuclide		Mev (%)		
		R = resonance integal, absorption					
		R_a = resonance integal, activation					

Sub-Section A-1b: Neutron Activation Analysis Methods

Reaction		References
R-1	Use of thermal neutron reaction, R-1, for activation analysis; matrix; special irradiation or assay technique; sensitivity; flux; observed interfering reactions; special comments.	Q23
R-2	Use of thermal neutron reaction, R-2, for activation analysis; matrix; special irradiation or assay technique; sensitivity; flux; observed interfering reactions; special comments.	Z15
	Other: A99, G57, etc ----- other references for thermal neutron activation analysis.	
R-3	Use of fast neutron reaction, R-3, for activation analysis; matrix; special irradiation or assay technique; sensitivity; flux; observed interfering reactions; special comments.	J27
	Threshold, cross-sections, or excitation function for reaction R-3.	D39 G27

Sub-Section A-1c: Data for Other Neutron Reactions

R-4	Threshold, cross-sections, or excitation function for reaction R-4.	X16

Section B-1: Evaluation of Neutron Reactions

R-1	Listing of possible interfering primary reactions; secondary reactions; second-order reactions; self-shielding effects.

Section C-1: Standard Sensitivities

R-1	Micrograms of element detectable under a standard set of irradiation and measurement conditions using reaction R-1; (see page 17).

Section A-2: Nuclear Data and Analysis Methods for Charged Particle or Photon Activation

Sub-Section A-2a: Charged Particle and Photon Activation Analysis Methods

References

R-1   Use of reaction, R-1, for activation analysis; matrix; special irradiation or assay technique;
             sensitivity; beam intensity; observed interfering reactions; special comments.   A30 R42
             Threshold, cross-sections, or excitation function for reaction R-1.

Sub-Section A-2b: Data for Other Charged Particle or Photon Reactions

R-2   Threshold, cross-sections, or excitation function for charged particle reaction R-2.   B92 L77 Q17

R-3   Threshold, cross-sections, or excitation function for photon reaction R-3.

Section B-2: Evaluation of Charged Particle and Photon Reactions

R-1   See Section B-1.

Section C-2: Standard Sensitivities

R-1   Micrograms per square centimeter of element detectable under a standard set of irradiation and
             measurement conditions using reaction R-1; (see page 17).

TABLE III

A Tabulation of Nuclear Data and

Experimental Methods for Activation Analysis

H^1	~100	332 ± 2 mb	s		
H^2	0.015	0.46 ± 0.10 mb			
		0.57 ± 0.01 mb a	12.26 y	0.018 (100)	none

$H^2(n,\gamma)H^3$	Possible interference from $Li^6(n,\alpha)H^3$; from $He^3(n,p)H^3$; from other (n,t) reactions.

$H^2(n,\gamma)H^3$	2×10^3 μg.

He^3	0.00013	5500 ± 300	
		(n,p) 5400 ± 200 a	12.26-y H^3
He^4	~100	0	
		0 a	

$He^3(n,p)H^3$	Determination of isotopic abundance of He by direct counting of disintegration products of thermal neutron induced reactions.	C29

$He^3(n,p)H^3$	Possible interference from $Li^6(n,\alpha)H^3$; from $H^2(n,\gamma)H^3$ with a H matrix; from other (n,t) reactions.

$H^2(\gamma, n)H^1$	Determination of 0.1 percent D_2O in 25 ml solution using a 1-curie source of Na^{24} as source of γ's; detected prompt neutrons with boron-coated ionization chamber after moderation with paraffin.	F2 H1
$H^2(d, p)H^3$	Excitation function from 0.013 Mev to 4.0 Mev; E_{th} = 0.013 Mev; $E_p \sim$ 3 Mev; $\sigma(3)$ = 90 mb.	J8
$H^2(d, p)H^3$	Possible interference from $Li^6(d, t)Li^5$; from $Be^9(d, t)Be^8$; from other (d, t) reactions; possible interference from the following secondary reactions: $Li^6(n, \alpha)H^3$; $He^3(n, p)H^3$; other (n, t) or (p, t) reactions.	
$H^2(d, p)H^3$	1×10^3 $\mu g/cm^2$ at 3 Mev.	

$He^4(p, 2p)H^3$	$\sigma(28)$ = 8.9 ± 1.0 mb.	W9
$He^4(\alpha, n)Be^7$	$\sigma(39.9) \leq$ 0.7 mb.	W2
$He^4(\gamma, p)H^3$	Excitation function from 20 Mev to 36 Mev; E_{th} < 20 Mev; $E_p \sim$ 26 Mev; $\sigma(26) \sim$ 1.8 mb.	F16
$He^4(p, 2p)H^3$	Possible interference from $Be^9(p, t)$ and other (p, t) reactions; possible interference from secondary reactions: $Li^6(n, \alpha)H^3$ and other (n, t) reactions.	

Li^6	7.52	28 ± 8 mb (n, α) 945	s 12.26-y H^3	
Li^7	92.48	$33 \pm$ mb a	0.84 s	
		$R = 28^\dagger$		†M9

$Li^6(n, \alpha)H^3$	Determination of Li^6 in aqueous solutions using the second-order reaction $Li^6(n, \alpha)H^3$, $O^{16}(H^3, n)F^{18}$.	W20
	Determination of isotopic composition of Li in Li salts using nuclear emulsions during thermal neutron irradiation.	H24
	Determination and localization of Li in minerals using emulsions; sensitivity = 10^{-4} μg.	P8
	Determination of Li^6 by direct counting of prompt α particles.	K18
	Determination of Li with thermal neutrons by tritium counting; observed interference from Li content in quartz irradiation tubes; sensitivity is limited by self-shielding.	K3
	Determination of Li with 100 mc Ra-Be source by direct counting of tritium in "infinitely" thick samples.	W4
	Excitation function from 0.025 Mev to 14 Mev; E_p = 0.25 and 1.86 Mev; $\sigma(0.25) = 3.4$ b; $\sigma(1.86) = 0.21$ b; $\sigma(14) = 26$ mb.	H49 R4

$Li^7(n, t)He^5 \xrightarrow{n} He^4$	$\sigma(3) = 72 \pm 18$ mb; σ(Po-Be neutrons) = 30 ± 20 mb; $\sigma(14) = 55 \pm 8$ mb.	A3

$Li^6(n, \alpha)H^3$	Possible interference from $H^2(n, \gamma)H^3$ with a H matrix; from $He^3(n, p)H^3$ with a He matrix; from other (n, t) reactions; possible interference from self-shielding in comparator samples.

$Li^6(n, \alpha)H^3$	6×10^{-6} μg.

$Li^7(p,n)Be^7$	Excitation function from E_{th}(1.9 Mev) to 6.8 Mev; E_p = 2.24 Mev; 4.5 Mev, and > 6.8 Mev; $\sigma(2.24)$ = 0.51 b.	B27 F13 J8 M6
	Thick-target yield at 22 Mev = 170 mc/ma-hr.	M15
$Li^6(d,n)Be^7$	Excitation function from E_{th}(0.12 Mev) to 0.35 Mev; E_p > 0.35 Mev; $\sigma(0.33)$ = 39 mb.	J8
$Li^6(d,t)Li^5$	Excitation function from 0.4 Mev to 4.1 Mev; $E_{th} \sim$ 0.28 Mev; E_p > 4.1 Mev; $\sigma(\sim 1.0)$ = 0.19 b; $\sigma(3.8)$ = 0.29 b.	J8 M5
$Li^7(d,t)Li^6$	Excitation function from 0.4 Mev to 4.1 Mev; E_{th} = 1.27 Mev; E_p > 4 Mev; $\sigma(2.4)$ = 95 mb; $\sigma(4.1)$ = 0.16 b.	J8 M5

$Li^7(p,n)Be^7$	Possible interference from $B^{10}(p,\alpha)Be^7$; from $Be^9(p,t)Be^7$.
$Li^6(d,n)Be^7$	Possible interference from $B^{10}(d,\alpha n)Be^7$; from $Be^9(d,2n)Be^7$ at E > 5 Mev; possible interference from secondary reactions: $B^{10}(p,\alpha)Be^7$; $Be^9(p,t)Be^7$.
Li(d,t)	Possible interference from Be(d,t); from other (d,t) reactions; possible interference from secondary reactions: $H^2(n,\gamma)H^3$; $He^3(n,p)H^3$; other (n,t) or (p,t) reactions.

$Li^7(p,n)Be^7$	2×10^{-3} $\mu g/cm^2$ at 2.24 Mev.
$Li^6(d,n)Be^7$	2×10^{-1} $\mu g/cm^2$ at 0.33 Mev.

Be^9	100	10 ± 1 mb			
		9 ± 3 mb a	2.5×10^6 y	0.555 (100)	none

$Be^9(n, \gamma)Be^{10}$ Possible interference from $B^{10}(n, p)Be^{10}$; from $C^{13}(n, \alpha)Be^{10}$.

$Be^9(n, \gamma)Be^{10}$ 1×10^4 μg.

$Be^9(\alpha, n\gamma)C^{12}$ — Determination of Be by direct counting of 4.4 Mev prompt γ's; B, Al, Mg, and other elements interfere.   G9 O3

Excitation function from 0.8 Mev to 5.0 Mev; $E_{th} \sim 0.75$ Mev; $E_p = 1.75$ Mev; $\sigma(1.75) = 0.15$ b; $\sigma(5.0) = 0.4$ b.   H6 T2

$Be^9(\gamma, n)Be^8----2\alpha$ — Non-destructive determination of Be in ores by direct counting of photo-neutrons using an ~ 1 curie Sb^{124} source with a sensitivity of 1 ppm; B, Cd, and other neutron absorbers may interfere.   A22 G1

Excitation function from E_{th}(1.63 Mev) to 24 Mev; $E_p = 9$ Mev and 22 Mev; $\sigma(9) = 1.6$ mb; $\sigma(22) = 3.0$ mb.   E2 N2

- -

$Be^9(p, t)Be^7$ or $Be^9(p, p2n)Be^7$ — Excitation function from 14 Mev to 160 Mev; $E_{th} < 14$ Mev; $E_p = 18.5$ Mev and 55 Mev; $\sigma(18.5) = 12$ mb; $\sigma(22) = 9$ mb; $\sigma(55) = 12$ mb.   B13 C22 / J8 R1 S8

$Be^9(d, t)Be^8$ — Excitation function from 0.5 Mev to 19 Mev; $E_{th} < 0.35$ Mev; $E_p \sim 5$ Mev; $\sigma(5) = 187$ mb; $\sigma(1.5 - 7.7) = 230 \pm 10$ mb.   H22 W16

$Be^9(d, d2n)Be^7$ — $E_{th} = 20$ Mev; $\sigma(90) = 12$ mb.   B13

$Be^9(\alpha, \alpha 2n)Be^7$ — $E_{th} \sim 23$ Mev; $\sigma(90) = 15$ mb.   B13

$Be^9(p, t)Be^7$ — Possible interference in Be^7 measurements from $Li^7(p, n)Be^7$; from $B^{10}(p, \alpha)Be^7$; possible interference in H^3 measurements from many (p, t) reactions; possible interference from secondary reactions: $H^2(n, \gamma)H^3$; $He^3(n, p)H^3$; $Li^6(n, \alpha)H^3$; other (n, t) reactions.

$Be^9(d, t)Be^8$ — Possible interference from Li(d, t); from other (d, t) reactions; possible interference from secondary reactions: $H^2(n, \gamma)H^3$; $He^3(n, p)H^3$; $Li^6(n, \alpha)H^3$; other (n, t) or (p, t) reactions.

$Be^9(d, d2n)Be^7$ — Possible interference from $B^{10}(d, \alpha n)Be^7$; from $Li^6(d, n)Be^7$ or $Li^7(d, 2n)Be^7$; possible interference from secondary reactions: $Li^7(p, n)Be^7$; $B^{10}(p, \alpha)Be^7$.

$Be^9(\alpha, \alpha 2n)Be^7$ — Possible interference from $Li(\alpha,)Be^7$; possible interference from secondary reactions: $Li^7(p, n)Be^7$; $B^{10}(p, \alpha)Be^7$.

$Be^9(p, t)Be^7$ — 8×10^{-2} $\mu g/cm^2$ at 18.5 Mev.

$Be^9(d, t)Be^8--->2\alpha$ — 4×10^{-1} $\mu g/cm^2$ at 5 Mev.

B^{10}	18.8	0.5 ± 0.2 (n, α) 3813 (n, p) <0.2 a	Li^7 (s) 2.7×10^6-y Be^{10}
B^{11}	81.2	<50 mb a	0.03 s 0.019 s
		$R = 280 \pm 40$[†]	†K23

B(n,)	Determination of B by direct counting of 120-Kev prompt γ's or of prompt neutrons using a Po-Be source for activation.	H10
B^{10}(n, α)Li^7	Determination of B^{10} in biological specimens using autoradiography.	E3
	Determination of B in tissues using a Po-Be source and nuclear emulsions.	M17 M18
	Determination of B^{10} in a methyl-ether BF_3 complex by direct counting of prompt α's; precision = 0.4% at B^{10} concentrations of 17% to 30%.	H44
	Determination of B^{10} by direct counting of prompt α's or tritons using a Ra-Be source with efficient moderator for activation	K34 K35 W4

B^{10}(n, p)Be^{10}	Possible interference from Be^9(n, γ)Be^{10}; from C^{13}(n, α)Be^{10}; possible interference from self-shielding in comparator samples.
B^{10}(n, α)Li^7	Possible interference from Li^6(n, α)H^3 with prompt α-counting technique; possible interference from self-shielding in comparator samples.

$B^{11}(p,n)C^{11}$ Determination of B in Si using 20-Mev protons with a sensitivity of 1×10^{-3} μg;
sensitivity limited by interference from reaction $N^{14}(p,\alpha)C^{11}$.   G30

Excitation function from $E_{th}(2.5$ Mev$)$ to 400 Mev; $E_p \sim 10$ Mev; $\sigma(10) = 100$ mb.   B27 H34
                                                                                                    R6   K24

$B^{10}(d,n)C^{11}$ Determination of B using cyclotron irradiations with a sensitivity of 0.5 μg.   S61

Determination of B in Si using 7-Mev protons with a sensitivity of ~ 50 ppb.   E12

$B^{10}(\alpha,n)N^{13}$ Determination of B by activation with 5.3 Mev α's from a 160-mc Po^{210} source; Al and Mg
interfere if no chemical separation is used.   O1 O4

Excitation function from 0.5 Mev to 5.3 Mev; $E_{th} < 0.5$ Mev; $E_p \sim 5$ Mev; $\sigma(1.51) = 32$ mb;
$\sigma(1.64) = 11$ mb.   S25 W3

- -

$B^{10}(p,\alpha)Be^{7}$ Excitation function from $E_{th}(0.06$ Mev$)$ to 1.6 Mev; $E_p = 1.15$ Mev; $\sigma(1.15) = 0.2$ b.   J8 W10

Thick-target yield at 0.70 Mev $= 3 \times 10^{-8}$ Be^{7} atoms/proton.   W10

$B^{11}(p,n)C^{11}$ Possible interference from $N^{14}(p,\alpha)C^{11}$; from $C^{12}(p,pn)C^{11}$ at $E > 20$ Mev.

$B^{10}(p,\alpha)Be^{7}$ Possible interference from $Li^{7}(p,n)Be^{7}$; from $Be^{9}(p,t)Be^{7}$ at $E > 14$ Mev.

$B^{10}(d,n)C^{11}$ Possible interference from $N^{14}(d,\alpha n)C^{11}$; from $C^{12}(d,dn)C^{11}$; possible interference from secondary
reaction: $N^{14}(p,\alpha)C^{11}$.

$B^{10}(\alpha,n)N^{13}$ Possible interference from $C(\alpha,)N^{13}$; from $N^{14}(\alpha,\alpha n)N^{13}$; possible interference from secondary
reactions: $C^{13}(p,n)N^{13}$; $O^{16}(p,\alpha)N^{13}$.

$B^{11}(p,n)C^{11}$ 6×10^{-5} μg/cm^2 at 10 Mev.

C^{12}	98.89	3.3 ± 0.2 mb	s				
C^{13}	1.11	0.5 ± 0.2 mb					
		0.9 ± 0.3 mb a	5568 y	0.155 (100)	none	<200	
						<1 μb a	2.4 s

$C^{12}(n, 2n)C^{11}$ — Excitation function from E_{th} (20.2 Mev) to 27 Mev; $E_p > 27$ Mev; $\sigma(27) = 9$ mb; $\sigma(25) = 5 \pm 1$ mb.   A3 B39

$C^{13}(n, \gamma)C^{14}$ — Possible interference from $N^{14}(n, p)C^{14}$; from $O^{17}(n, \alpha)C^{14}$.

$C^{12}(n, 2n)C^{11}$ — No apparent interference from primary reactions at E < 25 Mev; possible interference from secondary reactions: $B^{11}(p, n)C^{11}$; $N^{14}(p, \alpha)C^{11}$.

$C^{13}(n, \gamma)C^{14}$ — 4×10^4 μg.

$C^{12}(p,\gamma)N^{13}$ Determination of C in Fe using 0.46 Mev protons by coincidence counting with a sensitivity of 3 ppm.   P12

Determination of C in steel using 0.80 Mev protons with a sensitivity of 400 ppm.   V2

$C^{12}(d,n)N^{13}$ Determination of C in organic matter sealed in thin quartz tubes using gross counting technique; ultimate sensitivity = 0.015 μg.   S59

Determination of C in steel and aluminum using gross counting or autoradiography after irradiation with 6.7 deuterons; Fe does not interfere; sensitivity = 1 ppm; ultimate sensitivity much better than that observed.   A4 A7 C12 C37 C38 R7 T1 V2

Excitation function from E_{th}(0.328 Mev) to 20 Mev; E_p = 3.1 Mev and 8 Mev; $\sigma(3.1)$ = 40 mb; $\sigma(8)$ = 100 mb.   A3 B1 N2 N5 N6 W11

$C^{12}(\gamma,n)C^{11}$ Determination of C in Be with a sensitivity of ~ 160 ppm.   B57

Determination of C by x-ray irradiation.   L11

Excitation function from E_{th}(18.7 Mev) to 260 Mev; E_p = 22.5 Mev; Average $\sigma(22.5)$ = 10 mb.   A3 B4 K7 K9 M45 S51 T6

$C^{13}(p,n)N^{13}$ Excitation function from E_{th}(3.23 Mev) to 6.8 Mev; E_p > 6.8 Mev; $\sigma(6.8)$ = 200 mb.   B27 E5 R2

$C^{12}(p,pn)C^{11}$ Excitation function from E_{th}(~ 19 Mev) to 3.0 Bev; E_p ~ 45 Mev; $\sigma(45)$ ~ 100 mb.   A1 C13 C34 H21 H34 P1 R12 W15 W19

$C^{12}(d,t)C^{11}$ Excitation function from 14 Mev to 20 Mev; E_{th} < 14.5 Mev; E_p > 20 Mev; $\sigma(20)$ = 10 mb.   W11

$C^{12}(\alpha,\alpha n)C^{11}$ Excitation function from E_{th}(~ 20 Mev) to 380 Mev; E_p ~ 60 Mev; $\sigma(60)$ = 47 mb.   L15

$C^{13}(p,n)N^{13}$ Possible interference from $O^{16}(p,\alpha)N^{13}$; from $N^{14}(p,pn)N^{13}$ at E > 15 Mev.

$C^{12}(p,pn)C^{11}$ Possible interference from $B^{11}(p,n)C^{11}$; from $N^{14}(p,\alpha)C^{11}$.

$C^{12}(d,n)N^{13}$ Possible interference from $N^{14}(d,dn)N^{13}$; from $O^{16}(d,\alpha n)N^{13}$; possible interference from secondary reaction: $O^{16}(p,\alpha)N^{13}$.

$C^{12}(d,t)C^{11}$ Possible interference from $B^{10}(d,n)C^{11}$ or $B^{11}(d,2n)C^{11}$; from $N^{14}(d,\alpha n)C^{11}$; possible interference from secondary reactions: $B^{11}(p,n)C^{11}$; $N^{14}(p,\alpha)C^{11}$.

$C^{12}(\alpha,\alpha n)C^{11}$ Possible interference from $Be^9(\alpha,2n)C^{11}$; from $B(\alpha,\ )C^{11}$; possible interference from secondary reactions: $B^{11}(p,n)C^{11}$; $N^{14}(p,\alpha)C^{11}$.

$C^{12}(\gamma,n)C^{11}$ No apparent interference from primary reactions; possible interference from secondary reactions: $B^{10}(p,\gamma)C^{11}$ or $B^{11}(p,n)C^{11}$; $N^{14}(p,\alpha)C^{11}$.

$C^{13}(p,n)N^{13}$ 3×10^{-3} μg/cm^2 at 6.8 Mev.

$C^{12}(d,n)N^{13}$ 1×10^{-4} μg/cm^2 at 3.1 Mev.

37

N^{14}	99.63	0.08 ± 0.02	s		
		(n, p) 1.75 ± 0.05	5570-y C^{14}		<200
					<1 μb a 2.4 s
N^{15}	0.37	24 ± 8 μb	7.35 s		
		$R = 4.8 \pm 2.4^{\dagger}$			$\dagger$K23

N^{14}(n, p)C^{14}	Excitation function from 0.15 Mev to 3.6 Mev; E_p = 1.4, 2.26 and 2.80 Mev; $\sigma(1.4) \sim$ 195 mb; $\sigma(2.26)$ = 3 mb; $\sigma(2.80)$ = 3 mb; several peaks at E < 1.0 Mev.	B32 H49
N^{14}(n, 2n)N^{13}	E_{th} = 10.6 Mev; $\sigma(14.5)$ = 5.67 mb.	C20 P2

N^{14}(n, p)C^{14}	Possible interference from O^{17}(n, α)C^{14}; from C^{13}(n, γ)C^{14} with a C matrix.
N^{14}(n, 2n)N^{13}	No apparent interference from primary reactions at E < 20 Mev; interference in fast neutron activation from secondary reactions: C^{13}(p, n)N^{13}; O^{16}(p, α)N^{13}.

$N^{14}(d,n)O^{15}$	Determination of N using a gross counting technique with a sensitivity of 1.0 μg.	S60 S61
	Excitation function from 2.0 Mev to 5.0 Mev; $E_{th} < 2$ Mev; $E_p = 3.68$ Mev; $\sigma(3.68) = 28$ mb.	J8 N6
$N^{14}(\gamma,n)N^{13}$	Determination of N using a gross counting technique; only O interferes at $E < 15$ Mev; interference from C at $E > \sim 24$ Mev.	L11
	Excitation function from E_{th}(10.5 Mev) to 25 Mev; $E_p = 22.5$ Mev; $\sigma(22.5) = 15$ mb.	F5 J14

$N^{14}(p,\gamma)O^{15}$	Excitation function from 0.55 Mev to 2.6 Mev; $E_p = 1.05$ Mev and 2.5 Mev; $\sigma(1.05) = 0.36$ mb; $\sigma(2.5) = 0.4$ mb.	J8
$N^{15}(p,n)O^{15}$	$E_{th} = 3.78$ Mev.	A3
$N^{14}(p,\alpha)C^{11}$	Excitation function from 4.0 Mev to 6.7 Mev; $E_{th} \sim 3$ Mev; $E_p > 6.7$ Mev; $\sigma(6.7) = 95$ mb.	B28 J8

$N^{14}(p,\gamma)O^{15}$	Possible interference from $O^{16}(p,pn)O^{15}$ at $E > 10$ Mev.
$N^{15}(p,n)O^{15}$	Possible interference from $O^{16}(p,pn)O^{15}$ at $E > 10$ Mev.
$N^{14}(p,\alpha)C^{11}$	Possible interference from $B^{11}(p,n)C^{11}$; from $C^{12}(p,pn)C^{11}$ at $E > 20$ Mev.
$N^{14}(d,n)O^{15}$	Possible interference from $O^{16}(d,dn)O^{15}$; possible interference from secondary reactions: $N^{14}(p,\gamma)O^{15}$ or $N^{15}(p,n)O^{15}$.
$N^{14}(\gamma,n)N^{13}$	No apparent interference from primary reactions at $E < 20$ Mev; possible interference in fast neutron activation from secondary reactions: $C^{13}(p,n)N^{13}$; $O^{16}(p,\alpha)N^{13}$.

$N^{14}(p,\alpha)C^{11}$	7×10^{-5} μg/cm^2 at 6.7 Mev.
$N^{14}(d,n)O^{15}$	2×10^{-4} μg/cm^2 at 3.68 Mev.

O^{16}	99.59	0.2 mb	s			
		(n, p) 3.8 μb a[†]	7.4-s N^{16}			
O^{17}	0.037	(n, α) 0.4 ± 0.1 a	5570-y C^{14}		<200	
		(n, p) 3.2 μb[†]	4.14-s N^{17}		<1 μb a	2.4 s
O^{18}	0.204	0.21 ± 0.04 mb a	29.4 s			†F4

O^{16}(n, p)N^{16}	Determination of O in various matrices using 14-Mev neutrons.	L20
	Determination of O in Be using 14.5-Mev neutrons with a sensitivity of 100 ppm.	C40
	Excitation function from 12 Mev to 18 Mev; E_{th} = 10.0 ± 0.7 Mev; E_p = 13.3 Mev;	
	σ(13.3) ~ 90 mb; σ(14.5) = 49 mb.	M12 P2

O^{17}(n, α)C^{14}	σ(~ 1.0) = 0.46 ± 0.11 b.	A3

O^{16}(n, p)N^{16}	Possible interference from N^{15}(n, γ)N^{16}; from F^{19}(n, α)N^{16}.
O^{17}(n, p)N^{17}	No apparent interference.
O^{17}(n, α)C^{14}	Possible interference from C^{13}(n, γ)C^{14}; from N^{14}(n, p)C^{14}.

$O^{18}(p,n)F^{18}$	Determination of O^{18} on paper chromatograms with a sensitivity of < 1 μg.	F8
	Excitation function from $E_{th}(2.59$ Mev$)$ to 6.8 Mev; $E_p > 6.8$ Mev; $\sigma(6.8) = 0.50$ b.	A3 B25 B27 R6
$O^{16}(d,n)F^{17}$	Determination of O in Al using gross counting techniques with a sensitivity of 4.0 μg.	S61
	Excitation function from 2.0 Mev to 5.0 Mev; $E_p = 3.2$ Mev; $\sigma(3.2) = 60$ mb.	N5 N6
$O^{16}(t,n)F^{18}$	Determination of O using tritons from $Li^6(n, \ )$ reaction; chemical separation of F^{18} required; effective $\sigma = 0.5$ mb.	O8
	Determination of O in oxide films using tritons from $Li^6(n, \ )$ reaction.	W21
	Excitation function from 0.68 Mev to 2.13 Mev; $E_{th} < 0.68$ Mev; $\sigma(2.1) \sim 0.10$ b; $\sigma(2.7) = 0.5 \pm 0.2$ b.	J7 S22
$O^{16}(\gamma,n)O^{15}$	Determination of O in Be with a sensitivity of 38 ppm.	B57
	Determination of O in Al; no interference from C at $E < 15.6$ Mev; interference from N and from secondary reaction: $Al^{27}(n, \alpha)Al^{28}$.	L11
	Excitation function from $E_{th}(15.5$ Mev$)$ to 25 Mev; $E_p = 24.2$ Mev; $\sigma(24.2) = 11.4$ mb.	F5 J14 K9 M44 M45 P5 S50

$O^{16}(p,\alpha)N^{13}$	Excitation function from 6 Mev to 16 Mev; $E_{th} < 6$ Mev; $E_p = 8.6$, 11.3, and 14.6 Mev; $\sigma(8.6) \sim 40$ mb; $\sigma(11.3) \sim 50$ mb; $\sigma(14.6) \sim 40$ mb.	W19
$O^{16}(d,\gamma)F^{18}$	$\sigma(1.1) < 0.5$ mb.	A3
$O^{16}(\gamma,p)N^{17}$	Excitation function from $E_{th}(16.35)$ Mev to 25 Mev; $E_p = 24$ Mev; $\sigma(24) \sim 37$ mb.	S55

$O^{18}(p,n)F^{18}$	Possible interference from $Ne^{21}(p,\alpha)F^{18}$; from $F^{19}(p,pn)F^{18}$ at $E > 10$ Mev.
$O^{16}(d,\gamma)F^{18}$	Possible interference from $F^{19}(d,t)F^{18}$ at $E > 6$ Mev; from $Ne^{20}(d,\alpha)F^{18}$; possible interference from secondary reaction: $Ne^{21}(p,\alpha)F^{18}$.
$O^{16}(d,n)F^{17}$	Possible interference with gross counting technique from $N^{14}(d,n)O^{15}$; possible interference from secondary reaction: $Ne^{20}(p,\alpha)F^{17}$.
$O^{16}(t,n)F^{18}$	No apparent interference from primary reactions at $E < 10$ Mev; possible interference from secondary reaction: $Ne^{21}(p,\alpha)F^{18}$.
$O^{16}(\gamma,n)O^{15}$	Possible interference with gross counting techniques from $N^{14}(\gamma,n)N^{13}$; from $P^{31}(\gamma,n)P^{30}$; from $C^{12}(\gamma,n)C^{11}$; from other (γ,n) reactions.

$O^{18}(p,n)F^{18}$	8×10^{-3} μg/cm^2 at 6.8 Mev.
$O^{16}(d,n)F^{17}$	1×10^{-4} μg/cm^2 at 3.2 Mev.

41

F^{19}	100	<10 mb		
		9 ± 2 mb a	10.7 s	
		$R = 2.3 \pm 0.5^{\dagger}$		†K23

$F^{19}(n, \gamma)F^{20}$	Determination of F in chemical reagents and plastics.	L12
	Determination of F with a gross counting technique using a Van de Graaff - Be source with efficient moderator; sensitivity = 0.5 mg; interference from $Ne^{23}(n, \alpha)F^{20}$.	A18
	Determination of F in natural and industrial materials.	L11

$F^{19}(n, p)O^{19}$	$\sigma(14.5) = 0.135$ b.	P2
$F^{19}(n, 2n)F^{18}$	$E_{th} = 10.4$ Mev; $\sigma(14.5) = 61$ mb.	C20 P2

$F^{19}(n, \gamma)F^{20}$	Possible interference from $Na^{23}(n, \alpha)F^{20}$; from $Ne^{20}(n, p)F^{20}$.
$F^{19}(n, p)O^{19}$	Possible interference from $O^{18}(n, \gamma)O^{19}$; from $Na^{22}(n, \alpha)O^{19}$.
$F^{19}(n, 2n)F^{18}$	No apparent interference from primary reactions at E < 25 Mev; possible interference from secondary reactions: $O^{17}(p, \gamma)F^{18}$ or $O^{18}(p, n)F^{18}$; $Ne^{21}(p, \alpha)F^{18}$.

Z = 10   NEON

Ne^{20}	90.92		
Ne^{21}	0.26		
Ne^{22}	8.82	36 ± 15 mb a	40.2 s

$Ne^{22}(n, \gamma)Ne^{23}$	Possible interference from $Na^{23}(n, p)Ne^{23}$; from $Mg^{26}(n, \alpha)Ne^{23}$.

$F^{19}(p,\alpha)O^{16}$	Determination of F in glass using 1.4-Mev p's by counting prompt α's.	R15
$F^{19}(\alpha,n)Na^{22}$	Determination of F using 5.3-Mev α's from a 160-mc Po^{210} source; $E_{th} \sim 2.4$ Mev.	E8 O1 O4

$F^{19}(p,n)Ne^{19}$	Excitation function from $E_{th}(\sim 5.8$ Mev) to 6.8 Mev; $E_p > 6.8$ Mev; $\sigma(6.6) = 50$ mb.	B27
$F^{19}(p,pn)F^{18}$	Excitation function from $E_{th}(9$ Mev) to 25 Mev; $E_p = 20$ Mev; $\sigma(20) = 0.12$ b.	W19
	Thick-target yield at 22 Mev = 500 mc/ma-hr.	M15
$F^{19}(d,t)F^{18}$	Excitation function from 5.3 Mev to 8.7 Mev; $E_{th} \sim 5.3$ Mev; $E_p > 8.7$ Mev; $\sigma(8.7) = 3.9$ mb.	J8 K29
$F^{19}(\gamma,n)F^{18}$	Excitation function from $E_{th}(10.4$ Mev) to 23 Mev; $E_p = 12$ Mev and 20 Mev; $\sigma(12) = 2.5$ mb; $\sigma(20) \sim 3.5$ mb.	F5 G14 H36 T6

$F^{19}(p,n)Ne^{19}$	Possible interference from $Ne^{20}(p,pn)Ne^{19}$ at $E > 15$ Mev.	
$F^{19}(p,pn)F^{18}$	Possible interference from $O^{18}(p,n)F^{18}$; from $Ne^{21}(p,\alpha)F^{18}$; from $Na^{23}(p,p\alpha n)F^{18}$ at $E > 20$ Mev; from $Mg^{25}(p,2\alpha)F^{18}$ at $E > 15$ Mev.	
$F^{19}(d,t)F^{18}$	Possible interference from $O^{17}(d,n)F^{18}$; from $Ne^{20}(d,\alpha)F^{18}$; from $Na^{23}(d,d\alpha n)F^{18}$ at $E > 20$ Mev; from $Mg^{25}(d,2\alpha)F^{18}$ at $E > 12$ Mev; possible interference from secondary reactions: $Ne^{21}(p,\alpha)F^{18}$; $O^{17}(p,\gamma)F^{18}$ or $O^{18}(p,n)F^{18}$.	
$F^{19}(\alpha,n)Na^{22}$	Possible interference from $Ne(\alpha,\quad)Na^{22}$; from $Na^{23}(\alpha,\alpha n)Na^{22}$; possible interference from secondary reactions: $Ne^{22}(p,n)Na^{22}$ or $Ne^{21}(p,\gamma)Na^{22}$; $Mg^{25}(p,\alpha)Na^{22}$.	
$F^{19}(\gamma,n)F^{18}$	No apparent interference from primary reactions at $E < 20$ Mev; possible interference from secondary reactions: $O^{17}(p,\gamma)F^{18}$ or $O^{18}(p,n)F^{18}$; $Ne^{21}(p,\alpha)F^{18}$.	

$F^{19}(p,n)Ne^{19}$	2×10^{-4} $\mu g/cm^2$ at 6.6 Mev.

$Ne^{22}(p,n)Na^{22}$	$E_{th} = 3.35$ Mev.	R5
$Ne^{20}(\gamma,n)Ne^{19}$	Excitation function from $E_{th}(16.9$ Mev) to 25 Mev; $E_p = 21.5$ Mev; $\sigma(21.5) = 7.7$ mb.	F5
$Ne^{20}(\gamma,pn)F^{18}$	$E_{th} = 23$ Mev.	F5

$Ne^{22}(p,n)Na^{22}$	Possible interference from $Mg^{25}(p,\alpha)Na^{22}$; possible interference from $Na^{23}(p,pn)Na^{22}$ at $E > 12$ Mev.

Na^{23}	100	0.51 ± 0.01				
		0.53 ± 0.02 a	14.97 h	$1.394 \; (\sim 100)$	1.368	
					2.754	
		$R = 0.27^{\dagger}$				
		$R_a \sim 0.24^{\dagger}$				$\dagger$ M9

$Na^{23}(n,\gamma)Na^{24}$	Determination of Na in high purity Al with a sensitivity of 0.2 ppm.	A4 A5 C12 G28
	Determination of Na in Ge and Ge compounds using γ-spectrometry with a sensitivity of 0.24 ppm; flux = 3.4×10^{12}.	M49
	Determination of Na in Si using γ-spectrometry with a sensitivity of 0.08 ppm; flux = 3.4×10^{12}.	M47 M48
	Determination of Na in Si with a sensitivity of 4×10^{-5} ppm; flux = 2×10^{14}.	T16
	Determination of Na in Li with a sensitivity of 3×10^{-4} μg.	S35
	Determination of Na in Al alloys with a sensitivity of 1 ppm and with precision within 1.0%; interference from $Al^{27}(n,\alpha)Na^{24}$ and $Mg^{24}(n,p)Na^{24}$ limits ultimate sensitivity.	P11
	Determination of Na in blood using Ra-Be and Van de Graaff-Be sources.	S48
	Others: B60, B65, B67, D13, F7, J11, K16, K17, L4, L8, O5, R3, S2, S6, S7, S33, S47, W22.	

$Na^{23}(n,p)Ne^{23}$	Excitation function from E_{th}(3.5 Mev) to 8.2 Mev; $E_p > 8.2$ Mev; $\sigma(8.2) = 12$ mb; $\sigma(14.5) = 33.9$ mb.	H46 P2 W12
$Na^{23}(n,2n)Na^{22}$	Excitation function from 15 Mev to 120 Mev; $E_{th} \sim 10$ Mev; $E_p \sim 30$ Mev; $\sigma(30) \sim 0.12$ b.	M27 P16

$Na^{23}(n,\gamma)Na^{24}$	Possible interference from $Mg^{24}(n,p)Na^{24}$; from $Al^{27}(n,\alpha)Na^{24}$.
$Na^{23}(n,p)Ne^{23}$	Possible interference from $Ne^{22}(n,\gamma)Ne^{23}$; from $Mg^{26}(n,\alpha)Ne^{23}$.
$Na^{23}(n,2n)Na^{22}$	No apparent interference from primary reactions at E < 20 Mev; possible interference from secondary reactions: $Ne^{22}(p,n)Na^{22}$; $Mg^{25}(p,\alpha)Na^{22}$.

$Na^{23}(n,\gamma)Na^{24}$	2×10^{-5} μg.

$Na^{23}(d,p)Na^{24}$	Determination of Na in glass using 1.4-Mev d's.	R15
	Determination of location of Na in an industrial product using autoradiography.	E7
	Determination of Na in Al with gross counting technique using 4-Mev deuterons; sensitivity $\sim$ 80 ppm.	R7
	Excitation function from 1 Mev to 13 Mev; $E_{th} \sim 1$ Mev; $E_p \sim 5.5$ Mev; $\sigma(5.5) \sim 0.47$ b; thick-target yields.	C15
$Na^{23}(\alpha,n)Al^{26m}$	Determination of Na in urine with gross counting technique using 5.3-Mev α's from a 160-mc Po^{210} source; possible interference from Mg.	O1 O4

- -

$Na^{23}(p,n)Mg^{23}$	Excitation function from 5.0 Mev to 6.8 Mev; $E_{th} < 5$ Mev; $E_p > 6.8$ Mev; $\sigma(6.8) = 40$ mb.	B27
$Na^{23}(p,pn)Na^{22}$	Excitation function from E_{th}(11.6 Mev) to 110 Mev; $E_p \sim 32$ Mev; $\sigma(32) \sim 0.12$ b.	M27
	Thick-target yield at 22 Mev = 3.1 mc/ma-hr.	M15
$Na^{23}(p,p\alpha n)F^{18}$	Excitation function from E_{th}(20.3 Mev) to 110 Mev; $E_p \sim 40$ Mev; $\sigma(40) \sim 35$ mb.	C21 M27
$Na^{23}(\gamma,n)Na^{22}$	Excitation function from E_{th}(12.05 Mev) to 24 Mev; $E_p \sim 18.5$ Mev; $\sigma(18.5) \sim 13$ mb.	M45

$Na^{23}(p,n)Mg^{23}$	Possible interference from $Mg^{24}(p,pn)Mg^{23}$ at $E > \sim 15$ Mev.
$Na^{23}(p,pn)Na^{22}$	Possible interference from $Ne^{22}(p,n)Na^{22}$; from $Mg^{25}(p,\alpha)Na^{22}$; from $Al^{27}(p,p\alpha n)Na^{22}$ at $E > 25$ Mev.
$Na^{23}(p,p\alpha n)F^{18}$	Possible interference from $O^{18}(p,n)F^{18}$; from $F^{19}(p,pn)F^{18}$; from $Ne^{21}(p,\alpha)F^{18}$; from $Mg^{25}(p,2\alpha)F^{18}$; possible interference from secondary reaction: $O^{17}(p,\gamma)F^{18}$.
$Na^{23}(d,p)Na^{24}$	Possible interference from $Mg^{26}(d,\alpha)Na^{24}$; from $Ne^{22}(d,\gamma)Na^{24}$; from $Al^{27}(d,\alpha p)Na^{24}$ at $E > 12$ Mev; possible interference from secondary reactions: $Na^{23}(n,\gamma)Na^{24}$; $Mg^{24}(n,p)Na^{24}$; $Al^{27}(n,\alpha)Na^{24}$.
$Na^{23}(\alpha,n)Al^{26m}$	Possible interference from $Mg(\alpha,)Al^{26m}$; from $Al^{27}(\alpha,\alpha n)Al^{26m}$.
$Na^{23}(\gamma,n)Na^{22}$	No apparent interference from primary reactions; possible interference from secondary reactions: $Ne^{21}(p,\gamma)Na^{22}$ or $Ne^{22}(p,n)Na^{22}$; $Mg^{25}(p,\alpha)Na^{22}$.

$Na^{23}(p,n)Mg^{23}$	3×10^{-4} $\mu g/cm^2$ at 6.8 Mev.
$Na^{23}(d,p)Na^{24}$	7×10^{-5} $\mu g/cm^2$ at 5.5 Mev.

Mg^{24}	78.60	34 ± 10 mb	s				
Mg^{25}	10.11	280 ± 90 mb	s				
Mg^{26}	11.29	60 ± 60 mb					
		27 ± 5 mb a	9.45 m	1.75 (58)	0.834 (70)	30 mb* a	21 h
				1.59 (42)	1.015 (30)		
		$R = 0.9^{\dagger}$					$\dagger$ M9

$Mg^{26}(n,\gamma)Mg^{27}$	Determination of Mg in drinking water.	B60
	Determination of Mg in blood using Ra-Be and Van de Graaff - Be sources.	S33
	Others: J11, L4.	
$Mg^{24}(n,p)Na^{24}$	Determination of Mg in Si using reactor neutrons with a sensitivity of 0.08 ppm; fast flux $\sim 7 \times 10^{10}$.	T16
	$E_{th} = 4.9$ Mev; $\sigma(13) = 0.22$ b; $\sigma(14.5) = 0.19$ b.	H46 K32 P2

$Mg^{25}(n,p)Na^{25}$	$E_{th} = 4.1$ Mev; $\sigma(14.5) = 45$ mb.	H46 P2

$Mg^{26}(n,\gamma)Mg^{27}$	Possible interference from $Al^{27}(n,p)Mg^{27}$; from $Si^{30}(n,\alpha)Mg^{27}$.
$Mg^{24}(n,p)Na^{24}$	Possible interference from $Na^{23}(n,\gamma)Na^{24}$; from $Al^{27}(n,\alpha)Na^{24}$.
$Mg^{25}(n,p)Na^{25}$	No apparent interference.

$Mg^{26}(n,\gamma)Mg^{27}$	2×10^{-3} µg.

$Mg^{25}(\alpha, p)Al^{28}$	Determination of Mg using 5.3 Mev α's from a 160-mc Po^{210} source; B and Al interfere if direct counting technique used; $E_{th} \sim 4$ Mev.	O1 O4 S67

$Mg(p,)Na^{22}$	Excitation function from $E_{th}(\sim 7$ Mev) to 31 Mev; $E_p \sim 15$ Mev; $\sigma(15) \sim 70$ mb.	B7
$Mg^{25}(p, \alpha)Na^{22}$	Excitation function from $E_{th}(\sim 3.5$ Mev) to 95 Mev; $E_p \sim 15$ Mev and 42 Mev; $\sigma(15) = 115$ mb; $\sigma(42) \sim 45$ mb.	B12 C26 M28
	Thick-target yield at 22 Mev = 0.4 mc/ma-hr.	M15
$Mg^{25}(p, 2p)Na^{24}$	Excitation function from $E_{th}(\sim 11.6)$ to 110 Mev; $E_p \sim 30$ Mev; $\sigma(30) = 52$ mb.	C26 M27
$Mg^{25}(p, 2\alpha)F^{18}$	Excitation function from $E_{th}(12$ Mev) to 110 Mev; $E_p \sim 27$ Mev; $\sigma(27) \sim 20$ mb.	B7 M27
$Mg^{26}(p, \alpha n)Na^{22}$	Excitation function from $E_{th}(\sim 15$ Mev) to 95 Mev; $E_p \sim 30$ Mev; $\sigma(30) = 43$ mb.	M28
$Mg^{24}(d, \alpha)Na^{22}$	Excitation function from $E_{th}(\sim 2$ Mev) to 15 Mev; $E_p \sim 9.5$ Mev; $\sigma(9.5) = 0.15$ b; $\sigma(7.8) = 94 \pm 4$ mb.	C16 H3 H53 I2
$Mg^{26}(d, \alpha)Na^{24}$	Excitation function from $E_{th}(\sim 2$ Mev) to 15 Mev; $E_p \sim 8.5$ Mev; $\sigma(8.5) \sim 90$ mb; $\sigma(7.8) = 151 \pm 6$ mb.	C16 H3 H53 I2
$Mg^{24}(d, 2\alpha)F^{18}$	Excitation function from $E_{th}(\sim 10$ Mev) to 190 Mev; $E_p \sim 20$ Mev; $\sigma(20) \sim 24$ mb.	B7
$Mg^{24}(\gamma, n)Mg^{23}$	Excitation function from $E_{th}(\sim 17$ Mev) to 24 Mev; $E_p = 19.5$ Mev; $\sigma(19.5) = 8.4$ mb.	N4
$Mg^{25}(\gamma, p)Na^{24}$	Excitation function from $E_{th}(10.6$ Mev) to 24 Mev; $E_p = 20.5$ Mev; $\sigma(20.5) = 27$ mb.	K8 T19

$Mg(p,)Na^{22}$	Possible interference from $Ne^{22}(p, n)Na^{22}$; from $Na^{23}(p, pn)Na^{22}$ at $E > 12$ Mev.
$Mg^{25}(p, 2p)Na^{24}$	Possible interference from $Al^{27}(p, 3pn)Na^{24}$ at $E > 20$ Mev; possible interference from secondary reactions: $Na^{23}(n, \gamma)Na^{24}$; $Al^{27}(n, \alpha)Na^{24}$.
$Mg^{25}(p, 2\alpha)F^{18}$	Possible interference from $O^{18}(p, n)F^{18}$; from $F^{19}(p, pn)F^{18}$; from $Ne^{21}(p, \alpha)F^{18}$; from $Na^{23}(p, p\alpha n)F^{18}$ at $E > 20$ Mev; possible interference from secondary reactions: $O^{17}(p, \gamma)F^{18}$; $Ne^{21}(n, \alpha)F^{18}$.
$Mg^{24}(d, \alpha)Na^{22}$	Possible interference from $Ne^{21}(d, n)Na^{22}$ or $Ne^{22}(d, 2n)Na^{22}$; from $Na^{23}(d, dn)Na^{22}$.
$Mg^{26}(d, \alpha)Na^{24}$	Possible interference from $Na^{23}(d, p)Na^{24}$; from $Ne^{22}(d, \gamma)Na^{24}$; from $Al^{27}(d, \alpha p)Na^{24}$ at $E > 11$ Mev; possible interference from secondary reactions: $Na^{23}(n, \gamma)Na^{24}$; $Mg^{24}(n, p)Na^{24}$; $Al^{27}(n, \alpha)Na^{24}$.
$Mg^{24}(d, 2\alpha)F^{18}$	Possible interference from $O^{17}(d, n)F^{18}$ or $O^{18}(d, 2n)F^{18}$; from $F^{19}(d, dn)F^{18}$; from $Ne^{20}(d, \alpha)F^{18}$; possible interference from secondary reactions: $O^{17}(p, \gamma)F^{18}$ or $O^{18}(p, n)F^{18}$; $Ne^{21}(p, \alpha)F^{18}$.
$Mg^{25}(\alpha, p)Al^{28}$	Possible interference from $Al^{27}(\alpha, 2pn)Al^{28}$; possible interference from secondary reactions: $Al^{27}(n, \gamma)Al^{28}$; $P^{31}(n, \alpha)Al^{28}$.
$Mg^{25}(\gamma, p)Na^{24}$	No apparent interference from primary reactions; possible interference from secondary reactions: $Na^{23}(n, \gamma)Na^{24}$; $Al^{27}(n, \alpha)Na^{24}$.

$Mg^{25}(p, \alpha)Na^{22}$	4 $\mu g/cm^2$ at 15 Mev.
$Mg^{26}(d, \alpha)Na^{24}$	4×10^{-5} $\mu g/cm^2$ at 8.5 Mev.

Al^{27}	100	0.230 ± 0.005			
		0.21 ± 0.02 a	2.27 m	2.87 (100)	1.78 ($\sim$100)
		$R = 0.18^{\dagger}$			
		$R_a \sim 0.16^{\dagger}$			$\dagger$ M9

$Al^{27}(n, \gamma)Al^{28}$	Determination of Al in silicate rocks using moderated Po-Be neutrons.	B67
	Determination of Al with a calculated sensitivity of 10^{-4} μg.	J11
$Al^{27}(n, \alpha)Na^{24}$	Determination of Al in Si using cyclotron produced neutrons; detection by x-ray film.	S54
	Determination of relatively high quantities of Al in ceramics by γ-spectrometry after activation by 14-Mev neutrons; interference from Mg and Fe; $\sigma(14) = 135$ mb.	T20
	Determination of Al in Si using pile neutrons with a sensitivity of 0.1 ppm; fast flux $\sim 7 \times 10^{10}$.	T16
	Excitation function from 6 Mev to 14 Mev; $E_{th} = 3.3$ Mev; $E_p > 14$ Mev; $\sigma(13) = 0.14$ b; $\sigma(14) = 116$ mb.	F9 G26 H46 K32

$Al^{27}(n, p)Mg^{27}$	$E_{th} = 2.1$ Mev; average $\sigma(14) = 79$ mb.	C20 F9 H2 H46 P2
$Al^{27}(n, 2n)Al^{26m}$	$\sigma(14) = 87.2$ mb.	Y1

$Al^{27}(n, \gamma)Al^{28}$	Possible interference from $Si^{28}(n, p)Al^{28}$; from $P^{31}(n, \alpha)Al^{28}$; possible interference from second-order reaction: $Mg^{26}(n, \gamma)Mg^{27} \xrightarrow{\beta^-} Al^{27}(n, \gamma)Al^{28}$ with a Mg matrix.
$Al^{27}(n, p)Mg^{27}$	Possible interference from $Mg^{26}(n, \gamma)Mg^{27}$; from $Si^{30}(n, \alpha)Mg^{27}$.
$Al^{27}(n, \alpha)Na^{24}$	Possible interference from $Mg^{24}(n, p)Na^{24}$; possible interference from secondary reaction: $Na^{23}(n, \gamma)Na^{24}$.
$Al^{27}(n, 2n)Al^{26m}$	No apparent interference from primary reactions; possible interference from secondary reactions: $Mg^{26}(p, n)Al^{26m}$ or $Mg^{25}(p, \gamma)Al^{26m}$; $Si^{29}(p, \alpha)Al^{26m}$.

$Al^{27}(n, \gamma)Al^{28}$	4×10^{-5} μg.

$Al^{27}(\alpha, n)P^{30}$ — Determination of Al with a gross counting technique using 5.3 Mev α's from a 160—mc Po^{210} source; interference from B and Mg; precision about 5%; E_{th} = 3.4 Mev; $\sigma(5) \sim$ 20 mb.   O1 O4 H6

- -

$Al^{27}(p, n)Si^{27}$ — Excitation function from $E_{th}(\sim$ 5.8 Mev) to 6.8 Mev; $E_p >$ 6.8 Mev; $\sigma(6.3)$ = 10 mb.   B27

$Al^{27}(p, 3pn)Na^{24}$ — Excitation function from $E_{th}(\sim$ 20 Mev) to 980 Mev; $E_p \sim$ 75 Mev; $\sigma(75)$ = 16 mb.   C9 C35 H32 H34

$Al^{27}(p, p\alpha n)Na^{22}$ — Excitation function from E_{th}(25 Mev) to 110 Mev; $E_p \sim$ 45 Mev; $\sigma(45)$ = 23 mb.   B12 H34

$Al^{27}(d, \alpha p)Na^{24}$ — Excitation function from E_{th}(11 Mev) to 190 Mev; E_p = 22 Mev; $\sigma(22)$ = 53 mb.   B14 C14 H33

$Al^{27}(d, d\alpha n)Na^{22}$ — Excitation function from $E_{th}(\sim$ 25 Mev) to 190 Mev; E_p = 40 Mev; $\sigma(40)$ = 30 mb.   H33 R8

$Al^{27}(\alpha, \alpha 2pn)Na^{24}$ — Excitation function from $E_{th}(\sim$ 33 Mev) to 380 Mev; $E_p \sim$ 100 Mev; $\sigma(100) \sim$ 35 mb.   L14

$Al^{27}(\gamma, n)Al^{26m}$ — Excitation function from E_{th}(13.4 Mev) to 25 Mev; E_p = 19.5 Mev; $\sigma(19.5)$ = 22 mb.   M45 S23

$Al^{27}(p, n)Si^{27}$ — Possible interference from $Si^{28}(p, pn)Si^{27}$ at E > 15 Mev.

$Al^{27}(p, 3n)Na^{24}$ — Possible interference from $Mg(p,\ )Na^{24}$; possible interference from secondary reactions: $Na^{23}(n, \gamma)Na^{24}$; $Mg^{24}(n, p)Na^{24}$.

$Al^{27}(d, \alpha p)Na^{24}$ — Possible interference from $Na^{23}(d, p)Na^{24}$; from $Mg(d,\ )Na^{24}$; possible interference from secondary reactions: $Na^{23}(n, \gamma)Na^{24}$; $Mg^{24}(n, p)Na^{24}$.

$Al^{27}(\gamma, n)Al^{26m}$ — No apparent interference from primary reactions; possible interference from secondary reactions: $Mg^{25}(p, \gamma)Al^{26m}$ or $Mg^{26}(p, n)Al^{26m}$; $Si^{29}(p, \alpha)Al^{26m}$.

Si^{28}	92.27	0.08 ± 0.03	s			
Si^{29}	4.68	0.28 ± 0.09	s			
Si^{30}	3.05	0.4 ± 0.4				
		0.11 ± 0.01 a	2.62 h	1.47 (99+)	1.26 (.07)	
		$R = 0.5$ †				† M9

$Si^{30}(n, \gamma)Si^{31}$	Determination of Si in Zr with a calculated sensitivity of ~ 600 ppm; flux = 5×10^{11}.	L10
	Determination of Si in drinking water.	B60
	Determination of Si in high purity Al with a sensitivity of 3 ppm.	A4 C12
	Others: J11, L4, S33.	
$Si^{28}(n, p)Al^{28}$	Determination of Si in silicate rocks using a Po-Be source.	B66
	Determination of high concentration (> 0.1 g) Si in various matrices with a gross counting technique using 14-Mev neutrons; a quick method for routine assay; interference from Pr and Ca.	L20 T20
	Excitation function from 4.0 Mev to 8.0 Mev; $E_{th} = 3.9$ Mev; $E_p = 7.45$ Mev; $\sigma(7.45) = 0.37$ b; $\sigma(13.5) = 0.38$ b; $\sigma(14.5) = 0.22$ b.	C20 E8 H46 K32 M11 P2
$Si^{29}(n, p)Al^{29}$	$E_{th} = 1.8$ Mev; $\sigma(3.3) = 2.7$ mb; $\sigma(14.5) = 0.10$ b.	C20 H46 P2
$Si^{30}(n, \alpha)Mg^{27}$	$\sigma(14.5) = 45.9$ mb.	P2

$Si^{30}(n, \gamma)Si^{31}$	Possible interference from $P^{31}(n, p)Si^{31}$; from $S^{34}(n, \alpha)Si^{31}$ with a S matrix.
$Si^{28}(n, p)Al^{28}$	Possible interference from $Al^{27}(n, \gamma)Al^{28}$; from $P^{31}(n, \alpha)Al^{28}$.
$Si^{29}(n, p)Al^{29}$	No apparent interference.
$Si^{30}(n, \alpha)Mg^{27}$	Possible interference from $Al^{27}(n, p)Mg^{27}$; from $Mg^{26}(n, \gamma)Mg^{27}$.

$Si^{30}(n, \gamma)Si^{31}$	2×10^{-3} μg.

$Si^{30}(d,p)Si^{31}$	Determination of Si in Al with a direct counting technique using 4 Mev deuterons; observed sensitivity = 3.7×10^{3} ppm.	R7

$Si^{29}(p,2p)Al^{28}$	Excitation function from E_{th}(11.8 Mev) to $\sim$ 30 Mev; $E_{p} \sim$ 28 Mev; $\sigma(28) \sim$ 0.18 b; $\sigma(21.5) = 0.11$ b.	C21 C25
$Si^{28}(\gamma,n)Si^{27}$	Excitation function from E_{th}(16.9 Mev) to 24 Mev; $E_{p} = 20.9$ Mev; $\sigma(20.9) = 21$ mb.	S64
$Si^{30}(\gamma,p)Al^{29}$	Excitation function from E_{th}(12.3 Mev) to $\sim$ 22 Mev; $E_{p} = 21$ Mev; $\sigma(21) = 32$ mb.	K8

$Si^{29}(p,2p)Al^{28}$	No apparent interference from primary reactions at E < 20 Mev; possible interference from secondary reactions: $Al^{27}(n,\gamma)Al^{28}$; $P^{31}(n,\alpha)Al^{28}$.
$Si^{29}(d,n)P^{30}$	Possible interference from $P^{31}(d,dn)P^{30}$; from $S^{32}(d,\alpha)P^{30}$; possible interference from secondary reaction: $S^{33}(p,\alpha)P^{30}$.
$Si^{30}(d,p)Si^{31}$	No apparent interference from primary reactions; possible interference from secondary reactions: $P^{31}(n,p)Si^{31}$; $S^{34}(n,\alpha)Si^{31}$.

P^{31}	100	0.20 ± 0.02			
		0.19 ± 0.01 a	14.22 d	1.707 (100)	none
		$R_a \sim 92$ mb†			$\dagger$M9

$P^{31}(n,\gamma)P^{32}$	Determination of P in high purity Fe and Al with a sensitivity of 1 ppm.	A4 T1
	Determination of P in I with a sensitivity of 0.1 ppm.	J5
	Determination of P in Mg with a sensitivity of 3×10^{-3} µg; flux = 5×10^{11}.	A17
	Determination of P in Si with a sensitivity of 0.01 ppm; flux = 3×10^{12}; corrected for Si interference from second-order reaction: $Si^{30}(n,\gamma)Si^{31} \xrightarrow{\beta^-} P^{31}(n,\gamma)P^{32}$; limiting irradiation time to 1 week minimizes effect of this reaction.	C5 J3 K2
	Others (n,γ): F10, H25, H38, L3, L4, L23, O5, R3, S33, T16.	
$P^{31}(n,p)Si^{31}$	Determination of P in electrophorograms.	S12
	Excitation function from 1.6 Mev to 14 Mev; $E_{th} \sim 0.7$ Mev; $E_p \sim$ 5-10 Mev; $\sigma(5\text{-}10)$ = 142 mb; $\sigma(14)$ = 86 mb.	C20 F9 G25 G26 H46 M39 P6 R22
$P^{31}(n,\alpha)Al^{28}$	Determination of P in various matrices using 14-Mev neutrons.	L20
	E_{th} = 2.0 Mev; $\sigma(14.5)$ = 0.146 b.	H46 P2

$P^{31}(n,\gamma)P^{32}$	Possible interference from $S^{32}(n,p)P^{32}$; from $Cl^{35}(n,\alpha)P^{32}$ with a Cl matrix; possible interference from second-order reaction: $Si^{30}(n,\gamma)Si^{31} \xrightarrow{\beta^-} P^{31}(n,\gamma)P^{32}$ with a Si matrix.
$P^{31}(n,p)Si^{31}$	Possible interference from $Si^{30}(n,\gamma)Si^{31}$; from $S^{34}(n,\alpha)Si^{31}$.
$P^{31}(n,\alpha)Al^{28}$	Possible interference from $Al^{27}(n,\gamma)Al^{28}$; from $Si^{28}(n,p)Al^{28}$.
$P^{31}(n,2n)P^{30}$	No apparent interference from primary reactions at E < 20 Mev; possible interference from secondary reactions: $Si^{30}(p,n)P^{30}$ or $Si^{29}(p,\gamma)P^{30}$; $S^{33}(p,\alpha)P^{30}$.

$P^{31}(n,\gamma)P^{32}$	6×10^{-5} µg.

$P^{31}(p,pn)P^{30}$ E_{th} = 12.8 Mev; $\sigma(21.5)$ = 0.24 b.   C25

$P^{31}(\gamma,n)P^{30}$ Excitation function from E_{th}(12.33 Mev) to 25 Mev; E_p = 19 Mev; $\sigma(19)$ = 16.4 mb.   B9 K7
                                                                                                                                    K13 M45

$P^{31}(p,pn)P^{30}$ Possible interference from $Si^{30}(p,n)P^{30}$; from $S^{33}(p,\alpha)P^{30}$; possible interference from secondary
                             reaction: $Si^{29}(p,\gamma)P^{30}$.

$P^{31}(\gamma,n)P^{30}$ No apparent interference from primary reactions; possible interference from secondary reactions:
                             $Si^{29}(p,\gamma)P^{30}$ or $Si^{30}(p,n)P^{30}$; $S^{33}(p,\alpha)P^{30}$.

S^{32}	95.018	(n, α) 1.8 ± 1.0 mb	Si^{29} (s)		
S^{33}	0.750	(n, p) 15 ± 10 mb a	25.1-d P^{33}		
		(n, α) 8 mb	Si^{30}(s)		
S^{34}	4.215	0.26 ± 0.05 a	87 d	0.167 (100)	none
S^{36}	0.017	0.14 ± 0.04 a	5.04 m	1.6 (90)	3.09 (~90)
				4.3 (10)	
		R = 0.6 †			† M9

$S^{34}(n, \gamma)S^{35}$	Determination of S in Mg with a sensitivity of 10 µg; flux = 5×10^{11}.	A17
	Determination of S with a calculated sensitivity of 0.1 µg; flux $\sim 10^{12}$.	S33
	Others: J11, L4.	
$S^{32}(n, p)P^{32}$	Determination of S in paper chromatograms using a cyclotron-Be source.	S13
	Excitation function from $E_{th}(\sim 1.0$ Mev) to 15 Mev; E_p = (6-10) Mev; $\sigma(6$-$10)$ = 0.30 b; $\sigma(15)$ = 0.31 b.	A8 C20 G25 H46 H52 P2 S4

| $S^{34}(n, p)P^{34}$ | $\sigma(14.5)$ = 55.2 mb. | P2 |
| $S^{34}(n, \alpha)Si^{31}$ | E_{th} = 0.9 Mev; $\sigma(14.5)$ = 0.138 b. | H46 P2 |

$S^{34}(n, \gamma)S^{35}$	Possible interference from $Cl^{35}(n, p)S^{35}$; from $A^{38}(n, \alpha)S^{35}$ with an A matrix.
$S^{36}(n, \gamma)S^{37}$	Possible interference from $Cl^{37}(n, p)S^{37}$; from $A^{40}(n, \alpha)S^{37}$ with an A matrix.
$S^{32}(n, p)P^{32}$	Possible interference from $P^{31}(n, \gamma)P^{32}$; from $Cl^{35}(n, \alpha)P^{32}$.
$S^{33}(n, p)P^{33}$	No apparent interference.
$S^{34}(n, p)P^{34}$	Possible interference from $Cl^{37}(n, \alpha)P^{34}$.
$S^{34}(n, \alpha)Si^{31}$	Possible interference from $Si^{30}(n, \gamma)Si^{31}$; from $P^{31}(n, p)Si^{31}$.

| $S^{34}(n, \gamma)S^{35}$ | 4×10^{-3} µg. |
| $S^{36}(n, \gamma)S^{37}$ | 4×10^{-1} µg. |

$S^{33}(d, n)Cl^{34, 34m}$ Determination of S using a gross counting technique with a sensitivity of 10^3 μg.   S61

$S^{32}(d, \alpha)P^{30}$ Determination of S using a gross counting technique with a sensitivity of 0.3 μg.   S61 S62

$S^{34}(p, n)Cl^{34, 34m}$ Excitation function from 8 Mev to 110 Mev; E_{th} < 8 Mev; E_p = 12 Mev; $\sigma(12) \sim$ 65 mb.   H34

$S^{34}(d, \alpha)P^{32}$ Excitation function from 1.0 Mev to 7.75 Mev; E_{th} < 1.0 Mev; E_p > 7.75 Mev; $\sigma(7.75)$ = 0.33 b.   A12 H3 H53

$S^{32}(\gamma, n)S^{31}$ Excitation function from E_{th} ($\sim$ 11.5 Mev) to 23 Mev; $E_p \sim$ 20 Mev; average $\sigma(20.1)$ = 19 mb.   H19 M45

$S^{32}(\gamma, np)P^{30}$ Excitation function from E_{th} (15 Mev) to $\sim$ 27 Mev; E_p = 26 Mev; $\sigma(26)$ = 1.5 ± 0.2 mb; $\sigma(26) \sim$ 6 mb.   K7 K13

$S^{34}(p, n)Cl^{34, 34m}$ Possible interference from $Cl^{35}(p, pn)Cl^{34, 34m}$ at E > 15 Mev.

$S^{33}(d, n)Cl^{34, 34m}$ Possible interference from $A^{36}(d, \alpha)Cl^{34, 34m}$; from $Cl^{35}(d, dn)Cl^{34, 34m}$.

$S^{32}(d, \alpha)P^{30}$ Possible interference from $Si^{29}(d, n)P^{30}$ or $Si^{30}(d, 2n)P^{30}$; from $P^{31}(d, dn)P^{30}$; possible interference from secondary reactions: $Si^{29}(p, \gamma)P^{30}$ or $Si^{30}(p, n)P^{30}$.

$S^{34}(d, \alpha)P^{32}$ No apparent interference from primary reactions; possible interference from secondary reactions: $P^{31}(n, \gamma)P^{32}$; $Cl^{35}(n, \alpha)P^{32}$.

$S^{34}(p, n)Cl^{34m}$ 5×10^{-3} μg/cm^2 at 12 Mev.

Cl^{35}	75.4	30 ± 20 a	3.08×10^5 y		90 ± 30	s
		$(n,p)\, 0.19 \pm 0.05$ a	87-d S^{35}			
		$(n,\alpha) < 0.05$ mb a	14.3-d P^{32}			
Cl^{37}	24.6	5 ± 3 mb* a	1.0 s			
		0.56 ± 0.12	37.29 m	M	2.15	
					1.60	
		$R = 12.8 \pm 1.7^{\dagger}$				†K23

$Cl^{37}(n,\gamma)Cl^{38}$	Determination of Cl in paper chromatograms using a cyclotron-Be source.	S13
	Determination of Cl using a Van de Graaff - Be source with efficient moderator; sensitivity = 20 μg.	A18 S48
	Determination of Cl in Ti with a sensitivity of 3 ppm; flux $\sim 10^{12}$.	B44
	Determination of Cl in ZnS scintillators with a sensitivity of 1 μg; flux = 3×10^{12}; sensitivity limited by interference from reaction $S^{36}(n,\gamma)S^{37} \xrightarrow{\beta^-} Cl^{37}(n,\gamma)Cl^{38}$.	B3 C41
	Others: B43, B60, D2, D3, J11, L4, L11, L12, S33.	

- -

$Cl^{35}(n,p)S^{35}$	$E_{th} = 0.7$ Mev.	H46
$Cl^{37}(n,p)S^{37}$	$E_{th} = 3.5$ Mev; $\sigma(14.5) = 33.4$ mb.	H46 P2 S70
$Cl^{35}(n,\alpha)P^{32}$	$E_{th} = 1.0$ Mev; $\sigma(14.5) = 0.19$ b.	H46 P2
$Cl^{37}(n,\alpha)P^{34}$	$\sigma(14.5) = 52.4$ mb.	P2
$Cl^{35}(n,2n)Cl^{34m}$	$\overline{\sigma}(14.5) = 4.5$ mb.	P2 S70
$Cl^{35}(n,2n)Cl^{34}$	$\sigma(14.8) = 2.8$ mb.	S70

$Cl^{37}(n,\gamma)Cl^{38}$	Possible interference from $A^{38}(n,p)Cl^{38}$ in an A matrix; from $K^{41}(n,\alpha)Cl^{38}$ in a K matrix; possible interference from second-order reaction: $S^{36}(n,\gamma)S^{37} \xrightarrow{\beta^-} Cl^{37}(n,\gamma)Cl^{38}$ with a S matrix; possible interference from self-shielding in comparator samples.
$Cl^{35}(n,p)S^{35}$	Possible interference from $S^{34}(n,\gamma)S^{35}$ or $S^{36}(n,2n)S^{35}$; from $A^{38}(n,\alpha)S^{35}$.
$Cl^{37}(n,p)S^{37}$	Possible interference from $S^{36}(n,\gamma)S^{37}$; from $A^{40}(n,\alpha)S^{37}$.
$Cl^{35}(n,\alpha)P^{32}$	Possible interference from $P^{31}(n,\gamma)P^{32}$; from $S^{32}(n,p)P^{32}$.

$Cl^{37}(n,\gamma)Cl^{38}$	7×10^{-5} μg.

- -

$Cl^{37}(p,n)A^{37}$ Relative excitation function from $E_{th}(\sim 1.3$ Mev$)$ to 6.8 Mev; $E_p > 6.8$ Mev.   B27 R6

$Cl^{35}(p,pn)Cl^{34m}$ $E_{th} = 13.6$ Mev; $\sigma(21.5) = 0.12$ b.   C25

$Cl^{35}(\gamma,n)Cl^{34m}$ $E_{th} = 9.95$ Mev; $\sigma(17.6) = 4.4$ mb.   D8

$Cl^{37}(p,n)A^{37}$ Possible interference from $K^{40}(p,\alpha)A^{37}$ with a K matrix; possible interference from secondary reaction: $A^{36}(n,\gamma)A^{37}$.

$Cl^{35}(p,pn)Cl^{34,34m}$ Possible interference from $S^{33}(p,\gamma)Cl^{34,34m}$; $S^{34}(p,n)Cl^{34,34m}$; or $S^{35}(p,2n)Cl^{34,34m}$.

A^{36}	0.34	6 ± 2 a	35 d	EC (100)	none		
A^{38}	0.063	0.8 ± 0.2 a	~ 265 y	0.565 (100)	none		
A^{40}	99.600	0.53 ± 0.02 a	110 m	1.20 (99+)	1.29 (~100)	>60 mb	>3.5 y

$A^{36}(n, \gamma)A^{37}$	Determination of age of meteorites by comparison to K activation.	S74
$A^{40}(n, \gamma)A^{41}$	Determination of age of K minerals by analysis for radiogenic A^{40}; sensitivity = 3 x 10^{-6} µg; flux = 1 x 10^{11}; $K^{41}(n, p)A^{41}$ interferes and requires pre-irradiation separation of A from matrix.	M43
	Determination of age of meteorites by comparison to K activation.	S74
	Determination of A in drinking water.	B6

$A^{36}(n, \gamma)A^{37}$	Possible interference from $Ca^{40}(n, \alpha)A^{37}$ with a Ca matrix.
$A^{40}(n, \gamma)A^{41}$	Possible interference from $K^{41}(n, p)A^{41}$ with a K matrix; from $Ca^{44}(n, \alpha)A^{41}$ with a Ca matrix.

$A^{36}(n, \gamma)A^{37}$	1 x 10^{-3} µg.
$A^{40}(n, \gamma)A^{41}$	2 x 10^{-5} µg.

$A^{40}(\alpha, p)K^{43}$ $\sigma(7.4) = 0.26$ mb.   S14

$A^{40}(\gamma, n)A^{39}$ Excitation function from 10 Mev to 25 Mev; $E_{th} < 10$ Mev; $E_p = 20$ Mev; $\sigma(20) = 38$ mb.   F5 M23
                                                                                                                                P17 S49

$A^{40}(\gamma, p)Cl^{39}$ Excitation function from E_{th}(12.44 Mev) to 35 Mev; $E_p = 23.5$ Mev; $\sigma(23.5) = 67$ mb.   M23 P17 S49

$A^{40}(\gamma, np)Cl^{38}$ Excitation function from 20 Mev to 40 Mev; $E_{th} < 20$ Mev; $E_p = 27.5$ Mev; $\sigma(27.5) = 20$ mb.   P17

$A^{40}(\alpha, p)K^{43}$ Possible interference from $K^{41}(\alpha, 2p)K^{43}$; possible interference from secondary reactions: $Ca^{43}(n, p)K^{43}$; $Ca^{46}(n, \alpha)A^{43} \xrightarrow{\beta^-} K^{43}$; $Ca^{46}(p, \alpha)K^{43}$.

$A^{40}(\gamma, n)A^{39}$ Possible interference from $Ca^{43}(\gamma, \alpha)A^{39}$ with a Ca matrix; possible interference from secondary reaction: $K^{39}(n, p)A^{39}$.

$A^{40}(\gamma, p)Cl^{39}$ No apparent interference.

K^{39}	93.08	1.94 ± 0.15				
		$3 \pm 2^{*}$ a	1.25×10^{9} y			70 ± 20 s
K^{40}	0.012	70 ± 20	s			
$(1.3 \times 10^{9}$ y$)$		$(n,p) < 1$ a	$A^{40}(s)$			
K^{41}	6.91	1.24 ± 0.10				
		1.1 ± 0.1 a	12.52 h	3.55 (82)	1.53	
				1.99 (18)	1.32	
		$R = 3.5 \pm 1.7^{\dagger}$				$\dagger$ K23

$K^{41}(n,\gamma)K^{42}$ Determination of the age of meteorites by comparison to A activation.   S74

Determination of K in Si using γ spectrometry with a sensitivity of 0.9 ppm; flux = 3.4×10^{12}.   M47   M48

Determination of K in Mg with a sensitivity of 0.1 μg; flux = 5×10^{11} A17

Determination of K in minerals with a sensitivity of 32 ppm.   S7

Determination of K in blood using Ra-Be and Van de Graaff - Be sources.   S48

Others: B60, B65, G28, J11, K17, L4, L8, P3, R3, S33, W22.

$K^{41}(n,p)A^{41}$ $\sigma(14.5) = 81.2$ mb.   P2

$K^{41}(n,\alpha)Cl^{38}$ $\sigma(14.5) = 31.4$ mb.   P2

$K^{39}(n,2n)K^{38}$ $E_{th} = 13.2$ Mev; $\sigma(14.5) = 10.0$ mb.   C20   P2

$K^{41}(n,\gamma)K^{42}$ Possible interference from $Ca^{42}(n,p)K^{42}$ with a Ca matrix; from $Sc^{45}(n,\alpha)K^{42}$ with a Sc matrix; possible interference from second-order reaction: $A^{40}(n,\gamma)A^{41} \xrightarrow{\beta^{-}} K^{41}(n,\gamma)K^{42}$.

$K^{41}(n,p)A^{41}$ Possible interference from $A^{40}(n,\gamma)A^{41}$; from $Ca^{44}(n,\alpha)A^{41}$.

$K^{41}(n,\alpha)Cl^{38}$ Possible interference from $Cl^{37}(n,\gamma)Cl^{38}$; from $A^{38}(n,p)Cl^{38}$.

$K^{39}(n,2n)K^{38}$ No apparent interference from primary reactions at E < 20 Mev; possible interference from secondary reaction: $A^{38}(p,n)K^{38}$.

$K^{41}(n,\gamma)K^{42}$ 2×10^{-4} μg.

$K^{39}(p,pn)K^{38}$ E_{th} = 13.5 Mev; $\sigma(21.5)$ = 0.105 b.   C25

$K^{39}(\gamma,n)K^{38}$ E_{th} = 13.2 Mev; $\sigma(17.5)$ = 5.4 mb.   E8

$K^{39}(p,pn)K^{38}$ Possible interference from $A^{38}(p,n)K^{38}$.

$K^{39}(\gamma,n)K^{38}$ No apparent interference from primary reactions; possible interference from secondary reaction: $A^{38}(p,n)K^{38}$.

Ca^{40}	96.97	0.22 ± 0.04	1.1×10^5 y		
Ca^{42}	0.64	42 ± 3	s		
Ca^{43}	0.145		s		
Ca^{44}	2.06	0.67 ± 0.07 a	164 d	0.254 (100)	none
Ca^{46}	0.0033	0.25 ± 0.10 a	4.7 d	0.66 (83) 1.94 (17)	M
Ca^{48}	0.185	1.1 ± 0.1	8.8 m	1.95 ($\sim$100)	M
	$R = 2^{\dagger}$				$\dagger$ M9

$Ca^{44}(n,\gamma)Ca^{45}$	Determination of Ca in Si with a sensitivity of 5 ppm; flux = 2×10^{14}.	T16
	Determination of Ca in blood using Ra-Be and Van de Graaff - Be sources.	S48
	Determination of Ca in Mg with a sensitivity of 2 μg; flux = 5×10^{11}.	A17
	Others: B60, B65, G28, J11, L4.	

$Ca^{42}(n,p)K^{42}$	$E_{th} = 2.9$ Mev.	C20

$Ca^{44}(n,\gamma)Ca^{45}$	Possible interference from $Sc^{45}(n,p)Ca^{45}$ with a Ca matrix; from $Ti^{48}(n,\alpha)Ca^{45}$ with a Ti matrix.
$Ca^{48}(n,\gamma)Ca^{49}$	No apparent interference from primary reactions.
$Ca^{42}(n,p)K^{42}$	Possible interference from $K^{41}(n,\gamma)K^{42}$; from $Sc^{45}(n,\alpha)K^{42}$.

$Ca^{44}(n,\gamma)Ca^{45}$	7×10^{-3} μg.
$Ca^{48}(n,\gamma)Ca^{49}$	7×10^{-3} μg.
$Ca^{48}(n,\gamma)Ca^{49} \xrightarrow{\beta^-} Sc^{49}$	7×10^{-3} μg.

$Ca^{43}(p,n)Sc^{43}$ E_{th} = 3.8 Mev.   C25

$Ca^{44}(p,2n)Sc^{43}$ E_{th} = ~ 14 Mev.   C25

$Ca^{43}(p,2p)K^{42}$ E_{th} = 10.9 Mev; $\sigma(21.5)$ = 15 mb.   C25

$Ca^{44}(p,2p)K^{43}$ E_{th} = 12.7 Mev; $\sigma(21.5)$ = 5 mb.   C25

$Ca^{40}(\gamma,n)Ca^{39}$ Excitation function from E_{th}(15.8 Mev) to 24 Mev; E_p = 19.3 Mev; $\sigma(19.3)$ = 15 mb.   G13 S64

$Ca^{43}(p,n)Sc^{43}$ Possible interference from $Ti^{46}(p,\alpha)Sc^{43}$.

$Ca^{44}(p,2n)Sc^{43}$ Possible interference from $Ti^{46}(p,\alpha)Sc^{43}$.

$Ca^{43}(p,2p)K^{42}$ No apparent interference from primary reactions at E < 25 Mev; possible interference from secondary
                             reactions: $K^{41}(n,\gamma)K^{42}$; $Sc^{45}(n,\alpha)K^{42}$.

$Ca^{44}(p,2p)K^{43}$ No apparent interference at E < 25 Mev.

63

Sc^{45}	100	24.0 ± 1.0			
		10 ± 4 a	19.5 s		IT (100)
		12 ± 6 a	83.9 d	0.36 (99+)	0.885
		22 ± 2 a	83.9 d + 19.5 s		1.119
		$R_a \sim 10.7$			M9

$Sc^{45}(n, \gamma)Sc^{46}$	Determination of Sc in high purity Fe and Al with a sensitivity of 1×10^{-3} μg.	G28
	Determination of Sc in Si with a sensitivity of 2×10^{-5} ppm; flux = 2×10^{14}.	T16
	Determination of Sc with a calculated sensitivity of 2×10^{-3} μg; flux = 5×10^{11}.	L4
	Determination of Sc with a calculated sensitivity of 1×10^{-6} μg.	J11

$Sc^{45}(n, \gamma)Sc^{46}$	Possible interference from $Ti^{46}(n, p)Sc^{46}$ with a Ti matrix; possible interference from self-shielding in comparator samples.

$Sc^{45}(n, \gamma)Sc^{46 + 46m}$	3×10^{-6} μg.

Sc^{45}(p, n)Ti^{45} $E_{th} \sim 2.9$ Mev.   B47

Sc^{45}(p, pn)Sc$^{44, 44m}$ Excitation functions from $\sim$ 10 Mev to 100 Mev; $E_p \sim$ 22.5 Mev; $\sigma(22.5) = 0.39$ and 0.21 mb,
                                 respectively.   M26

Sc^{45}(p, n)Ti^{45} Possible interference from Ti^{46}(p, pn)Ti^{45} at E > 16 Mev.

Sc^{45}(p, pn)Sc$^{44, 44m}$ Possible interference from Ca^{44}(p, n)Sc$^{44, 44m}$; from Ti^{47}(p, α)Sc$^{44, 44m}$; possible interference
                                 from secondary reaction: Ca^{43}(p, γ)Ca$^{44, 44m}$.

Sc^{45}(p, pn)Sc$^{44, 44m}$ 7×10^{-5} μg/cm^2 and 1×10^{-3} μg/cm^2, respectively, at 22.5 Mev.

Ti^{46}	7.95	0.6 ± 0.2	s		
		(n,p) 4.1 mb*†	85-d Sc^{46}		
Ti^{47}	7.75	1.7 ± 0.3	s		
		(n,p) 0.21 mb*†	3.4-d Sc^{47}		
Ti^{48}	73.45	8.3 ± 0.6	s		
		(n,p) 0.077 mb*†	44-h Sc^{48}		
		(n,α) 0.0055 mb*†	160-d Ca^{45}		
Ti^{49}	5.51	1.9 ± 0.5	s		
Ti^{50}	5.34	<0.2			
		0.14 ± 0.03 a	5.79 m	2.13 (94.5)	M
		(n,α) 0.0002 mb*†	4.7-d Ca^{47}	1.50 (5.5)	
		$R = 3.8 \pm 0.9^{\dagger\dagger}$			†M37
					†† K23

$Ti^{46}(n,p)Sc^{46}$	Determination of Ti in Al with a sensitivity of 130 ppm.	B40 B66
$Ti^{48}(n,p)Sc^{48}$	Determination of Ti in Al with a sensitivity of 130 ppm.	B40 B66
	$E_{th} = 1.3$ Mev; $\sigma(14.5) = 92.7$ mb.	C20 P2
$Ti^{49}(n,p)Sc^{49}$	$E_{th} = 1.1$ Mev.	C20
$Ti^{46}(n,2n)Ti^{45}$	$E_{th} = 12.3$ Mev.	C20

$Ti^{50}(n,\gamma)Ti^{51}$	Possible interference from $V^{51}(n,p)Ti^{51}$ with a V matrix; from $Cr^{54}(n,\alpha)Ti^{51}$ with a Cr matrix.
$Ti^{46}(n,p)Sc^{46}$	Possible interference from $Sc^{45}(n,\gamma)Sc^{46}$; possible interference from secondary reaction: $Ca^{46}(p,n)Sc^{46}$.
$Ti^{48}(n,p)Sc^{48}$	Possible interference from $V^{51}(n,\alpha)Sc^{48}$; possible interference from secondary reaction: $Ca^{48}(p,n)Sc^{48}$.
$Ti^{49}(n,p)Sc^{49}$	Possible interference from $Ca^{48}(n,\gamma)Ca^{49} \xrightarrow{\beta^-} Sc^{49}$ with a Ca matrix.
$Ti^{46}(n,2n)Ti^{45}$	No apparent interference from primary reactions at E < 25 Mev; possible interference from secondary reaction: $Sc^{45}(p,n)Ti^{45}$.

$Ti^{50}(n,\gamma)Ti^{51}$	2×10^{-3} μg.

$Ti^{48}(p, n)V^{48}$	E_{th} = 4.7 Mev.	C23
$Ti^{48}(p, 2n)V^{47}$	E_{th} = 15.3 Mev; $\sigma(21.5)$ = 0.12 b.	C23
$Ti^{46}(p, pn)Ti^{45}$	E_{th} = 15.2 Mev; $\sigma(21.5)$ < 0.50 b.	C25
$Ti^{46}(d, \alpha)Sc^{44}$	$\sigma(7.7)$ = 52.4 mb.	A12
$Ti^{48}(d, \alpha)Sc^{46}$	$\sigma(7.0)$ = 0.44 mb; $\sigma(7.7)$ = 28.5 mb.	A12 H3 H53
$Ti^{48}(d, 2n)V^{48}$	Excitation function from E_{th}(2 Mev) to 20 Mev; E_p = 17 Mev; $\sigma(17)$ = 0.38 b.	B49

$Ti^{48}(p, n)V^{48}$	No apparent interference at E < 20 Mev.
$Ti^{48}(p, 2n)V^{47}$	Possible interference from $Cr^{50}(p, \alpha)V^{47}$.
$Ti^{46}(p, pn)Ti^{45}$	Possible interference from $Sc^{45}(p, n)Ti^{45}$.
$Ti^{48}(d, 2n)V^{48}$	Possible interference from $Cr^{50}(d, \alpha)V^{48}$.
$Ti^{46}(d, \alpha)Sc^{44, 44m}$	Possible interference from $Ca^{43}(d, n)Sc^{44, 44m}$ or $Ca^{44}(d, 2n)Sc^{44, 44m}$; from $Sc^{45}(d, dn)Sc^{44, 44m}$; possible interference from secondary reactions: $Ca^{43}(p, \gamma)Sc^{44, 44m}$ or $Ca^{44}(p, n)Sc^{44, 44m}$.

$Ti^{46}(d, \alpha)Sc^{44}$	7×10^{-3} $\mu g/cm^2$ at 7.7 Mev.

V^{50}	0.24	250 ± 200	s		
$(4 \times 10^{14} y)$					
V^{51}	99.76	4.5 ± 0.9 a	3.76 m	2.47 (100)	1.44 ($\sim$100)

$R = 3.3 \pm 0.8^{\dagger}$

$R_a^{51} \sim 2.2^{\dagger\dagger}$

$\dagger$ K23
$\dagger\dagger$ M9

$V^{51}(n, \gamma)V^{52}$	Determination of V in steels using Mn activation for flux monitoring; interference from reactions $Cr^{52}(n, p)V^{52}$ and $Mn^{55}(n, \alpha)V^{52}$ was negligible.	L22
	Determination of V in Ti with a sensitivity of 10 ppm; flux = 10^{12}.	B44
	Determination of V in Si with a sensitivity of 5 ppm; flux = 1×10^{13}.	T16
	Determination of V in graphite using a gross β counting technique.	S36 S37
	Others: B42, B58, J11.	

- -

$V^{51}(n, p)Ti^{51}$	$\sigma(14.5) = 27$ mb.	P2
$V^{51}(n, \alpha)Sc^{48}$	$E_{th} < 2.4$ mb; $\sigma(2.4) = 0.08$ mb; $\sigma(14.5) = 28.6$ mb.	H46 P2

$V^{51}(n, \gamma)V^{52}$	Possible interference from $Cr^{52}(n, p)V^{52}$ with a V matrix; from $Mn^{55}(n, \alpha)V^{52}$ with a Mn matrix; possible interference from second-order reaction: $Ti^{50}(n, \gamma)Ti^{51} \xrightarrow{\beta^-} V^{51}(n, \gamma)V^{52}$ with a Ti matrix.
$V^{51}(n, p)Ti^{51}$	Possible interference from $Ti^{50}(n, \gamma)Ti^{51}$; from $Cr^{54}(n, \alpha)Ti^{51}$.
$V^{51}(n, \alpha)Sc^{48}$	Possible interference from $Ti^{48}(n, p)Sc^{48}$; possible interference from secondary reaction: $Cr^{48}(p, n)Sc^{48}$.

$V^{51}(n, \gamma)V^{52}$	3×10^{-6} μg.

$V^{51}(p,n)Cr^{51}$ E_{th} = 1.56 Mev.   R6

$V^{51}(\gamma,\alpha)Sc^{47}$ Yield with 23 Mev bremsstrahlung = 10^4 α/mole-r.   G22

$V^{51}(p,n)Cr^{51}$ Possible interference from $Fe^{54}(p,\alpha)Mn^{51} \xrightarrow{\beta^+} Cr^{51}$; from $Cr^{52}(p,pn)Cr^{51}$ at E > 15 Mev; possible interference from secondary reactions: $Cr^{50}(n,\gamma)Cr^{51}$; $Fe^{54}(n,\alpha)Cr^{51}$.

$V^{51}(\gamma,\alpha)Sc^{47}$ Possible interference from $Ti^{48}(\gamma,p)Sc^{47}$; possible interference from secondary reactions: $Ti^{47}(n,p)Sc^{47}$; $Ca^{46}(p,\gamma)Sc^{47}$.

Cr^{50}	4.31	17.0 ± 1.4			
		13.5 ± 1.4 a	27.8 d	EC	0.325 (9)
Cr^{52}	83.76	0.76 ± 0.06	s		
Cr^{53}	9.55	18.2 ± 1.5	s		
Cr^{54}	2.38	<0.3			
		0.38 ± 0.04 a	3.52 m	2.85 (100)	none
		$R = 2.6 \pm 1.1^\dagger$			$\dagger$ K23

$Cr^{50}(n,\gamma)Cr^{51}$	Determination of Cr in Si with a sensitivity of 0.1 ppm; flux = 2×10^{14}.	T16
	Determination of Cr in Al with a sensitivity of 2.5 µg; flux = 3.4×10^{12}.	M47
	Determination of Cr in liquid metals with a sensitivity of 0.2 ppm.	S32
	Determination of Cr in Mg with a sensitivity of 5 µg; flux = 5×10^{11}.	A17
	Others: C5, J11, L4, S33, S71.	

$Cr^{52}(n,p)V^{52}$	$E_{th} = 2.8$ Mev; $\sigma(12.3) = 125$ mb; $\sigma(14.5) = 77.7$ mb.	C20 K32 P2
$Cr^{50}(n,2n)Cr^{49}$	$E_{th} = 13.4$ Mev.	C20

$Cr^{50}(n,\gamma)Cr^{51}$	Possible interference from $Fe^{54}(n,\alpha)Cr^{51}$ with a Cr matrix.
$Cr^{54}(n,\gamma)Cr^{55}$	Possible interference from $Mn^{55}(n,p)Cr^{55}$ with a Mn matrix; from $Fe^{58}(n,\alpha)Cr^{55}$ with an Fe matrix.
$Cr^{52}(n,p)V^{52}$	Possible interference from $V^{51}(n,\gamma)V^{52}$; from $Mn^{55}(n,\alpha)V^{52}$.
$Cr^{50}(n,2n)Cr^{49}$	No apparent interference at E < 20 Mev.

$Cr^{50}(n,\gamma)Cr^{51}$	5×10^{-5} µg.
$Cr^{54}(n,\gamma)Cr^{55}$	2×10^{-3} µg.

$Cr^{52}(p,n)Mn^{52m}$ Excitation function from E_{th} (5.4 Mev) to 16 Mev; $E_p \sim$ 12.5 Mev; $\sigma(12.5)$ = 0.41 b.   C25 L24

$Cr^{52}(p,n)Mn^{52}$ Excitation function from E_{th} ($\sim$ 7 Mev) to 16 Mev; $E_p \sim$ 12.5 Mev; $\sigma(12.5)$ = 0.20 b.   L24

Thick-target yield from natural Cr at 22 Mev = 80 mc/ma-hr.   M15

$Cr^{54}(p,n)Mn^{54}$ Thick-target yield from natural Cr at 22 Mev = 0.5 mc/ma-hr.   M15

$Cr^{52}(p,2n)Mn^{51}$ E_{th} = 16 Mev; $\sigma(21.5)$ = 155 mb.   C23

$Cr^{52}(p,pn)Cr^{51}$ E_{th} = 12 Mev; $\sigma(21.5)$ = 425 mb.   C23

$Cr^{53}(d,n)Mn^{54}$ Excitation function from E_{th} ($\sim$ 0.5 Mev) to 15 Mev; E_p = 5.5 Mev; $\sigma(5.5)$ = 0.26 b; $\sigma(15)$ = 0.17 b; thick-target yields for energies less than 15 Mev.   K1

$Cr^{50}(d,p)Cr^{51}$ Excitation function from E_{th} ($\sim$ 0.5 Mev) to 15 Mev; E_p = 5.2 Mev; $\sigma(5.2)$ = 0.66 b; $\sigma(15)$ = 0.33 b; thick-target yields for E < 15 Mev.   K1

$Cr^{50}(d,\alpha)V^{48}$ Excitation function from E_{th} ($\sim$ 1 Mev) to 15 Mev; $E_p \sim$ 9 Mev; $\sigma(9)$ = 70 mb; thick-target yields for E < 15 Mev.   K1

$Cr^{52}(d,2n)Mn^{52}$ Excitation function from E_{th} ($\sim$ 6.5 Mev) to 20 Mev; E_p = 18.5 Mev; $\sigma(18.5)$ = 0.19 b; thick-target yields for E < 15 Mev.   B49 K1

$Cr^{50}(\gamma,n)Cr^{49}$ Excitation function from E_{th} (13.4 Mev) to 22 Mev; E_p = 19 Mev; $\sigma(19)$ = 52 mb.   G13

$Cr^{53}(\gamma,p)V^{52}$ Excitation function from E_{th} ($\sim$ 12 Mev) to 22 Mev; E_p = 19.7 Mev; $\sigma(19.7) \sim$ 27 mb.   G13

$Cr^{52}(p,n)Mn^{52}$ No apparent interference at E < 20 Mev.

$Cr^{54}(p,n)Mn^{54}$ Possible interference from $Fe^{57}(p,\alpha)Mn^{54}$; from $Mn^{55}(p,pn)Mn^{54}$ at E > 12 Mev; possible interference from secondary reaction: $Fe^{54}(n,p)Mn^{54}$.

$Cr^{52}(p,2n)Mn^{51}$ Possible interference from $Fe^{54}(p,\alpha)Mn^{51}$.

$Cr^{52}(p,pn)Cr^{51}$ Possible interference from $V^{51}(p,n)Cr^{51}$; from $Fe^{54}(p,\alpha)Mn^{51} \xrightarrow{\beta^+} Cr^{51}$; possible interference from secondary reaction: $Fe^{54}(n,\alpha)Cr^{51}$.

$Cr^{53}(d,n)Mn^{54}$ Possible interference from $Mn^{55}(d,dn)Mn^{54}$; from $Fe^{54}(d,2p)Mn^{54}$ or $Fe^{56}(d,\alpha)Mn^{54}$; possible interference from secondary reactions: $Fe^{54}(n,p)Mn^{54}$; $Fe^{57}(p,\alpha)Mn^{54}$.

$Cr^{50}(d,p)Cr^{51}$ Possible interference from $V^{50}(d,n)V^{51}$ or $V^{51}(d,2n)V^{51}$; possible interference from secondary reactions: $Fe^{54}(n,\alpha)Cr^{51}$; $V^{50}(p,\gamma)Cr^{51}$ or $V^{51}(p,n)Cr^{51}$.

$Cr^{50}(d,\alpha)V^{48}$ Possible interference from $Ti^{47}(d,n)V^{48}$ or $Ti^{48}(d,2n)V^{48}$; possible interference from secondary reactions: $Ti^{47}(p,\gamma)V^{48}$ or $Ti^{48}(p,n)V^{48}$.

$Cr^{50}(\gamma,n)Cr^{49}$ No apparent interference.

$Cr^{52}(d,p)Cr^{51}$ 5×10^{-3} $\mu g/cm^2$ at 5.2 Mev.

Mn^{55}	100	13.2 ± 0.2			
		13.3 ± 0.2 a	2.576 h	M	M

$R = 11.7 \pm 1.5^{†}$

$R_a \sim 11.8^{††}$

†K23
††M9

$Mn^{55}(n, \gamma)Mn^{56}$

Determination of Mn in biological material with a sensitivity of 0.1 μg; flux $\sim 10^{12}$.   B34

Determination of Mn in Al by γ spectrometry with a sensitivity of 340 ppm.   B40   B66

Determination of Mn in Ti with a sensitivity of 1.4 ppm; flux $= 10^{12}$.   B44

Determination of Mn in Si with a sensitivity of 3×10^{-6} ppm; flux $= 3 \times 10^{12}$.   C5   K2   T16

Determination of Mn in high purity Fe and Al with a sensitivity of 0.3 ppm; flux $\sim 10^{12}$.   A4   A6   G28   T1

Others: B42, B60, B62, C18, J11, L4, L23, S33.

- -

$Mn^{55}(n, \alpha)V^{52}$ $\sigma(14.5) = 52.5$ mb; $\sigma(14.8) = 96 \pm 14$ mb.   K31   P2

$Mn^{55}(n, \gamma)Mn^{56}$ Possible interference from $Fe^{56}(n, p)Mn^{56}$ with an Fe matrix; from $Co^{59}(n, \alpha)Mn^{56}$ with a Co matrix; possible interference from second-order reaction: $Cr^{54}(n, \gamma)Cr^{55} \xrightarrow{\beta^-} Mn^{55}(n, \gamma)Mn^{56}$.

$Mn^{55}(n, \alpha)V^{52}$ Possible interference from $V^{51}(n, \gamma)V^{52}$; from $Cr^{52}(n, p)V^{52}$.

$Mn^{55}(n, \gamma)Mn^{56}$ 1×10^{-6} μg.

$Mn^{55}(p,n)Fe^{55}$	Excitation function from E_{th}(1.002 Mev) to 2.85 Mev.	M19
	Thick-target yield at 22 Mev = 10 mc/ma-hr.	M22
$Mn^{55}(p,pn)Mn^{54}$	E_{th} = 10.3 Mev; $\sigma(21.5)$ = 0.62 b.	C16
	Thick-target yield at 22 Mev = 20 mc/ma-hr.	M15
$Mn^{55}(d,p)Mn^{56}$	Excitation function from 50 Mev to 190 Mev; E_p < 50 Mev; $\sigma(50)$ = 25 mb.	S27
$Mn^{55}(\gamma,n)Mn^{54}$	Excitation function from E_{th}(10.0 Mev) to 24 Mev; $E_p \sim$19 Mev; $\sigma(19)$ = 100 mb.	M45

$Mn^{55}(p,n)Fe^{55}$ — Possible interference from $Ni^{58}(p,\alpha)Co^{55} \xrightarrow{\beta^+} Fe^{55}$; from $Fe^{56}(p,pn)Fe^{55}$ or $Fe^{56}(p,2n)Co^{55} \xrightarrow{\beta^+} Fe^{55}$ at E > 15 Mev; possible interference from secondary reactions: $Fe^{54}(n,\gamma)Fe^{55}$; $Ni^{58}(n,\alpha)Fe^{55}$.

$Mn^{55}(p,pn)Mn^{54}$ — Possible interference from $Cr^{54}(p,n)Mn^{54}$; from $Fe^{57}(p,\alpha)Mn^{54}$; possible interference from secondary reactions: $Fe^{54}(n,p)Mn^{54}$; $Cr^{53}(p,\gamma)Mn^{54}$.

$Mn^{55}(d,p)Mn^{56}$ — Possible interference from $Cr^{54}(d,\gamma)Mn^{56}$ with a Cr matrix; possible interference from secondary reactions: $Fe^{56}(n,p)Mn^{56}$; $Co^{59}(n,\alpha)Mn^{56}$.

$Mn^{55}(\gamma,n)Mn^{54}$ — No apparent interference from primary reactions; possible interference from secondary reactions: $Fe^{54}(n,p)Mn^{54}$; $Cr^{53}(p,\gamma)Mn^{54}$ or $Cr^{54}(p,n)Mn^{54}$; $Fe^{57}(p,\alpha)Mn^{54}$.

Fe^{54}	5.84	2.3 ± 0.2			
		2.5 ± 0.4 a	2.60 y	EC	none
		(n, p) 23.0 mb*†	300-d Mn^{54}		
		(n, α) 0.37 mb*†	27-d Cr^{51}		
Fe^{56}	91.68	2.7 ± 0.2	s		
		(n, p) 0.44 mb*†	2.58-h Mn^{56}		
Fe^{57}	2.17	2.5 ± 0.2	s		
Fe^{58}	0.31	2.5 ± 2.0			
		0.98 ± 0.10 a	45.1 d	M	M
		(n, α) < 1.5 mb a	3.6-m Cr^{55}		
		R = 2.3 ± 0.4†			†M37
					††K23

Fe^{58}(n, γ)Fe^{59}	Determination of Fe in Mg with a sensitivity of 0.05 μg.	A17
	Determination of Fe in Si with a sensitivity of 0.1 ppm	C5 K2 T16
	Determination of Fe in Ge with a sensitivity of 0.1 ppm; flux ~ 3 x 10^{12}.	C5
	Determination of Fe in Si using γ spectrometry with a sensitivity of 20 ppm; flux = 3.4 x 10^{12}.	M47 M48
	Determination of Fe in Al with a sensitivity of 0.2%; flux = 2 x 10^{6}.	B40 B66
	Determination of Fe in W using γ spectrometry with a sensitivity of 2.1 μg; flux = 3 x 10^{12}.	C33
	Others: B43, B60, C12, G28, L4, S33.	
Fe^{54}(n, p)Mn^{54}	Determination of Fe using pile neutrons with a sensitivity of 6 x 10^{2} μg; flux = 5 x 10^{11}.	M54
Fe^{56}(n, p)Mn^{56}	Determination of Fe using pile neutrons with a sensitivity of 40 μg; flux = 5 x 10^{11}.	M54
	Excitation function from 3.4 Mev to 17.9 Mev; E_{th} = 2.9 Mev; E_p = 13.5 Mev; σ(13.5) = 0.11 b.	C20 F9 P2 T13 Y1

Fe^{54}(n, 2n)Fe^{53}	E_{th} = 13.9 Mev; σ(16.9) = 0.12 b; σ(17.9) = 0.18 b.	C20 T13

Fe^{58}(n, γ)Fe^{59}	Possible interference from Co^{59}(n, p)Fe^{59}; from Ni^{62}(n, α)Fe^{59}.
Fe^{54}(n, p)Mn^{54}	Possible interference from Mn^{55}(n, 2n)Mn^{54} at E > 10 Mev; possible interference from secondary reactions: Cr^{53}(p, γ)Mn^{54} or Cr^{54}(p, n)Mn^{54}.
Fe^{56}(n, p)Mn^{56}	Possible interference from Co^{59}(n, α)Mn^{56}; from Mn^{55}(n, γ)Mn^{56}.

Fe^{58}(n, γ)Fe^{59}	1 x 10^{-2} μg.

$Fe^{56}(p,n)Co^{56}$ E_{th} = 5.3 Mev; thick-target yield at 20 Mev = 70 mc/ma-hr.   C23 M15

$Fe^{56}(p,2n)Co^{55}$ E_{th} = 15.7 Mev; $\sigma(21.5)$ = 0.11 b.   C23

$Fe^{56}(p,pn)Fe^{55}$ E_{th} = 11.5 Mev; $\sigma(21.5)$ = 0.76 b.   C23

$Fe^{57}(p,2p)Mn^{56}$ E_{th} = 10.5 Mev; $\sigma(21.5)$ = 13 mb.   C25

$Fe^{54}(d,n)Co^{55}$ Excitation function from 3 Mev to 9 Mev; E_{th} < 3 Mev; $E_p \sim$ 8 Mev; $\sigma(8) \sim$ 50 mb.   C31

$Fe^{54}(d,\alpha)Mn^{52}$ Excitation function from 3 Mev to 9 Mev; $E_{th} \sim$ 3 Mev; E_p > 9 Mev; $\sigma(9) \sim$ 17 mb.   C31

$Fe^{56}(d,2n)Co^{56}$ Excitation function from E_{th}($\sim$ 6 Mev) to 20 Mev; E_p = 17.2 Mev; $\sigma(17.2)$ = 0.31 b.   B49

$Fe^{54}(\gamma,n)Fe^{53}$ Excitation function from E_{th}(13.8 Mev) to 24 Mev; E_p = 18.3 Mev; $\sigma(18.3)$ = 67 mb.   H14 K7 K10
     M45 S1

$Fe^{56}(p,n)Co^{56}$ No apparent interference at E < 20 Mev.

$Fe^{56}(p,2n)Co^{55}$ Possible interference from $Ni^{58}(p,\alpha)Co^{55}$.

$Fe^{57}(p,2p)Mn^{56}$ No apparent interference from primary reactions at E < 25 Mev; possible interference from secondary reactions: $Mn^{55}(n,\gamma)Mn^{56}$; $Co^{59}(n,\alpha)Mn^{56}$.

$Fe^{54}(d,n)Co^{55}$ No apparent interference from primary reactions; possible interference from secondary reaction: $Ni^{58}(p,\alpha)Co^{55}$.

$Fe^{54}(d,\alpha)Mn^{52}$ Possible interference from $Cr^{50}(d,\gamma)Mn^{52}$ or $Cr^{52}(d,2n)Mn^{52}$; possible interference from secondary reaction: $Cr^{52}(p,n)Mn^{52}$.

$Fe^{56}(d,2n)Co^{56}$ Possible interference from $Ni^{58}(d,\alpha)Co^{56}$.

$Fe^{54}(\gamma,n)Fe^{53}$ No apparent interference.

$Fe^{54}(d,\alpha)Mn^{52}$ 7×10^{-1} $\mu g/cm^2$ at 9 Mev.

Co^{59}	100	37.0 ± 1.5	10.47 m				100 ± 50	99 m
		16 ± 3 a	5.24 y	0.312 (99+)	1.17 (~100)		6 ± 2	99 m
		20 ± 3 a			1.33 (~100)			
		36.3 ± 1.5 a	10.4 m + 5.24 y					
		(n, p) 22.0 mb*†	46-d Fe^{59}					
		$R = 38.3 \pm 4.0^{\dagger\dagger}$						†M37
		$R_a = 49.3^{\dagger\dagger\dagger}$						††K23
								†††M9

$Co^{59}(n, \gamma)Co^{60m}$	Determination of Co with a sensitivity of 2 μg; flux = 5×10^{11}.	W18
$Co^{59}(n, \gamma)Co^{60}$	Determination of Co in liquid metals with a sensitivity of 0.02 ppm.	S32
	Determination of Co in Al with a sensitivity of 4.0 μg; flux = 5×10^{11}.	B40
	Determination of Co in high purity Fe with a sensitivity of 1 ppm.	A4　A6　G28　T1
	Determination of Co with a sensitivity of 0.01 μg; flux ~ 10^{12}.	S38
	Determination of Co in Si with a sensitivity of 6×10^{-4} ppm; flux = 2×10^{14}.	T16
	Determination of Co with a sensitivity of ~ 0.04 μg; flux = 5×10^{11}.	B42
	Others: B58, D7, J11, L4, S33.	

$Co^{59}(n, p)Fe^{59}$	Yield of Fe^{59} in pile neutron irradiation ~ 0.04 μc/hr-g Co_3O_4; flux ~ 3×10^{12}.	W1
$Co^{59}(n, \alpha)Mn^{56}$	Average $\sigma(14) = 35$ mb.	B30　P2

$Co^{59}(n, \gamma)Co^{60, 60m}$	Possible interference from $Ni^{60}(n, p)Co^{60, 60m}$ with a Ni matrix; from $Cu^{63}(n, \alpha)Co^{60, 60m}$ with a Cu matrix; possible interference from second-order reaction: $Co^{60m}(n, \gamma)Co^{61}$; possible interference from self-shielding in comparator sample.
$Co^{59}(n, p)Fe^{59}$	Possible interference from $Fe^{58}(n, \gamma)Fe^{59}$; from $Ni^{62}(n, \alpha)Fe^{59}$.
$Co^{59}(n, \alpha)Mn^{56}$	Interference from $Mn^{55}(n, \gamma)Mn^{56}$; from $Fe^{56}(n, p)Mn^{56}$.

$Co^{59}(n, \gamma)Co^{60m}$	1×10^{-6} μg.
$Co^{59}(n, \gamma)Co^{60 + 60m}$	4×10^{-5} μg.

$Co^{59}(p,pn)Co^{58,58m}$ Excitation functions from 12 Mev to 100 Mev; $E_{th} \sim 10$ Mev; $E_p = 28$ Mev; $\sigma(28) = 0.23$ b and 0.36 b, respectively.   M26 S13

$Co^{59}(p,p2n)Co^{57}$ Excitation function from 25 Mev to 100 Mev; $E_{th} \sim 25$ Mev; $E_p \sim 40$ Mev; $\sigma(40) = 157$ mb.   S19

$Co^{59}(d,p)Co^{60+60m}$ Excitation function from E_{th} (~ 2.5 Mev) to 12 Mev; $E_p \sim 7$ Mev; $\sigma(7) = 0.27$ b.   P4

$Co^{59}(\gamma,n)Co^{58}$ Excitation function from E_{th} (10.25 Mev) to 22 Mev; $E_p = 16.9$ Mev; $\sigma(16.9) = 0.13$ b.   H14 M45

$Co^{59}(p,pn)Co^{58,58m}$ Possible interference from $Fe^{58}(p,n)Co^{58,58m}$; from $Ni^{61}(p,\alpha)Co^{58,58m}$; possible interference from secondary reactions: $Ni^{58}(n,p)Co^{58,58m}$; $Fe^{57}(p,\gamma)Co^{58,58m}$.

$Co^{59}(p,p2n)Co^{57}$ Possible interference from $Ni^{60}(p,\alpha)Co^{57}$; from $Ni^{58}(p,pn)Ni^{57} \xrightarrow{\beta^+} Co^{57}$ or $Ni^{58}(p,2p)Co^{57}$; from $Fe^{57}(p,n)Co^{57}$ or $Fe^{56}(p,\gamma)Co^{57}$.

$Co^{59}(d,p)Co^{60,60m}$ Possible interference from $Fe^{58}(d,\gamma)Co^{60,60m}$; from $Ni^{60}(d,2p)Co^{60,60m}$ or $Ni^{62}(d,\alpha)Co^{60,60m}$; possible interference from secondary reactions: $Ni^{60}(n,p)Co^{60,60m}$; $Cu^{63}(n,\alpha)Co^{60,60m}$.

$Co^{59}(\gamma,n)Co^{58,58m}$ No apparent interference from primary reactions; possible interference from secondary reactions: $Fe^{57}(p,\gamma)Co^{58,58m}$ or $Fe^{58}(p,n)Co^{58,58m}$; $Ni^{61}(p,\alpha)Co^{58,58m}$; $Ni^{58}(n,p)Co^{58,58m}$.

$Co^{59}(p,pn)Co^{58m}$ 2×10^{-4} $\mu g/cm^2$ at 28 Mev.

Ni^{58}	67.76	4.4 ± 0.3	8×10^4 y	EC	none
		(n, p) 32.0 mb*†	71-d Co^{58}		
		(n, p) 13.0 mb*†	9.0-h Co^{58m}		
Ni^{60}	26.16	2.6 ± 0.2	s		
		(n, p) 5 ± 2 mb*†	5.2-y Co^{60}		
Ni^{61}	1.25	2.0 ± 1.0	s		
Ni^{62}	3.66	15 ± 2	125 y	0.067	none
		(n, α) 5.7 mb*†	45-d Fe^{59}		
Ni^{64}	1.16	1.6 ± 0.2 a	2.564 h	M	M
		$R = 3.2 \pm 0.5^{\dagger\dagger}$			$\dagger$ M37
					$\dagger\dagger$ K23

$Ni^{64}(n, \gamma)Ni^{65}$	Determination of Ni in high purity Fe with a sensitivity of 1 ppm.	A4 A6 G28 T1
	Determination of Ni in Si with a sensitivity of 3×10^{-3} ppm; flux $= 3 \times 10^{12}$.	C5
	Determination of Ni in crude petroleum oil with a sensitivity of 1.0 ppm; flux $\sim 10^{10}$.	B43
	Determination of Ni in geochemical samples and in Ge with a sensitivity of 10^{-3} μg; flux $\sim 10^{12}$.	S33
	Determination of Ni in Ti with a sensitivity of 13 ppm; flux $= 10^{12}$.	B44
	Determination of Ni in Al with a sensitivity of 300 ppm; flux $\sim 10^{10}$.	B40 B66
	Others: J11, L4, S38, T16.	
$Ni^{58}(n, p)Co^{58}$	Determination of Ni using pile neutrons with a sensitivity of 8 μg; flux $= 5 \times 10^{11}$; $\sigma(14.1) = 0.56$ b.	M54 P18
$Ni^{60}(n, p)Co^{60}$	Determination of Ni using pile neutrons with a sensitivity of 2×10^4 μg; flux $= 5 \times 10^{11}$.	M54
$Ni^{61}(n, p)Co^{61}$	$\sigma(14.5) = 0.18$ b.	P6
$Ni^{58}(n, 2n)Ni^{57}$	Relative excitation function from E_{th}(12 Mev) to 19 Mev; $E_p > 19$ Mev; $\sigma(14.5) = 40.6$ mb.	M7 P6
$Ni^{58}(n, np)Co^{57}$	$\sigma(14.1) = 0.16$ b.	P18

$Ni^{62}(n, \gamma)Ni^{63}$	Possible interference from $Cu^{63}(n, p)Ni^{63}$; from $Zn^{66}(n, \alpha)Ni^{63}$ with a Zn matrix.
$Ni^{64}(n, \gamma)Ni^{65}$	Possible interference from $Cu^{65}(n, p)Ni^{65}$; from $Zn^{68}(n, \alpha)Ni^{65}$ with a Zn matrix; possible interference from second-order reaction: $Cu^{63}(n, \gamma)Cu^{64} \xrightarrow{\beta^+} Ni^{64}(n, \gamma)Ni^{65}$.
$Ni^{61}(n, p)Co^{61}$	No apparent interference from primary reactions at E < 20 Mev.
$Ni^{58}(n, 2n)Ni^{57}$	No apparent interference.

$Ni^{64}(n, \gamma)Ni^{65}$	9×10^{-4} μg.

$Ni^{60}(p,n)Cu^{60}$ E_{th} = 5.1 Mev; $\sigma(6.7)$ < 10 mb.   B26

$Ni^{61}(p,n)Cu^{61}$ E_{th} = 3.1 Mev; $\sigma(6.7)$ = 0.24 b.   B26

$Ni^{62}(p,n)Cu^{62}$ Excitation function from E_{th}(4.7 Mev) to 6.8 Mev; E_p > 6.8 Mev; $\sigma(6.7)$ = 0.43 b.   B26

$Ni^{64}(p,n)Cu^{64}$ Excitation function from E_{th}(2.5 Mev) to 6.8 Mev; from 90 Mev to 410 Mev; E_p > 6.8 Mev;
                         $\sigma(6.7)$ = 0.40 b.   B26 D9 K24

$Ni^{62}(p,2n)Cu^{61}$ E_{th} = 13.5 Mev; $\sigma(21.5)$ = 0.385 b.   C23

$Ni^{58}(p,pn)Ni^{57}$ E_{th} = 11.9 Mev; $\sigma(21.5)$ = 0.24 b.   C25

$Ni^{58}(p,2p)Co^{57}$ E_{th} = 8.0 Mev; $\sigma(21.5)$ = 0.68 b.   C25
                         Thick-target yield from natural nickel at 22 Mev = 50 mc/ma-hr.   M15

$Ni^{60}(\alpha,n)Zn^{63}$ Excitation function from E_{th}($\sim$ 10 Mev) to 39 Mev; $E_p \sim$ 20 Mev; $\sigma(20) \sim$ 0.68 b.   G4

$Ni^{60}(\alpha,2n)Zn^{62}$ Excitation function from E_{th}($\sim$ 22 Mev) to 39 Mev; $E_p \sim$ 31 Mev; $\sigma(31) \sim$ 0.24 b.   G4

$Ni^{60}(\alpha,pn)Cu^{62}$ Excitation function from E_{th}($\sim$ 20 Mev) to 39 Mev; $E_p \sim$ 31 Mev; $\sigma(31) \sim$ 0.95 b.   G4

$Ni^{58}(\gamma,n)Ni^{57}$ Excitation function from E_{th}(11.7 Mev) to 24 Mev; E_p = 18.5 Mev; $\sigma(18.5)$ = 57 mb.   G13 H14
                                                                                                                              K7 K10

$Ni^{60}(p,n)Cu^{60}$ No apparent interference at E < 20 Mev.

$Ni^{61}(p,n)Cu^{61}$ Possible interference from $Zn^{64}(p,\alpha)Cu^{61}$.

$Ni^{62}(p,n)Cu^{62}$ Possible interference from $Cu^{63}(p,pn)Cu^{62}$ at E > 12 Mev.

$Ni^{64}(p,n)Cu^{64}$ Possible interference from $Zn^{67}(p,\alpha)Cu^{64}$; from $Cu^{65}(p,pn)Cu^{64}$ at E > 6 Mev; possible interference
                         from secondary reactions: $Cu^{63}(n,\gamma)Cu^{64}$; $Zn^{64}(n,p)Cu^{64}$.

$Ni^{62}(p,2n)Cu^{61}$ Possible interference from $Zn^{64}(p,\alpha)Cu^{61}$.

$Ni^{58}(p,pn)Ni^{57}$ No apparent interference.

$Ni^{58}(p,2p)Co^{57}$ Possible interference from $Fe^{57}(p,n)Co^{57}$; possible interference from secondary reaction:
                         $Fe^{56}(p,\gamma)Co^{57}$.

$Ni^{60}(\alpha,n)Zn^{63}$ No apparent interference from primary reactions at E < 25 Mev; possible interference from
                              secondary reaction: $Cu^{63}(p,n)Zn^{63}$.

$Ni^{60}(\alpha,2n)Zn^{62}$ No apparent interference at E < 25 Mev.

$Ni^{60}(\alpha,pn)Cu^{62}$ Possible interference from $Cu^{63}(\alpha,\alpha n)Cu^{62}$; possible interference from secondary reactions:
                              $Ni^{61}(p,\gamma)Cu^{62}$ or $Ni^{62}(p,n)Cu^{62}$.

$Ni^{58}(\gamma,n)Ni^{57}$ No apparent interference.

$Ni^{62}(p,n)Cu^{62}$ 2×10^{-3} $\mu g/cm^2$ at 6.7 Mev.

$Ni^{64}(p,n)Cu^{64}$ 2×10^{-2} $\mu g/cm^2$ at 6.7 Mev.

Cu^{63}	69.1	4.5 ± 0.1						
		4.3 ± 0.2 a	12.80 h	0.571 (39)	1.34			
				0.657 (19)				
				EC (42)				
		(n, p) 3.1 ± 0.5 mb*a†	80-y Ni^{63}					
Cu^{65}	30.9	2.2 ± 0.2						
		1.8 ± 0.4 a	5.10 m	2.63 (100)	1.04	130 ± 40 a*	58.5 h	
				1.5 (9)	0.83			

$R_a^{63} = 4.4^{\dagger\dagger\dagger}$

$R_a^{65} = 2.2^{\dagger\dagger\dagger}$

$R = 3.7 \pm 0.8^{\dagger\dagger}$

$\dagger$ P15
$\dagger\dagger$ K23
$\dagger\dagger\dagger$ M9

$Cu^{63}(n, \gamma)Cu^{64}$

Determination of Cu in W by γ spectrometry with a sensitivity of 1.1 μg; flux = 3×10^{12}.   C33

Determination of Cu in high purity Fe and Al with a sensitivity of 0.4 ppm.   A4   A5   A6   G28   C12   T1

Determination of Cu in Si with a sensitivity of 2×10^{-3} ppm.   K2   T16

Determination of Cu in Ge and Ge compounds using γ spectrometry with a sensitivity of 0.01 ppm; flux = 3.4×10^{12}.   M49

Determination of Cu in petroleum oils with a sensitivity of 0.05 ppm; flux $\sim 10^{11}$.   L10

Determination of Cu in Mg with a sensitivity of 0.03 μg; flux = 5×10^{11}.   A17

Determination of Cu in Ti with a sensitivity of 33 ppm; flux = 10^{12}.   B44

Determination of Cu in blood using Ra-Be and Van de Graaff-Be sources.   S48

Others: B40, B43, B60, B63, B66, G24, J11, L4, L23, M47, S33, S38, S39, S68, S71.

$Cu^{65}(n, p)Ni^{65}$ $E_{th} = 2.3$ Mev; $\sigma(14) = 19$ mb.   C20   F9

$Cu^{63}(n, 2n)Cu^{62}$ Excitation function from E_{th}(11.8 Mev) to 27 Mev; $E_p = 19$ Mev; $\sigma(19) \sim 0.9$ b; $\sigma(14) = 0.51$ b.   B39   F9   M47   P2   Y1

$Cu^{65}(n, 2n)Cu^{64}$ $\sigma(14) = 0.97$ b.   F9   P2

$Cu^{63}(n, \gamma)Cu^{64}$ Possible interference from $Zn^{64}(n, p)Cu^{64}$ with a Zn matrix; possible interference from second-order reaction: $Ni^{62}(n, \gamma)Ni^{63} \xrightarrow{\beta^-} Cu^{63}(n, \gamma)Cu^{64}$.

$Cu^{65}(n, \gamma)Cu^{66}$ Possible interference from $Zn^{66}(n, p)Cu^{66}$ with a Zn matrix; from $Ga^{69}(n, \alpha)Cu^{66}$ with a Ga matrix; possible interference from second-order reactions: $Ni^{64}(n, \gamma)Ni^{65} \xrightarrow{\beta^-} Cu^{65}(n, \gamma)Cu^{66}$; $Zn^{64}(n, \gamma)Zn^{65} \xrightarrow{K} Cu^{65}(n, \gamma)Cu^{66}$.

$Cu^{63}(n, p)Ni^{63}$ Possible interference from $Zn^{66}(n, \alpha)Ni^{63}$; from $Ni^{62}(n, \gamma)Ni^{63}$ or $Ni^{64}(n, 2n)Ni^{63}$ with a Ni matrix.

$Cu^{65}(n, p)Ni^{65}$ Possible interference from $Zn^{68}(n, \alpha)Ni^{65}$; from $Ni^{64}(n, \gamma)Ni^{65}$ with a Ni matrix.

$Cu^{63}(n, 2n)Cu^{62}$ No apparent interference from primary reactions at E < 20 Mev; possible interference from secondary reactions: $Ni^{61}(p, \gamma)Cu^{62}$ or $Ni^{62}(p, n)Cu^{62}$.

$Cu^{65}(n, 2n)Cu^{64}$ Possible interference from $Zn^{64}(n, p)Cu^{64}$; possible interference from secondary reactions: $Ni^{64}(p, n)Cu^{64}$; $Zn^{67}(p, \alpha)Cu^{64}$.

$Cu^{63}(n, \gamma)Cu^{64}$ 6×10^{-6} μg.

$Cu^{65}(n, \gamma)Cu^{66}$ 3×10^{-5} μg.

$Cu^{63}(p, n)Zn^{63}$ Excitation function from E_{th}(4.2 Mev) to 100 Mev; $E_p \sim 13$ Mev; $\sigma(13) \sim 0.42$ b; $\sigma(100) = 7$ mb.   B24 B26 D9 / G1 H38 M24 / M25

$Cu^{65}(p, n)Zn^{65}$ Excitation function from E_{th}(2.2 Mev) to 12 Mev; $E_p > 12$ Mev; $\sigma(12) = 0.80$ b; thick-target yield at 22 Mev = 9.3 mc/ma-hr.   B24 B26 B47 / H38 M15

$Cu^{63}(p, 2n)Zn^{62}$ $E_{th} = 13.4$ Mev; $\sigma(21.5) = 0.10$ b.   C23

$Cu^{63}(p, pn)Cu^{62}$ Excitation function from E_{th}(11.0 Mev) to 100 Mev; $E_p \sim 25$ Mev; $\sigma(25) = 0.57$ b; $\sigma(100) = 0.12$ b.   C23 G1 H34 / M24 M25

$Cu^{65}(p, pn)Cu^{64}$ Excitation function from E_{th}(~ 5 Mev) to 100 Mev; $E_p \sim 25$ Mev; $\sigma(25) = 0.53$ b; $\sigma(100) = 0.16$ b.   C24 M24 M25

$Cu^{63}(d, p)Cu^{64}$ $E_{th} = 2.0$ Mev; $\sigma(8) = 0.25$ b.   C16

$Cu^{63}(d, 2n)Zn^{63}$ $E_{th} = 7.0$ Mev; $\sigma(14) = 0.30$ b.   C16

$Cu^{65}(d, 2n)Zn^{65}$ $E_{th} = 5.5$ Mev; $\sigma(14) = 0.51$ b.   C16

$Cu(d, \quad)Zn^{63}$ Excitation function from 10 Mev to 190 Mev; $E_{th} \sim 7$ Mev; $E_p \sim 30$ Mev; $\sigma(30) = 0.38$ b.   B6

$Cu^{63, 65}(\alpha, n)Ga^{66, 68}$ Excitation function from 12 Mev to 40 Mev; $E_p = 17.5$ Mev; $\sigma(17.5) = 0.13$ b and 0.30 b, respectively.   P14

$Cu^{63, 65}(\alpha, 2n)Ga^{65, 67}$ Excitation functions from E_{th}(~ 16 Mev) to 40 Mev; $E_p = 30$ Mev and 28 Mev, respectively; $\sigma(30)$ and $\sigma(28) = 0.55$ b and 0.50 b, respectively.   P14

$Cu^{63}(\gamma, n)Cu^{62}$ Excitation function from E_{th}(11 Mev) to 36 Mev; $E_p = 17$ Mev; Average $\sigma(17) = 0.85$ b.   B21 B53 D12 / G8 H14 K7 / K30 S15

$Cu^{63}(p, n)Zn^{63}$ Possible interference from $Zn^{64}(p, pn)Zn^{63}$ at E > 15 Mev.

$Cu^{65}(p, n)Zn^{65}$ Possible interference from $Zn^{66}(p, pn)Zn^{64}$ at E > 12 Mev; possible interference from secondary reaction: $Zn^{64}(n, \gamma)Zn^{65}$.

$Cu^{63}(p, 2p)Zn^{62}$ No apparent interference from primary reactions at E < 20 Mev.

$Cu^{63}(p, pn)Cu^{62}$ Possible interference from $Ni^{62}(p, n)Cu^{62}$; possible interference from secondary reaction: $Ni^{61}(p, \gamma)Cu^{62}$.

$Cu^{65}(p, pn)Cu^{64}$ Possible interference from $Ni^{64}(p, n)Cu^{64}$; from $Zn^{67}(p, \alpha)Cu^{64}$; possible interference from secondary reaction: $Zn^{64}(n, p)Cu^{64}$.

$Cu^{63}(d, p)Cu^{64}$ Possible interference from $Ni^{64}(d, 2n)Cu^{64}$ or $Ni^{62}(d, \gamma)Cu^{64}$; from $Zn^{66}(d, \alpha)Cu^{64}$ or $Zn^{64}(d, 2p)Cu^{64}$; possible interference from secondary reactions: $Zn^{64}(n, p)Cu^{64}$; $Ni^{64}(p, n)Cu^{64}$; $Zn^{67}(p, \alpha)Cu^{64}$.

$Cu^{63}(d, 2n)Zn^{63}$ Possible interference from $Zn^{64}(d, dn)Zn^{63}$.

$Cu^{65}(d, 2n)Zn^{65}$ Possible interference from $Zn^{66}(d, dn)Zn^{65}$; possible interference from secondary reaction: $Zn^{64}(n, \gamma)Zn^{65}$.

$Cu^{63}(\alpha, n)Ga^{66}$ Possible interference from $Zn^{64}(\alpha, pn)Ga^{66}$; possible interference from secondary reaction: $Zn^{66}(p, n)Ga^{66}$.

$Cu^{65}(\alpha, n)Ga^{68}$ Possible interference from $Zn^{66}(\alpha, pn)Ga^{68}$; possible interference from secondary reactions: $Zn^{67}(p, \gamma)Ga^{68}$ or $Zn^{68}(p, n)Ga^{68}$.

$Cu^{63}(\gamma, n)Cu^{62}$ No apparent interference from primary reactions; possible interference from secondary reactions: $Ni^{61}(p, \gamma)Cu^{62}$ or $Ni^{62}(p, n)Cu^{62}$.

$Cu^{63}(p, n)Zn^{63}$ 1×10^{-4} $\mu g/cm^2$ at 13 Mev.

$Cu^{63}(d, p)Cu^{64}$ 4×10^{-4} $\mu g/cm^2$ at 8 Mev.

Zn^{64}	48.89	0.44 ± 0.05 a	245 d	EC (98.5)	1.119
		(n, p)< 10 μb a	12.8-h Cu^{64}		
		(n, α) 15 ± 10 μb	Ni^{61} (s)		
Zn^{66}	27.81		s		
		(n, α)<20 μb	80-y Ni^{63}		
Zn^{67}	4.11				
		(n, p) 1.3 mb a *†	s 61-h Cu^{67}		
		(n, α) 6 ± 4 μb	Ni^{64} (s)		
Zn^{68}	18.56	97 ± 10 mb a	13.8 h	none	IT (100)
		1.0 ± 0.2 a	52 m	0.897 (100)	none
		(n, α)<20 μb a	2.56-h Ni^{65}		
Zn^{70}	0.62	85 ± 20 mb	3 h	1.5	M
			2.2 m	2.4 (100)	M
		R = 3.4 ± 0.8 ††			†M37 ††K23

$Zn^{64}(n,\gamma)Zn^{65}$	Determination of Zn in Al with a sensitivity of 200 ppm; flux $\sim 10^{11}$.	B40 B66
$Zn^{68}(n,\gamma)Zn^{69m}$	Determination of Zn in Si using γ spectrometry with a sensitivity of 220 ppm.	M47
	Determination of Zn in Al with a sensitivity of 200 ppm; flux $\sim 10^{11}$.	B40 B66
$Zn^{68}(n,\gamma)Zn^{69}$	Determination of Zn in Si with a sensitivity of 7×10^{-3} ppm; flux = 2×10^{14}.	T16
	Determination of Zn in Si using γ spectrometry with a sensitivity of 2×10^{-8} ppm.	M48
	Determination of Zn in Ge and Ge compounds using γ spectrometry with a sensitivity of 1.3 ppm; flux = 3×10^{12}.	M49
	Others: B54, B60, B63, C12, C33, G28, J11, K2, L4, L23, S33, S48.	

$Zn^{64}(n,p)Cu^{64}$	$\sigma(2.0) = 12$ mb; $\sigma(3.55) = 56$ mb; $\sigma(14.5) = 0.39$ b.	P2 R18
$Zn^{66}(n,p)Cu^{66}$	$E_{th} = 3.5$ Mev; average $\sigma(14) = 0.08$ b.	C20 P2 Y1
$Zn^{68}(n,\alpha)Ni^{65}$	$\sigma(14) = 7.6 \pm 0.8$ mb.	B31 F3
$Zn^{64}(n,2n)Zn^{63}$	$E_{th} = 11.8$ Mev; average $\sigma(14) = 0.17$ b.	C20 P2 Y1

$Zn^{64}(n,\gamma)Zn^{65}$	No apparent interference from primary reactions; possible interference from second-order reaction: $Cu^{63}(n,\gamma)Cu^{64} \xrightarrow{\beta^-} Zn^{64}(n,\gamma)Zn^{65}$ with a Cu matrix.
$Zn^{68}(n,\gamma)Zn^{69,69m}$	Possible interference from $Ga^{69}(n,p)Zn^{69,69m}$; from $Ge^{72}(n,\alpha)Zn^{69,69m}$.
$Zn^{64}(n,p)Cu^{64}$	Possible interference from $Cu^{63}(n,\gamma)Cu^{64}$ or $Cu^{65}(n,2n)Cu^{64}$; possible interference from secondary reaction: $Ni^{64}(p,n)Cu^{64}$.
$Zn^{66}(n,p)Cu^{66}$	Possible interference from $Cu^{65}(n,\gamma)Cu^{66}$; from $Ga^{69}(n,\alpha)Cu^{66}$.
$Zn^{68}(n,\alpha)Ni^{65}$	Possible interference from $Ni^{64}(n,\gamma)Ni^{65}$; from $Cu^{65}(n,p)Ni^{65}$.
$Zn^{64}(n,2n)Zn^{63}$	No apparent interference from primary reactions at E < 20 Mev; possible interference from secondary reaction: $Cu^{63}(p,n)Zn^{63}$.

$Zn^{64}(n,\gamma)Zn^{65}$	1×10^{-3} μg.
$Zn^{68}(n,\gamma)Zn^{69m}$	1×10^{-3} μg.
$Zn^{68}(n,\gamma)Zn^{69}$	1×10^{-4} μg.

$Zn^{64}(p,n)Ga^{64}$	Excitation function from 8 Mev to 12 Mev; $E_{th} \sim 6$ Mev; $E_p > 12$ Mev; $\sigma(12) \sim 0.35$ b. C25 H38
$Zn^{66}(p,n)Ga^{66}$	Excitation function from 5.5 Mev to 12 Mev; $E_{th} < 5.5$ Mev; $E_p > 12$ Mev; $\sigma(12) = 0.70$ b. B24 B26 H38
$Zn^{67}(p,n)Ga^{67}$	Excitation function from E_{th}(2.2 Mev) to 12 Mev; $E_p > 12$ Mev; $\sigma(12) \sim 0.80$ b. B24 B26 H38
$Zn(p,\ )Ga^{67}$	Thick-target yield at 22 Mev = 600 mc/ma-hr. M15
$Zn^{68}(p,n)Ga^{68}$	Excitation function from E_{th}(3.7 Mev) to 6.8 Mev; $E_p > 6.8$ Mev; $\sigma(6.7) = 0.60$ b. B24 B26 B47
$Zn^{64}(p,\alpha)Cu^{61}$	Excitation function from ~ 7 Mev to 23.5 Mev; $E_{th} < 7$ Mev; $E_p = 15$ Mev; $\sigma(15) = 78$ mb. C24
$Zn^{68}(p,2n)Ga^{67}$	$E_{th} = 10.7$ Mev; $\sigma(21.5) = 0.78$ b. C23
$Zn^{64}(p,pn)Zn^{63}$	$E_{th} = 12.0$ Mev; $\sigma(21.5) = 0.68$ b; $\sigma(25) = 0.53$ b; $\sigma(100) = 0.16$ b. C25 M25
$Zn^{66}(p,pn)Zn^{65}$	$E_{th} = 10.8$ Mev; $\sigma(21.5) = 0.92$ b. C25
$Zn^{68}(p,2p)Cu^{67}$	$E_{th} = 8.7$ Mev; $\sigma(21.5) = 3.8$ mb. C25
$Zn^{64}(\gamma,n)Zn^{63}$	Excitation function from E_{th}(11.6 Mev) to 24 Mev; $E_p = 18.5$ Mev; $\sigma(18.5) = 0.123$ b. H14 K7 K10 S1

$Zn^{64}(p,n)Ga^{64}$	No apparent interference.
$Zn^{66}(p,n)Ga^{66}$	No apparent interference at E < 15 Mev.
$Zn^{67}(p,n)Ga^{67}$	Possible interference from $Ge^{70}(p,\alpha)Ga^{67}$.
$Zn^{68}(p,n)Ga^{68}$	Possible interference from $Ga^{69}(p,pn)Ga^{68}$ at E > 15 Mev.
$Zn^{64}(p,\alpha)Cu^{61}$	Possible interference from $Ni^{61}(p,n)Cu^{61}$ or $Ni^{62}(p,2n)Cu^{61}$; possible interference from secondary reaction: $Ni^{60}(p,\gamma)Cu^{61}$.
$Zn^{68}(p,2n)Ga^{67}$	Possible interference from $Ge^{70}(p,\alpha)Ga^{67}$.
$Zn^{64}(p,pn)Zn^{63}$	Possible interference from $Cu^{63}(p,n)Zn^{63}$.
$Zn^{66}(p,pn)Zn^{65}$	Possible interference from $Cu^{65}(p,n)Zn^{65}$.
$Zn^{68}(p,2p)Cu^{67}$	No apparent interference at E < $\sim$ 25 Mev.
$Zn^{64}(\gamma,n)Zn^{63}$	No apparent interference with primary reactions; possible interference from secondary reaction: $Cu^{63}(p,n)Zn^{63}$.

$Zn^{66}(p,n)Ga^{66}$	3×10^{-4} μg/cm^2 at 6.7 Mev.
$Zn^{68}(p,n)Ga^{68}$	3×10^{-4} μg/cm^2 at 6.7 Mev.

Ga^{69}	60.2	2.1 ± 0.2			
		1.4 ± 0.3 a	21.1 m	1.65 (99+)	
Ga^{71}	39.8	5.1 ± 0.4			
		4.0 ± 0.7 a	14.3 h	M	M

$R = 11.7 ± 2.7^{\dagger}$

$R_a^{69} = 9.2^{\dagger\dagger}$

$R_a^{71} = 15^{\dagger\dagger}$

† K23

†† M9

$Ga^{71}(n,\gamma)Ga^{72}$	Determination of Ga in Si with a sensitivity of 1×10^{-4} ppm; flux = 3×10^{12}.	C5 K2
	Determination of Ga in meteorites with a sensitivity of 1 ppm.	B45 G11
	Determination of Ga in biological material with a sensitivity of 0.05 µg; flux = 1×10^{12}.	B64
	Others: A4, B42, G28, J11, L4, M46, S33, T16.	

- -

$Ga^{69}(n,p)Zn^{69}$	$\sigma(14.5) = 24.2$ mb.	P2
$Ga^{69}(n,\alpha)Cu^{66}$	$\sigma(14.5) = 105$ mb.	P2
$Ga^{69}(n,2n)Ga^{68}$	$E_{th} = 10.5$ Mev; $\sigma(14.5) = 0.55$ b.	C20 P2
$Ga^{71}(n,2n)Ga^{70}$	$\sigma(14.5) = 0.70$ b.	P2

$Ga^{69}(n,\gamma)Ga^{70}$ Possible interference from $Ge^{70}(n,p)Ga^{70}$ with a Ge matrix; possible interference from second-order reaction: $Zn^{68}(n,\gamma)Zn^{69} \xrightarrow{\beta^-} Ga^{69}(n,\gamma)Ga^{70}$.

$Ga^{71}(n,\gamma)Ga^{72}$ Possible interference from $Ge^{72}(n,p)Ga^{72}$ with a Ge matrix; from $As^{75}(n,\alpha)Ga^{72}$ with an As matrix; from fission of U or Pu; possible interference from second-order reactions: $Zn^{70}(n,\gamma)Zn^{71,71m} \xrightarrow{\beta^-} Ga^{71}(n,\gamma)Ga^{72}$; $Ge^{70}(n,\gamma)Ge^{71} \xrightarrow{K} Ga^{71}(n,\gamma)Ga^{72}$.

$Ga^{69}(n,p)Zn^{69,69m}$ Possible interference from $Zn^{68}(n,\gamma)Zn^{69,69m}$ or $Zn^{70}(n,2n)Zn^{69,69m}$; from $Ge^{72}(n,\alpha)Zn^{69}$.

$Ga^{69}(n,\alpha)Cu^{66}$ Possible interference from $Cu^{65}(n,\gamma)Cu^{66}$; from $Zn^{66}(n,p)Cu^{66}$.

$Ga^{69}(n,2n)Ga^{68}$ No apparent interference from primary reactions at E < 20 Mev; possible interference from secondary reactions: $Zn^{67}(p,\gamma)Zn^{68}$ or $Zn^{68}(p,n)Ga^{68}$.

$Ga^{71}(n,2n)Ga^{70}$ Possible interference from $Ge^{70}(n,p)Ga^{70}$; possible interference from secondary reactions: $Zn^{70}(p,n)Ga^{70}$; $Ge^{73}(p,\alpha)Ga^{70}$.

$Ga^{69}(n,\gamma)Ga^{70}$ 2×10^{-5} µg.

$Ga^{71}(n,\gamma)Ga^{72}$ 1×10^{-5} µg.

$Ga^{69}(d,p)Ga^{70}$	Determination of Ga in Fe with a sensitivity of 6 ppm.	S16
$Ga^{71}(d,p)Ga^{72}$	Determination of Ga in Fe with a sensitivity of 6 ppm.	S16

$Ga^{69}(p,n)Ge^{69}$	Excitation function from 4 Mev to 6.8 Mev; E_{th} = 4.1 Mev; E_p > 6.8 Mev; $\sigma(6.7)$ = 0.47 b; $\sigma(100)$ = 15 mb.	B26 C16 M25
$Ga^{69}(p,2n)Ge^{68}$	E_{th} = 11.0 Mev; $\sigma(21.5)$ = 0.36 b; $\sigma(25)$ = 0.44 b; $\sigma(100)$ = 23 mb.	C23 M25
$Ga^{69}(p,pn)Ga^{68}$	E_{th} = 10.4 Mev; $\sigma(21.5)$ = 0.36 b; $\sigma(25)$ = 0.49 b; $\sigma(100)$ = 0.19 b.	C23 M25
$Ga^{71}(p,pn)Ga^{70}$	E_{th} = 9.0 Mev; $\sigma(21.5)$ = 0.26 b.	C23

$Ga^{69}(p,n)Ge^{69}$	Possible interference from $Ge^{70}(p,pn)Ge^{69}$ at E > 12 Mev.
$Ga^{71}(p,n)Ge^{71}$	Possible interference from $Ge^{72}(p,pn)Ge^{71}$ at E > 12 Mev; from $Se^{74}(p,\alpha)As^{71} \xrightarrow{\beta^+} Ge^{71}$; possible interference from secondary reactions: $Ge^{70}(n,\gamma)Ge^{71}$; $Se^{74}(n,\alpha)Ge^{71}$; $Ge^{70}(p,\gamma)As^{71} \xrightarrow{\beta^+} Ge^{71}$.
$Ga^{69}(p,2n)Ge^{68}$	No apparent interference at E < 20 Mev.
$Ga^{69}(p,pn)Ga^{68}$	Possible interference from $Zn^{68}(p,n)Ga^{68}$; possible interference from secondary reaction: $Zn^{67}(p,\gamma)Ga^{68}$.
$Ga^{71}(p,pn)Ga^{70}$	Possible interference from $Zn^{70}(p,n)Ga^{70}$; from $Ge^{73}(p,\alpha)Ga^{70}$; possible interference from secondary reactions: $Ga^{69}(n,\gamma)Ga^{70}$; $Ge^{70}(n,p)Ga^{70}$.

$Ga^{69}(p,n)Ge^{69}$	8×10^{-4} $\mu g/cm^2$ at 6.7 Mev.

Ge^{70}	20.55	3.4 ± 0.3			
		3.9 ± 1.2 a	11.4 d	EC	none
Ge^{72}	27.37	0.98 ± 0.09	s		
Ge^{73}	7.67	14 ± 1	s		
Ge^{74}	36.74	0.62 ± 0.06			
		40 ± 8 mb a	48 s		IT (100)
		0.21 ± 0.08 a	82 m	1.14 (85)	M
				0.614 (15)	
Ge^{76}	7.67	0.36 ± 0.07			
		80 ± 20 mb a	54 s	2.7 (86)	
					IT ($\sim$14)
		80 ± 20 mb a	11.3 h	M	M

$$R = 3.5 \pm 2.9^{\dagger} \qquad\qquad\qquad\qquad\qquad\qquad\qquad\qquad\qquad\qquad\qquad \dagger \, K23$$

$Ge^{74}(n,\gamma)Ge^{75}$	Determination of Ge with a calculated sensitivity of 0.04 µg; flux = 5×10^{11}.	L4
$Ge^{76}(n,\gamma)Ge^{77}$	Determination of Ge with a sensitivity of 0.4 µg; flux = 5×10^{11}.	L4
	Others: J4, S4, S71.	

- -

$Ge^{70}(n,p)Ga^{70}$	$E_{th} = 1.8$ Mev; $\sigma(14.5) = 0.13$ b.	C20 P2
$Ge^{72}(n,p)Ga^{72}$	$\sigma(14.5) = 65$ mb.	P2
$Ge^{73}(n,p)Ga^{73}$	$\sigma(14.5) = 0.14$ b.	P2
$Ge^{74}(n,\alpha)Zn^{71}$	$\sigma(14.5) = 14.9$ mb.	P2
$Ge^{70}(n,2n)Ge^{69}$	$\sigma(14.5) = 0.67$ b.	P2
$Ge^{76}(n,2n)Ge^{75}$	$\sigma(14.5) = 1.82$ b.	P2

$Ge^{70}(n,\gamma)Ge^{71}$	Possible interference from $Se^{74}(n,\alpha)Ge^{71}$ with a Se matrix; possible interference from second-order reaction: $Ga^{69}(n,\gamma)Ga^{70} \xrightarrow{\beta^-} Ge^{70}(n,\gamma)Ge^{71}$.
$Ge^{74}(n,\gamma)Ge^{75}$	Possible interference from $As^{75}(n,p)Ge^{75}$ with an As matrix; from $Se^{78}(n,\alpha)Ge^{75}$ with a Se matrix.
$Ge^{76}(n,\gamma)Ge^{77}$	Possible interference from $Se^{80}(n,\alpha)Ge^{77}$ with a Se matrix; from fission of U or Pu.
$Ge^{70}(n,p)Ga^{70}$	Possible interference from $Ga^{69}(n,\gamma)Ga^{70}$ or $Ga^{71}(n,2n)Ga^{70}$; possible interference from secondary reaction: $Zn^{70}(p,n)Ga^{70}$.
$Ge^{72}(n,p)Ga^{72}$	Possible interference from $Ga^{71}(n,\gamma)Ga^{72}$; from $As^{75}(n,\alpha)Ga^{72}$; from fission of Th, U, or Pu.
$Ge^{73}(n,p)Ga^{73}$	No apparent interference at E < 20 Mev.
$Ge^{74}(n,\alpha)Zn^{71}$	Possible interference from $Zn^{70}(n,\gamma)Zn^{71}$; from $Ga^{71}(n,p)Zn^{71}$.
$Ge^{70}(n,2n)Ge^{69}$	No apparent interference from primary reactions at E < 20 Mev; possible interference from secondary reaction: $Ga^{69}(p,n)Ge^{69}$.
$Ge^{76}(n,2n)Ge^{75}$	Possible interference from $As^{75}(n,p)Ge^{75}$; from $Se^{78}(n,\alpha)Ge^{75}$.

$Ge^{70}(n,\gamma)Ge^{71}$	3×10^{-5} µg.
$Ge^{74}(n,\gamma)Ge^{75+75m}$	2×10^{-4} µg.
$Ge^{76}(n,\gamma)Ge^{77+77m}$	2×10^{-3} µg.

$Ge^{74}(p,n)As^{74}$ Thick-target yield at 22 Mev = 50 mc/ma-hr.   M15

$Ge(d,)As^{71}$ Thick-target yield at 15 Mev = 7.6 µc/ua-hr.   W5

$Ge(d,)As^{72}$ Thick-target yield at 15 Mev = 64.9 µc/µa-hr.   W5

$Ge(d,)As^{73}$ Thick-target yield at 15 Mev = 1.1 µc/µa-hr.   W5

$Ge(d,)As^{74}$ Thick-target yield at 15 Mev = 5.2 µc/µa-hr.   W5

$Ge^{74}(p,n)As^{74}$ Possible interference from $Se^{77}(p,\alpha)As^{74}$; from $As^{75}(p,pn)As^{74}$ at E > 12 Mev; possible interference from secondary reaction: $Se^{74}(n,p)As^{74}$.

$Ge(d,)As^{74}$ Possible interference from $Se^{76}(d,\alpha)As^{74}$; from $As^{75}(d,dn)As^{74}$; possible interference from secondary reactions: $Se^{74}(n,p)As^{74}$; $Se^{77}(p,\alpha)As^{74}$.

$Ge(d,)As^{73}$ Possible interference from $Se^{76}(d,\alpha n)As^{73}$; possible interference from secondary reaction: $Se^{76}(p,\alpha)As^{73}$.

$Ge(d,)As^{72}$ Possible interference from $Se^{74}(d,\alpha)As^{72}$ with a Se matrix.

$Ge(d,)As^{71}$ Possible interference from $Se^{74}(d,\alpha n)As^{71}$ with a Se matrix.

As^{75}	100	4.3 ± 0.2			
		5.4 ± 1.0 a	26.4 h	M	M
		$R_a = 36.8^{\dagger}$			† M9

$As^{75}(n, \gamma)As^{76}$	Determination of As in Ge and Ge compounds using γ spectrometry with a sensitivity of 150 ppm; flux = 3.4×10^{12}.	M49
	Determination of As in biological specimens with a sensitivity of 0.4 ppm.	J11 S73
	Determination of As in Si and W using γ spectrometry with a sensitivity of ~ 200 ppm; flux $\sim 3 \times 10^{12}$.	C33 M47
	Determination of As in Mg with a sensitivity of 1×10^{-3} μg; flux = 5×10^{11}.	A17
	Determination of As in high purity Fe with a sensitivity of ~ 1 ppm; flux $\sim 10^{10}$.	A4 A6 G28 T1
	Determination of As in sea water with a sensitivity of 0.01 ppm; flux $\sim 5 \times 10^{11}$.	B43
	Determination of As in Si with a sensitivity of 10^{-5} ppm.	K2 T16
	Determination of As in Ge with a sensitivity of 10^{-5} ppm; flux = 3×10^{12}.	C5
	Others: B60, D11, G20, G23, J2, J4, K28, L4, L23, M40, S5, S24, S33, S34, S39, S40, S41, S42, S71.	

$As^{75}(n, p)Ge^{75}$	$\sigma(14.5) = 11.8$ mb.	P2
$As^{75}(n, \alpha)Ga^{72}$	$\sigma(14.5) = 12.3$ mb.	P2
$As^{75}(n, 2n)As^{74}$	$E_{th} = 10.3$ Mev; $\sigma(14.5) = 0.545$ b.	C20 P2

$As^{75}(n, \gamma)As^{76}$	Possible interference from $Se^{76}(n, p)As^{76}$ with a Se matrix; from $Br^{79}(n, \alpha)As^{76}$ with a Br matrix; possible interference from second-order reaction: $Ge^{74}(n, \gamma)Ge^{75} \xrightarrow{\beta^-} As^{75}(n, \gamma)As^{76}$.
$As^{75}(n, p)Ge^{75}$	Possible interference from $Ge^{74}(n, \gamma)Ge^{75}$ or $Ge^{76}(n, 2n)Ge^{75}$; from $Se^{78}(n, \alpha)Ge^{75}$; from fission of Th, U, or Pu.
$As^{75}(n, \alpha)Ga^{72}$	Possible interference from $Ga^{71}(n, \gamma)Ga^{72}$; from $Ge^{72}(n, p)Ga^{72}$; from fission of Th, U, or Pu.
$As^{75}(n, 2n)As^{74}$	Possible interference from $Se^{74}(n, p)As^{74}$; possible interference from secondary reactions: $Ge^{73}(p, \gamma)As^{74}$ or $Ge^{74}(p, n)As^{74}$.

$As^{75}(n, \gamma)As^{76}$	4×10^{-6} μg.

As^{75}(p, n)Se^{75} Excitation function from E$_{th}$(1. 6 Mev) to 6. 8 Mev; E$_p$ > 6. 8 Mev; σ(6. 7) = 0. 27 b.   B26

As^{75}(p, pn)As^{74} E$_{th}$ = 10. 3 Mev; σ(21. 5) = 0. 35 b; σ(25) = 0. 20 b; σ(100) = 0. 11 b.   C23 M25

As^{75}(γ, n)As^{74} Excitation function from E$_{th}$(10. 1 Mev) to 22 Mev; E$_p$ = 17 Mev; σ(17) = 91 mb.   M45 Y2

As^{75}(p, n)Se^{75} Possible interference from Se^{76}(p, pn)Se^{75} at E > 15 Mev; from Kr^{78}(p, α)Br^{75} $\xrightarrow{\beta^+}$ Se^{75} with
                                   a Kr matrix; possible interference from secondary reactions: Se^{74}(n, γ)Se^{75}; Kr^{78}(n, α)Se^{75};
                                   Se^{74}(p, γ)Br^{75} $\xrightarrow{\beta^+}$ Se^{75}.

As^{75}(p, pn)As^{74} Possible interference from Ge^{74}(p, n)As^{74}; from Se^{77}(p, α)As^{74}; possible interference from
                                   secondary reactions: Se^{74}(n, p)As^{74}; Ge^{73}(p, γ)As^{74}.

As^{75}(γ, n)As^{74} No apparent interference from primary reactions; possible interference from secondary reactions:
                                   Se^{74}(n, p)As^{74}; Ge^{73}(p, γ)As^{74} or Ge^{74}(p, n)As^{74}; Se^{77}(p, α)As^{74}.

As^{75}(p, n)Se^{75} 7 x 10^{-2} μg/cm^2 at 6. 7 Mev.

Se^{74}	0.87	50 ± 7			
		26 ± 6 a	121 d	EC (100)	M
Se^{76}	9.02	85 ± 7	s		
		7 ± 3 a	17.5 s	none	IT (100)
Se^{77}	7.58	42 ± 4	s		
Se^{78}	23.52	0.4 ± 0.4	3.91 m	none	IT (100)
			6.5 x 10^4 y	0.16 (100)	none
Se^{80}	49.82	0.61 ± 0.06			
		30 ± 10 mb a	56.8 m	none	IT (100)
		0.5 ± 0.1 a	18.2 m	1.38	none
Se^{82}	9.19	2.1 ± 1.5			
		50 ± 25 mb a	70 s	3.4	M
		4 ± 2 mb a	25 m	1.5 (100)	M
		R = 9.6 ± 1.3†			†K23

Se^{74}(n, γ)Se^{75}	Determination of Se in ore concentrates and industrial wastes with a sensitivity of 50 μg; flux = 4 x 10^{11}.	F17
	Determination of Se in high purity Al and Fe with a sensitivity of 4 x 10^{-3} μg.	G28
Se^{80}(n, γ)Se^{81}	Determination of Se with a calculated sensitivity of 0.05 μg; flux = 5 x 10^{11}.	L4
Se^{82}(n, γ)Se^{83}	Determination of Se with a calculated sensitivity of 2.0 μg; flux = 5 x 10^{11}.	L4
	Determination of Se with a calculated sensitivity of 10^{-3} μg; flux ∼ 10^{12}.	S33
	Determination of Se with a calculated sensitivity of 10^{-4} μg.	J11

Se^{77}(n, p)As^{77}	E_{th} = 0.1 Mev; σ(14.5) = 45.2 mb.	C20 P2
Se^{80}(n, α)Ge^{77+77m}	σ(14.5) = 37.7 mb.	P2
Se^{82}(n, 2n)Se^{81}	σ(14.5) = 1.50 b.	P2
Se^{80}(n, np)As^{79}	σ(14.5) ≤ 0.8 mb.	C19

Se^{74}(n, γ)Se^{75}	Possible interference from Kr^{78}(n, α)Se^{75} with a Kr matrix.
Se^{80}(n, γ)Se$^{81, 81m}$	Possible interference from Br^{81}(n, p)Se$^{81, 81m}$ with a Br matrix; from Kr^{84}(n, α)Se$^{81, 81m}$ with a Kr matrix; from fission of U or Pu.
Se^{82}(n, γ)Se^{83}	Possible interference from Kr^{86}(n, α)Se^{83} with a Kr matrix; from fission of U or Pu.
Se^{77}(n, p)As^{77}	Possible interference from Ge^{76}(n, α)Ge^{77} $\xrightarrow{\beta^-}$ As^{77}; from fission of Th, U, or Pu.
Se^{80}(n, α)Ge$^{77, 77m}$	Possible interference from Ge^{76}(n, γ)Ge$^{77, 77m}$; from fission of Th, U, or Pu.
Se^{82}(n, 2n)Se^{81}	Possible interference from Br^{81}(n, p)Se^{81}; from Kr^{84}(n, α)Se^{81}; from fission of Th, U, or Pu.

Se^{74}(n, γ)Se^{75}	6 x 10^{-4} μg.
Se^{80}(n, γ)Se^{81}	9 x 10^{-5} μg.
Se^{80}(n, γ)Se^{81m}	1 x 10^{-3} μg.
Se^{82}(n, γ)Se^{83}	6 x 10^{-2} μg.
Se^{82}(n, γ)Se$^{83, 83m}$ $\xrightarrow{\beta^-}$ Br^{83}	4 x 10^{-3} μg.

$Se^{78}(p,n)Br^{78}$ — Excitation function from $E_{th}(4.5\ Mev)$ to 6.8 Mev; $E_p > 6.8\ Mev$; $\sigma(6.7) = 0.30\ b.$ — B26 B48

$Se^{80}(p,n)Br^{80,80m}$ — Excitation function from $E_{th}(2.7\ Mev)$ to 6.8 Mev; $E_p > 6.8\ Mev$; $\sigma(6.7) = 0.33\ b$ and 0.12 b, respectively. — B26 B48

$Se^{82}(p,n)Br^{82}$ — Excitation function from $E_{th}(2.0\ Mev)$ to 6.8 Mev; $E_p > 6.8\ Mev$; $\sigma(6.7) = 0.45\ b.$ — B26 B48

$Se^{82}(d,2n)Br^{82}$ — Excitation function from $E_{th}(\sim 3.5\ Mev)$ to 9.7 Mev; $E_p > 9.7\ Mev$; $\sigma(9.7) = 0.93\ b.$ — M42

$Se^{78}(p,n)Br^{78}$ — Possible interference from $Br^{79}(p,pn)Br^{78}$ at $E > 15\ Mev$; possible interference from secondary reaction: $Kr^{78}(n,p)Br^{78}$.

$Se^{80}(p,n)Br^{80,80m}$ — Possible interference from $Kr^{83}(p,\alpha)Br^{80,80m}$; from $Br^{81}(p,pn)Br^{80,80m}$ at $E > 15\ Mev$; possible interference from secondary reactions: $Br^{79}(n,\gamma)Br^{80,80m}$; $Kr^{80}(n,p)Br^{80,80m}$.

$Se^{82}(p,n)Br^{82}$ — Possible interference from $Kr^{83}(p,2p)Br^{82}$ at $E > 15\ Mev$; possible interference from secondary reactions: $Br^{81}(n,\gamma)Br^{82}$; $Kr^{82}(n,p)Br^{82}$; $Rb^{85}(n,\alpha)Br^{82}$.

$Se^{82}(d,2n)Br^{82}$ — Possible interference from $Br^{81}(d,p)Br^{82}$; from $Kr^{84}(d,\alpha)Br^{82}$; possible interference from secondary reactions: $Br^{81}(n,\gamma)Br^{82}$; $Kr^{82}(n,p)Br^{82}$; $Rb^{85}(n,\alpha)Br^{82}$.

$Se^{78}(p,n)Br^{78}$ — $5 \times 10^{-4}\ \mu g/cm^2$ at 6.7 Mev.

$Se^{80}(p,n)Br^{80}$ — $2 \times 10^{-4}\ \mu g/cm^2$ at 6.7 Mev.

$Se^{80}(p,n)Br^{80m}$ — $8 \times 10^{-4}\ \mu g/cm^2$ at 6.7 Mev.

$Se^{82}(p,n)Br^{82}$ — $7 \times 10^{-3}\ \mu g/cm^2$ at 6.7 Mev.

Br^{79}	50.52	2.9 ± 0.5 a	4.38 h	none	IT (100)
		8.5 ± 1.4 a	17.6 m	1.99 (79)	0.62 (~11)
		10.4 ± 1.0 a	4.38 h + 17.6 m	1.38 (13)	
Br^{81}	49.48	3.1 ± 0.5 a	35.87 h	0.444 (100)	M

$$R = 118 \pm 14^{\dagger}$$
$$R_a^{79} = 147^{\dagger\dagger}$$

† K23
†† M9

$Br^{79}(n, \gamma)Br^{80}$	Determination of Br using a Van de Graaff-Be source with an efficient moderator with a sensitivity of 1.0 μg.	A18
$Br^{81}(n, \gamma)Br^{82}$	Determination of Br in naphthas with a sensitivity of 0.03 ppm.	B43
	Determination of Br on paper chromatograms with cyclotron-produced neutrons.	S13
	Determination of Br in blood using Ra-Be and Van de Graaff-Be sources.	S48
	Others: B60, C41, D2, D3, J11, L4, M53, W13.	

- -

$Br^{79}(n, \alpha)As^{76}$	$\sigma(14) = 10$ mb.	B30
$Br^{81}(n, \alpha)As^{78}$	$\sigma(14.5) = 0.103$ b.	P2
$Br^{79}(n, 2n)Br^{78}$	$\sigma(14.5) = 1.14$ b.	P2
$Br^{81}(n, 2n)Br^{80m}$	$\sigma(14.5) = 0.83$ b.	P2

$Br^{79}(n, \gamma)Br^{80, 80m}$	Possible interference from $Kr^{80}(n, p)Br^{80, 80m}$ with a Kr matrix.
$Br^{81}(n, \gamma)Br^{82}$	Possible interference from $Kr^{82}(n, p)Br^{82}$ with a Kr matrix; from $Rb^{85}(n, \alpha)Br^{82}$ with a Rb matrix; from fission of U or Pu; possible interference from second-order reaction: $Se^{80}(n, \gamma)Se^{81} \xrightarrow{\beta^-} Br^{81}(n, \gamma)Br^{82}$.
$Br^{79}(n, \alpha)As^{76}$	Possible interference from $As^{75}(n, \gamma)As^{76}$; from $Se^{76}(n, p)As^{76}$; from fission of Th, U, or Pu; possible interference from secondary reaction: $Ge^{76}(p, n)As^{76}$.
$Br^{81}(n, \alpha)As^{78}$	Possible interference from $Se^{78}(n, p)As^{78}$; from fission of Th, U, or Pu.
$Br^{79}(n, 2n)Br^{78}$	Possible interference from $Kr^{78}(n, p)Br^{78}$; possible interference from secondary reactions: $Se^{77}(p, \gamma)Br^{78}$ or $Se^{78}(p, n)Br^{78}$.
$Br^{81}(n, 2n)Br^{80, 80m}$	Possible interference from $Kr^{80}(n, p)Br^{80, 80m}$; possible interference from secondary reactions: $Se^{80}(p, n)Br^{80, 80m}$; $Kr^{83}(p, \alpha)Br^{80, 80m}$.

$Br^{79}(n, \gamma)Br^{80m}$	1×10^{-5} μg.
$Br^{79}(n, \gamma)Br^{80}$	5×10^{-6} μg.
$Br^{81}(n, \gamma)Br^{82}$	1×10^{-5} μg.

$Br^{79}(p,n)Kr^{79}$ $\sigma(6.7) = 0.14$ b.   B26

$Br^{81}(p,pn)Br^{80,80m}$ Excitation functions from 10 Mev to 100 Mev; $E_{th} < 10$ Mev; $E_p \sim 30$ Mev; $\sigma(30) = 80$ mb

                                    and 145 mb, respectively.   M26

$Br^{81}(d,p)Br^{82}$ Excitation function from $E_{th}(\sim 3$ Mev) to 9.7 Mev; $E_p \sim 9$ Mev; $\sigma(9) = 170$ mb.   M42

$Br^{79}(\gamma,n)Br^{78+78m}$ Excitation function from E_{th}(10 Mev) to 21 Mev; $E_p = 16$ Mev; $\sigma(16) \sim 100$ mb.   G13

$Br^{81}(\gamma,n)Br^{80,80m}$ Excitation functions from E_{th}(11 Mev) to 24 Mev; $E_p = 18$ Mev; $\sigma(18)$ 88 mb and 42 mb,

                                    respectively.   G13 K12

$Br^{81}(\gamma,\alpha)As^{77}$ Excitation function from 14 Mev to 26 Mev; $E_{th} < 10$ Mev; $E_p = 21.5$ Mev; $\sigma(10.2) = 0.12$ mb;

                                    $\sigma(21.5) = 0.27$ mb.   N1 T5

$Br^{79}(p,n)Kr^{79}$ Possible interference from $Kr^{80}(p,pn)Kr^{79}$ at E > 15 Mev; possible interference from secondary

                                    reactions: $Kr^{78}(n,\gamma)Kr^{79}$; $Kr^{78}(p,\gamma)Rb^{79} \xrightarrow{\beta^+} Kr^{79}$.

$Br^{81}(p,pn)Br^{80,80m}$ Possible interference from $Se^{80}(p,n)Br^{80,80m}$; from $Kr^{83}(p,\alpha)Br^{80,80m}$; possible interference

                                    from secondary reaction: $Kr^{80}(n,p)Br^{80,80m}$.

$Br^{81}(d,p)Br^{82}$ Possible interference from $Se^{80}(d,\gamma)Br^{82}$ or $Se^{82}(d,2n)Br^{82}$; from $Kr^{81}(d,\alpha)Br^{82}$; possible

                                    interference from secondary reactions: $Kr^{82}(n,p)Br^{82}$; $Rb^{85}(n,\alpha)Br^{82}$; $Se^{82}(p,n)Br^{82}$.

$Br^{79}(\gamma,n)Br^{78,78m}$ No apparent interference from primary reactions; possible interference from secondary reactions:

                                    $Kr^{78}(n,p)Br^{78,78m}$; $Se^{77}(p,\gamma)Br^{78,78m}$ or $Se^{78}(p,n)Br^{78,78m}$.

$Br^{81}(\gamma,n)Br^{80,80m}$ No apparent interference from primary reactions; possible interference from secondary reactions:

                                    $Kr^{80}(n,p)Br^{80,80m}$; $Se^{80}(p,n)Br^{80,80m}$; $Kr^{83}(p,\alpha)Br^{80,80m}$.

$Br^{79}(p,n)Kr^{79}$ 3×10^{-3} μg/cm^2 at 6.7 Mev.

$Br^{81}(d,p)Br^{82}$ 3×10^{-3} μg/cm^2 at 9 Mev.

Kr^{78}	0.35	2.0 ± 0.5 a	34.5 h	EC (95) 0.598 (~5)	M		
Kr^{80}	2.27	95 ± 15 a	13 s $+ 2.1 \times 10^5$ y	none EC (100)	IT (100) none		
Kr^{82}	11.56	45 ± 15	114 m s	none	IT (100)		
Kr^{83}	11.55	220 ± 40	s				
Kr^{84}	56.90	0.10 ± 0.03 a 60 ± 20 mb a	4.36 h 10.3 y	0.824 (77) 0.672 (9+)	IT (23) 0.150 (~75)		
Kr^{86}	17.37	60 ± 20 mb a	78 m	M	M	<600 a	2.77 h

$Kr^{78}(n, \gamma)Kr^{79}$ No apparent interference from primary or second-order reactions; possible interference from self-shielding in comparator samples.

$Kr^{84}(n, \gamma)Kr^{85, 85m}$ Possible interference from $Rb^{85}(n, p)Kr^{85, 85m}$ with a Rb matrix; from $Sr^{88}(n, \alpha)Kr^{85, 85m}$ with a Sr matrix; from fission of U or Pu; possible interference from self-shielding in comparator samples.

$Kr^{86}(n, \gamma)Kr^{87}$ Possible interference from $Rb^{87}(n, p)Kr^{87}$ with a Rb matrix; from fission of U or Pu; possible interference from self-shielding in comparator samples.

$Kr^{82}(n, \gamma)Kr^{83m}$ 5×10^{-6} μg.

$Kr^{84}(n, \gamma)Kr^{85m}$ 4×10^{-4} μg.

$Kr^{86}(n, \gamma)Kr^{87}$ 2×10^{-3} μg.

Rb^{85}	72.15	0.80 ± 0.08 a	1.02 m	none	IT (100)	
			18.66 d	1.78 (84)	1.08 (8.8)	
				0.71 (15)		
Rb^{87}	27.85	0.12 ± 0.03 a	17.8 m	M	M	1.0 ± 2 a
$(5.0 \times 10^{10}$ y)						

$$R = 9.0 \pm 2.8^{\dagger}$$

† K23

$Rb^{85}(n,\gamma)Rb^{86}$ Determination of Rb in sea water and related materials with a sensitivity of 10^{-2} µg.   S43

Determination of Rb in Na-K alloys with a sensitivity of < 0.2 ppm.   C4 S32

$Rb^{87}(n,\gamma)Rb^{88}$ Determination of Rb in sea water with a sensitivity of 5×10^{-4} ppm.   S33

Determination of Rb in geological specimens with a sensitivity of 0.034 ppm.   C3

Others: B60, G28, J11, L4, L8.

$Rb^{87}(n,p)Kr^{87}$ $E_{th} = 3.3$ Mev.   C20

$Rb^{87}(n,\alpha)Br^{84}$ $\sigma(14.5) = 38.9$ mb.   P2

$Rb^{85}(n,2n)Rb^{84}$ $E_{th} = 11.5$ Mev.   C20

$Rb^{85}(n,\gamma)Rb^{86}$ Possible interference from $Sr^{86}(n,p)Rb^{86}$ in a Rb matrix; from $Y^{89}(n,\alpha)Rb^{86}$ with an Y matrix; from fission of U or Pu; possible interference from second-order reaction: $Kr^{84}(n,\gamma)Kr^{85m} \xrightarrow{\beta^-} Rb^{85}(n,\gamma)Rb^{86}$.

$Rb^{87}(n,\gamma)Rb^{88}$ Possible interference from $Sr^{88}(n,p)Rb^{88}$ in a Sr matrix; from fission of U or Pu; possible interference from second-order reaction: $Kr^{86}(n,\gamma)Kr^{87} \xrightarrow{\beta^-} Rb^{87}(n,\gamma)Rb^{88}$.

$Rb^{87}(n,p)Kr^{87}$ Possible interference from $Kr^{86}(n,\gamma)Kr^{87}$; from fission of Th, U, or Pu.

$Rb^{87}(n,\alpha)Br^{84}$ Possible interference from $Kr^{84}(n,p)Br^{84}$; from fission of Th, U, or Pu.

$Rb^{87}(n,2n)Rb^{86}$ Possible interference from $Sr^{86}(n,p)Kr^{86}$; from $Y^{89}(n,\alpha)Rb^{86}$; from fission of Th, U, or Pu; possible interference from secondary reaction: $Kr^{86}(p,n)Rb^{86}$.

$Rb^{85}(n,\gamma)Rb^{86}$ 6×10^{-5} µg.

$Rb^{87}(n,\gamma)Rb^{88}$ 7×10^{-4} µg.

$Rb^{85}(p, n)Sr^{85}$ $\sigma(6.7) = 0.31$ b.   B26

$Rb^{87}(p, n)Sr^{87m}$ Excitation function from 2.5 Mev to 6.8 Mev; $E_{th} < 2.5$ Mev; $E_p > 6.8$ Mev; $\sigma(6.7) = 0.19$ b.   B26

$Rb^{87}(\gamma, n)Rb^{86}$ Excitation function from $E_{th}(9.3$ Mev) to 20 Mev; $E_p = 17.5$ Mev; $\sigma(17.5) = 0.23$ b.   K5

$Rb^{87}(\gamma, \alpha)Br^{83}$ Excitation function from $E_{th}(\sim 14$ Mev) to 27 Mev; $E_p = 24$ Mev; $\sigma(24) = 0.075$ mb.   H15   K7

$Rb^{85}(p, n)Sr^{85, 85m}$ Possible interference from $Sr^{86}(p, pn)Sr^{85, 85m}$ at E > 15 Mev; possible interference from secondary reactions: $Sr^{84}(n, \gamma)Sr^{85, 85m}$ or $Sr^{84}(p, \gamma)Y^{85} \xrightarrow{\beta^+} Sr^{85, 85m}$.

$Rb^{87}(p, n)Sr^{87m}$ No apparent interference from primary reactions; possible interference from secondary reactions: $Sr^{86}(n, \gamma)Sr^{87m}$; $Zr^{90}(n, \alpha)Sr^{87m}$.

$Rb^{87}(\gamma, n)Rb^{86}$ Possible interference from $Sr^{87}(\gamma, p)Rb^{86}$; possible interference from secondary reactions: $Sr^{86}(n, p)Rb^{86}$; $Y^{89}(n, \alpha)Rb^{86}$; $Kr^{86}(p, n)Rb^{86}$.

$Rb^{85}(p, n)Sr^{85}$ 5×10^{-2} $\mu g/cm^2$ at 6.7 Mev.

$Rb^{87}(p, n)Sr^{87m}$ 8×10^{-4} $\mu g/cm^2$ at 6.7 Mev.

Sr^{84}	0.56	<1 a	70 m	EC (14)	IT (86)		
		1.0 ± 0.3 a	64 d	EC (100)	0.513 ($\sim$ 100)		
Sr^{86}	9.86	1.3 ± 0.4 a	2.80 h	none	IT (100)		
			s				
Sr^{87}	7.02		s				
Sr^{88}	82.56	5 ± 1 mb a	51 d	1.463 (99+)		0.5 ± 0.1 a	28 y
		$R = 10.0 \pm 2.6^{\dagger}$					$\dagger$ K23

$Sr^{86}(n, \gamma)Sr^{87m}$	Determination of Sr in human bones with a sensitivity of 0.75 μg; flux = 1×10^{12}.	S46
	Determination of Sr in biological material with a sensitivity of 1.0 μg; flux = 2.0×10^{12}.	H13
$Sr^{88}(n, \gamma)Sr^{89}$	Determination of Sr in Mg with a sensitivity of 2 μg; flux = 5×10^{11}.	A17
	Determination of Sr in liquid metals with a sensitivity of 0.5 ppm.	S32
	Others: B35, B42, B60, G28, H51, J11, S33.	

$Sr^{88}(n, p)Rb^{88}$	$E_{th} = 4.3$ Mev; $\sigma(14.5) = 17.7$ mb.	C20 P2
$Sr^{88}(n, \alpha)Kr^{85}$	$\sigma(14.5) = 64$ mb.	P2

$Sr^{84}(n, \gamma)Sr^{85, 85m}$	No apparent interference.
$Sr^{86}(n, \gamma)Sr^{87m}$	Possible interference from $Zr^{90}(n, \alpha)Sr^{87m}$ with a Zr matrix; from fission of U or Pu.
$Sr^{88}(n, \gamma)Sr^{89}$	Possible interference from $Y^{89}(n, p)Sr^{89}$ with an Y matrix; from $Zr^{92}(n, \alpha)Sr^{89}$ with a Zr matrix; from fission of U or Pu; possible interference from second-order reactions: $Rb^{87}(n, \gamma)Rb^{88} \xrightarrow{\beta^-} Sr^{88}(n, \alpha)Sr^{89}$; $Sr^{89}(n, \gamma)Sr^{90}$.
$Sr^{88}(n, p)Rb^{88}$	Possible interference from $Rb^{87}(n, \gamma)Rb^{88}$; from fission of Th, U, or Pu.
$Sr^{88}(n, \alpha)Kr^{85, 85m}$	Possible interference from $Rb^{85}(n, p)Kr^{85, 85m}$; from $Kr^{84}(n, \gamma)Kr^{85, 85m}$; from fission of Th, U, or Pu.

$Sr^{84}(n, \gamma)Sr^{85}$	2×10^{-2} μg.
$Sr^{86}(n, \gamma)Sr^{87m}$	2×10^{-4} μg.
$Sr^{88}(n, \gamma)Sr^{89}$	2×10^{-2} μg.

$Sr^{87}(p,n)Y^{87, 87m}$ Excitation functions from E_{th} ($\sim$ 2.5 Mev) to 6.8 Mev; $E_p > 6.8$ Mev; $\sigma(6.7) = 0.23$ b and

0.10 b, respectively.   B26

$Sr^{88}(p,n)Y^{88}$ Excitation function from 4.7 Mev to 6.8 Mev; $E_{th} < 4.7$ Mev; $E_p > 6.8$ Mev; $\sigma(6.7) = 0.16$ b.   B26

Thick-target yield at 22 Mev = 20 mc/ma-hr.   M15

$Sr^{86}(\gamma,n)Sr^{85}$ Excitation function from E_{th}(11.5 Mev) to 23 Mev; E_p = 15.9 Mev; $\sigma(15.9) = 0.16$ b.   Y2

$Sr^{87}(p,n)Y^{87, 87m}$ Possible interference from $Zr^{90}(p,\alpha)Y^{87, 87m}$ at E > 20 Mev.

$Sr^{88}(p,n)Y^{88}$ Possible interference from $Zr^{91}(p,\alpha)Y^{88}$; from $Y^{89}(p,pn)Y^{88}$ at E > 15 Mev.

$Sr^{86}(\gamma,n)Sr^{85, 85m}$ No apparent interference from primary reactions; possible interference from secondary reaction:

$Rb^{85}(p,n)Sr^{85, 85m}$.

$Sr^{87}(p,n)Y^{87}$ 3×10^{-2} $\mu g/cm^2$ at 6.7 Mev.

$Sr^{87}(p,n)Y^{87m}$ 2×10^{-2} $\mu g/cm^2$ at 6.7 Mev.

$Sr^{88}(p,n)Y^{88}$ 1×10^{-1} $\mu g/cm^2$ at 6.7 Mev.

Y^{89}	100	1.26 ± 0.08					
		1.2 ± 0.3 a	64.2 h	2.26 (99+)	None	<7 a	57.5 d

$R_a = 0.91^\dagger$ † M9

$Y^{89}(n, \gamma)Y^{90}$ Determination of Y in high purity Fe and Al with a sensitivity of 3×10^{-3} μg.   G28

Determination of Y with a calculated sensitivity of 0.01 μg; flux = 5×10^{11}.   L4

Determination of Y with a calculated sensitivity of 10^{-3} μg; flux ~ 10^{12}.   S33

Determination of Y with a calculated sensitivity of 10^{-5} μg.   J11

- -

$Y^{89}(n, \alpha)Rb^{86}$ $\sigma(14.5) = 69.7$ mb.   P2

$Y^{89}(n, \gamma)Y^{90}$ Possible interference from $Zr^{90}(n, p)Y^{90}$ with Zr matrix; from $Nb^{93}(n, \alpha)Y^{90}$ with a Nb matrix; possible interference from fission of U or Pu.

$Y^{89}(n, \alpha)Rb^{86}$ Possible interference from $Rb^{85}(n, \gamma)Rb^{86}$ or $Rb^{87}(n, 2n)Rb^{86}$; from $Sr^{86}(n, p)Rb^{86}$; from fission of Th, U, or Pu; possible interference from secondary reaction: $Kr^{86}(p, n)Rb^{86}$.

$Y^{89}(n, \gamma)Y^{90}$ 2×10^{-5} μg.

$Y^{89}(p,n)Zr^{89,89m}$ Excitation functions from $E_{th}(\sim 3.5$ Mev) to 6.8 Mev; $E_p > 6.8$ Mev; $\sigma(6.7) = 0.29$ b

and 0.12 b, respectively.   B26

$Y^{89}(\gamma,n)Y^{88}$ Excitation function from $E_{th}(11.8$ Mev) to ~ 20 Mev; $E_p = 16.3$ Mev; $\sigma(16.3) = 0.19$ b.   Y2

$Y^{89}(p,n)Zr^{89,89m}$ Possible interference from $Zr^{90}(p,pn)Zr^{89,89m}$ at $E > 15$ Mev; from $Mo^{92}(p,\alpha)Nb^{89} \xrightarrow{\beta^+} Zr^{89}$; possible interference from secondary reaction: $Mo^{92}(n,\alpha)Zr^{89}$.

$Y^{89}(p,pn)Y^{88}$ Possible interference from $Sr^{88}(p,n)Y^{88}$; from $Zr^{91}(p,\alpha)Y^{88}$; possible interference from secondary reaction: $Sr^{87}(p,\gamma)Y^{88}$.

$Y^{89}(\gamma,n)Y^{88}$ No apparent interference from primary reactions; possible interference from secondary reactions: $Sr^{87}(p,\gamma)Y^{88}$ or $Sr^{88}(p,n)Y^{88}$; $Zr^{91}(p,\alpha)Y^{88}$.

$Y^{89}(p,n)Zr^{89m}$ 3×10^{-4} $\mu g/cm^2$ at 6.7 Mev.

$Y^{89}(p,n)Zr^{89}$ 2×10^{-3} $\mu g/cm^2$ at 6.7 Mev.

Zr^{90}	51.46	0.10 ± 0.07		s		
Zr^{91}	11.23	1.58 ± 0.12		s		
Zr^{92}	17.11	0.25 ± 0.12	1.1×10^6 y	0.056 (96)	0.03	<4
Zr^{94}	17.40	0.08 ± 0.06				
		0.09 ± 0.03 a	65 d	M	M	
Zr^{96}	2.80	0.1 ± 0.1				
		0.10 ± 0.05 a	17.0 h	1.91 (100)	0.75 ($\sim$100)	

$$R = 3.7 \pm 0.5^{\dagger} \qquad\qquad\qquad\qquad\qquad\qquad\qquad\qquad \dagger K23$$

$Zr^{94}(n,\gamma)Zr^{95}$ — Determination of Zr in Si with a sensitivity of 3×10^{-3} ppm; flux = 2×10^{14}. — T16

Determination of Zr in Zr-Hf mixtures by analysis for Nb^{95}; sensitivity < 1 ppm; flux $\sim 10^{12}$. — H41

$Zr^{96}(n,\gamma)Zr^{97}$ — Determination of Zr in Al with a sensitivity of 6 µg; flux $\sim 5 \times 10^{11}$. — B40 B66

Determination of Zr with a calculated sensitivity of 10^{-2} µg; flux $\sim 10^{12}$. — S33

Others: A19, G28, J11, L4.

- -

$Zr^{90}(n,p)Y^{90}$ — $E_{th} = 1.8$ Mev; $\sigma(14.5) = 0.247$ b. — C20 P2

$Zr^{94}(n,p)Y^{94}$ — $\sigma(14.5) = 10.6$ mb. — P2

$Zr^{90}(n,\alpha)Sr^{87m}$ — $\sigma(14.5) = 0.194$ b; $\sigma(14) = 3.3$ mb. — B30 P2

$Zr^{94}(n,\alpha)Sr^{91}$ — $\sigma(14) = 3.6$ mb. — B30

$Zr^{90}(n,2n)Zr^{89m}$ — $E_{th} = 12$ Mev; $\sigma(14.5) = 79.8$ mb. — C20 P2

$Zr^{94}(n,\gamma)Zr^{95}$ — Possible interference from $Mo^{98}(n,\alpha)Zr^{95}$ with a Mo matrix; from fission of U or Pu.

$Zr^{96}(n,\gamma)Zr^{97}$ — Possible interference from $Mo^{100}(n,\alpha)Zr^{97}$ with a Mo matrix; from fission of U or Pu.

$Zr^{90}(n,p)Y^{90}$ — Possible interference from $Nb^{93}(n,\alpha)Y^{90}$; $Y^{89}(n,\gamma)Y^{90}$; from fission of Th, U, or Pu.

$Zr^{94}(n,p)Y^{94}$ — Possible interference from fission of Th, U, or Pu.

$Zr^{90}(n,\alpha)Sr^{87m}$ — Possible interference from $Sr^{86}(n,\gamma)Sr^{87m}$ or $Sr^{88}(n,2n)Sr^{87m}$; possible interference from secondary reaction: $Rb^{87}(p,n)Sr^{87m}$.

$Zr^{94}(n,\alpha)Sr^{91}$ — Possible interference from fission of Th, U, or Pu.

$Zr^{90}(n,2n)Zr^{89}$ — Possible interference from $Mo^{92}(n,\alpha)Zr^{89}$; possible interference from secondary reaction: $Y^{89}(p,n)Zr^{89}$.

$Zr^{94}(n,\gamma)Zr^{95}$ — 6×10^{-3} µg.

$Zr^{96}(n,\gamma)Zr^{97}$ — 9×10^{-3} µg.

$Zr^{91}(p,n)Nb^{91m}$ Excitation function from 3.0 Mev to 6.8 Mev; $E_{th} < 3$ Mev; $E_p > 6.8$ Mev; $\sigma(6.7) = 50$ mb.   B26

$Zr^{92}(p,n)Nb^{92}$ Excitation function from $E_{th}(2.5$ Mev$)$ to 6.8 Mev; $E_p > 6.8$ Mev; $\sigma(6.7) = 0.18$ b.   B26

$Zr^{96}(p,n)Nb^{96}$ Excitation function from $E_{th}(2.6$ Mev$)$ to 6.8 Mev; $E_p > 6.8$ Mev; $\sigma(6.7) = 0.32$ b.   B26

$Zr^{96}(d,p)Zr^{97}$ Excitation function from 50 Mev to 190 Mev; $E_p < 50$ Mev; $\sigma(50) = 21$ mb.   S27

$Zr^{90}(d,\alpha)Y^{88}$ Excitation function from 7.0 Mev to 7.75 Mev; $E_p > 7.75$ Mev; $\sigma(7.75) = 2.28$ mb.   A12

$Zr^{92}(d,\alpha)Y^{90}$ Excitation function from 2.5 Mev to 7.75 Mev; $E_p > 7.75$ Mev; $\sigma(7.75) = 3.7$ mb.   A12

$Zr^{94}(d,\alpha)Y^{92}$ Excitation function from ~ 4 Mev to 7.75 Mev; $E_p > 7.75$ Mev; $\sigma(7.75) \sim 4.0$ mb.   A12

$Zr^{90}(\gamma,n)Zr^{89,89m}$ Excitation functions from ~ 12 Mev to 23 Mev; $E_{th} = 11.8$ Mev and 12.3 Mev, respectively; $E_p = 17.8$ Mev; $\sigma(17.8) = 0.12$ b and 0.15 b, respectively.   A21 K5 Y2

$Zr^{91}(p,n)Nb^{91m}$ Possible interference from $Mo^{94}(p,\alpha)Nb^{91m}$; from $Mo^{92}(p,2p)Nb^{91m}$ at $E > 15$ Mev; from $Mo^{92}(p,pn)Mo^{91} \xrightarrow{\beta^+} Nb^{91m}$ at $E > 15$ Mev.

$Zr^{92}(p,n)Nb^{92,92m}$ Possible interference from $Mo^{95}(p,\alpha)Nb^{92,92m}$; from $Nb^{93}(p,pn)Nb^{92,92m}$ at $E > 15$ Mev; possible interference from secondary reaction: $Mo^{92}(n,p)Nb^{92,92m}$.

$Zr^{96}(p,n)Nb^{96}$ Possible interference from $Mo^{97}(p,2p)Nb^{96}$ at $E > 15$ Mev; possible interference from secondary reaction: $Mo^{96}(n,p)Nb^{96}$.

$Zr^{96}(d,p)Zr^{97}$ No apparent interference from primary reactions at $E < 20$ Mev; possible interference from secondary reaction: $Mo^{100}(n,\alpha)Zr^{97}$.

$Zr^{90}(d,\alpha)Y^{88}$ Possible interference from $Sr^{87}(d,n)Y^{88}$ or $Sr^{88}(d,2n)Y^{88}$; from $Y^{89}(d,dn)Y^{88}$; possible interference from secondary reactions: $Sr^{87}(p,\gamma)Y^{88}$ or $Sr^{88}(p,n)Y^{88}$.

$Zr^{92}(d,\alpha)Y^{90}$ No apparent interference from primary reactions; possible interference from secondary reaction: $Y^{89}(n,\gamma)Y^{90}$.

$Zr^{94}(d,\alpha)Y^{92}$ No apparent interference.

$Zr^{90}(\gamma,n)Zr^{89,89m}$ No apparent interference from primary reactions; possible interference from secondary reactions: $Mo^{92}(n,\alpha)Zr^{89,89m}$; $Y^{89}(p,n)Zr^{89,89m}$; $Mo^{92}(p,\alpha)Nb^{89} \xrightarrow{\beta^+} Zr^{89,89m}$

$Zr^{92}(p,n)Nb^{92}$ 5×10^{-2} $\mu g/cm^2$ at 6.7 Mev.

$Zr^{96}(p,n)Nb^{96}$ 2×10^{-2} $\mu g/cm^2$ at 6.7 Mev.

Nb^{93}	100	1.15 ± 0.05					
		1.0 ± 0.5 a	6.6 m		IT (99+)	15 ± 4	35 d
		2×10^4 y		0.50 (100)	0.70 (92)		
					0.87 (92)		
					1.57 (8)		
		$R_a = 3.87^{\dagger}$					$\dagger$ M9

$Nb^{93}(n,\gamma)Nb^{94m}$ Determination of Nb with a calculated sensitivity of 1 μg; flux = 5×10^{11}.   L4

$Nb^{93}(n,\alpha)Y^{90}$ $\sigma(14) = 9.0$ mb.   B30

$Nb^{93}(n,\gamma)Nb^{94m}$ Possible interference from $Mo^{94}(n,p)Nb^{94m}$ with a Nb matrix.

$Nb^{93}(n,\alpha)Y^{90}$ Possible interference from $Y^{89}(n,\gamma)Y^{90}$; $Zr^{90}(n,p)Y^{90}$; fission of Th, U, or Pu.

$Nb^{93}(n,\gamma)Nb^{94m}$ 3×10^{-5} μg.

$Nb^{93}(\alpha,n)Tc^{96}$	Determination of Nb in silicates with 30-Mev α's; used reaction $Mo^{92}(\alpha,p)Tc^{95}$ as an internal beam monitor.	W23

$Nb^{93}(p,n)Mo^{93m}$	Excitation function from E_{th}(3.7 Mev) to 21 Mev; E_p = 15 Mev; $\sigma(15)$ = 0.26 b.	B26 J6
$Nb^{93}(\gamma,n)Nb^{92}$	Excitation function from 12.5 Mev to 25 Mev; E_{th} = 8.86 Mev; E_p = 17 Mev; $\sigma(17)$ = 0.23 b.	M45 N3 Y2

$Nb^{93}(p,n)Mo^{93m}$	Possible interference from $Mo^{94}(p,pn)Mo^{93m}$ at E > 15 Mev; possible interference from secondary reactions: $Mo^{92}(n,\gamma)Mo^{93m}$; $Ru^{96}(n,\alpha)Mo^{93m}$; $Mo^{92}(p,\gamma)Tc^{93} \xrightarrow{\beta^+} Mo^{93m}$.
$Nb^{93}(\gamma,n)Nb^{92,92m}$	No apparent interference from primary reactions; possible interference from secondary reactions: $Mo^{92}(n,p)Nb^{92,92m}$; $Zr^{91}(p,\gamma)Nb^{92,92m}$ or $Zr^{92}(p,n)Nb^{92,92m}$; $Mo^{95}(p,\alpha)Nb^{92,92m}$.

$Nb^{93}(p,n)Mo^{93m}$	3×10^{-4} $\mu g/cm^2$ at 15 Mev.

Mo^{92}	15.86	<0.3			
		<6 mb a	6.95 h	none	IT (100)
		$(n, p) > 0.1$ mb[*][†]	10-d Nb^{92}		
		$(n, \alpha) > 0.0005$ mb[*][†]	79-h Zr^{89}		
Mo^{94}	9.12		s		
Mo^{95}	15.70	13.9 ± 1.4	s		
		$(n, p) > 0.017$ mb[*][†]	35-d Nb^{95}		
Mo^{96}	16.50	1.2 ± 0.6	s		
Mo^{97}	9.45	2.2 ± 0.7	s		
Mo^{98}	23.75	0.4 ± 0.4			
		0.45 ± 0.10 a	66.0 h[††]	M	M
Mo^{100}	9.62	0.5 ± 0.5			
		0.20 ± 0.05	14.6 m	M	M

R = 13.8 ± 1.7[†††]

† M37
†† G27
††† K23

$Mo^{98}(n, \gamma)Mo^{99}$	Determination of Mo in Si with a sensitivity of 2×10^{-4} ppm; flux = 3×10^{12}; with a sensitivity of 1×10^{-3} ppm; flux = 1×10^{11}. C5 T16
	Determination of Mo in W using γ spectrometry with a sensitivity of 1.2 μg. C33
	Determination of Mo in biological material with a sensitivity of 3×10^{-4} μg; flux = 1×10^{12}. B64
	Others: A11, G28, J11, L4, S33.

$Mo^{97}(n, p)Nb^{97}$	$E_{th} = 1.5$ Mev; $\sigma(14.5) = 0.11$ b.	C20 P2
$Mo^{92}(n, 2n)Mo^{91}$	Excitation function from E_{th}(13.3 Mev) to 27 Mev; $E_p \sim 20$ Mev; $\sigma(14) = 0.13$ b; $\sigma(20) = 0.98$ b.	B39 Y1
$Mo^{100}(n, 2n)Mo^{99}$	$\sigma(14.5) = 3.79$ b.	P2

$Mo^{92}(n, \gamma)Mo^{93m}$	Possible interference from $Ru^{96}(n, \alpha)Mo^{93m}$.
$Mo^{98}(n, \gamma)Mo^{99}$	Possible interference from $Ru^{102}(n, \alpha)Mo^{99}$; from fission of U or Pu.
$Mo^{100}(n, \gamma)Mo^{101}$	Possible interference from $Ru^{104}(n, \alpha)Mo^{101}$; from fission of U or Pu.
$Mo^{97}(n, p)Nb^{97}$	Possible interference from $Zr^{96}(n, \gamma)Zr^{97} \xrightarrow{\beta^-} Nb^{97}$; from fission of Th, U, or Pu; possible interference from secondary reaction: $Mo^{100}(p, \alpha)Nb^{97}$.
$Mo^{92}(n, 2n)Mo^{91}$	No apparent interference.
$Mo^{100}(n, 2n)Mo^{99}$	Possible interference from $Ru^{102}(n, \alpha)Mo^{99}$; from fission of Th, U, or Pu.

$Mo^{98}(n, \gamma)Mo^{99}$	3×10^{-4} μg.
$Mo^{100}(n, \gamma)Mo^{101}$	1×10^{-3} μg.

$Mo^{94}(p,n)Tc^{94}$ Excitation function from E_{th}(5.1 Mev) to 6.8 Mev; $E_p > 6.8$ Mev; $\sigma(6.7) = 0.15$ b.   B26

$Mo^{95}(p,n)Tc^{95}$ Excitation function from E_{th}(3.6 Mev) to 6.8 Mev; $E_p > 6.8$ Mev; $\sigma(6.7) = 0.11$ b.   B26

$Mo^{96}(p,n)Tc^{96}$ Excitation function from E_{th}(3.8 Mev) to 6.8 Mev; $E_p > 6.8$ Mev; $\sigma(6.7) = 0.23$ b.   B26

$Mo^{92}(d,\alpha)Nb^{90}$ $\sigma(7.75) = 2.95$ mb.   A12

$Mo^{97}(d,\alpha)Nb^{95m}$ $\sigma(7.75) = 0.98$ mb.   A12

$Mo^{97}(d,\alpha)Nb^{95}$ Excitation function from 2.25 Mev to 7.75 Mev; $E_{th} < 2.25$ Mev; $E_p > 7.75$ Mev; $\sigma(7.75) = 2.35$ mb.   A12

$Mo^{98}(d,\alpha)Nb^{96}$ $\sigma(7.75) = 2.53$ mb.   A12

$Mo^{92}(\gamma,n)Mo^{91,91m}$ Excitation function from E_{th}(13.1 and 13.2 Mev, respectively) to 24 Mev; $E_p = 18.7$ Mev;

                              $\sigma(18.7) = 120$ mb and 24 mb, respectively.   K5

$Mo^{94}(p,n)Tc^{94}$ No apparent interference at $E < 20$ Mev.

$Mo^{95}(p,n)Tc^{95}$ Possible interference from $Ru^{98}(p,\alpha)Tc^{95}$; from $Ru^{96}(p,pn)Ru^{95} \xrightarrow{\beta^+} Tc^{95}$ at $E > 15$ Mev.

$Mo^{96}(p,n)Tc^{96}$ Possible interference from $Ru^{99}(p,\alpha)Tc^{96}$; possible interference from secondary reaction:

                              $Ru^{96}(n,p)Tc^{96}$.

$Mo^{92}(\gamma,n)Mo^{91,91m}$ No apparent interference.

$Mo^{92}(d,\alpha)Nb^{90}$ Possible interference from $Zr^{90}(d,2n)Nb^{90}$; possible interference from secondary reaction:

                              $Zr^{90}(p,n)Nb^{90}$.

$Mo^{97}(d,\alpha)Nb^{95,95m}$ Possible interference from $Zr^{94}(d,n)Nb^{95,95m}$.

$Mo^{98}(d,\alpha)Nb^{96}$ Possible interference from $Zr^{96}(d,2n)Nb^{96}$; possible interference from secondary reaction:

                              $Zr^{96}(p,n)Nb^{96}$.

$Mo^{94}(p,n)Tc^{94}$ 3×10^{-3} $\mu g/cm^2$ at 6.7 Mev.

$Mo^{95}(p,n)Tc^{95}$ 1×10^{-2} $\mu g/cm^2$ at 6.7 Mev.

$Mo^{96}(p,n)Tc^{96}$ 9×10^{-3} $\mu g/cm^2$ at 6.7 Mev.

NO STABLE ISOTOPES

Tc^{99} 22 ± 3 15.8 s

$(2.1 \times 10^{5}\ y)$

$Tc^{98}(n, \gamma)Tc^{99m}$ Search for naturally occurring Tc^{98} in terrestrial sources; technique requires correction for   A9   A11

interfering reactions: $Tc^{99}(n, n')Tc^{99m}$; $Mo^{98}(n, \gamma)Mo^{99} \xrightarrow{\beta^{-}} Tc^{99m}$; $Ru^{99}(n, p)Tc^{99m}$.   B37   H26

- -

$Tc^{98}(n, \gamma)Tc^{99m}$ Possible interference from $Mo^{98}(n, \gamma)Mo^{99} \xrightarrow{\beta^{-}} Tc^{99m}$; from $Ru^{99}(n, p)Tc^{99m}$; from fission of

U or Pu.

$Tc^{99}(n, \gamma)Tc^{100}$ Possible interference from $Ru^{100}(n, p)Tc^{100}$; from $Rh^{103}(n, \alpha)Tc^{100}$.

Ru^{96}	5.7	0.21 ± 0.02 a	2.88 d	EC (100)	M
Ru^{98}	2.2		s		
Ru^{99}	12.8		s		
Ru^{100}	12.7		s		
Ru^{101}	17.0		s		
Ru^{102}	31.3	1.44 ± 0.16 a	39.8 d	0.227 (90) 0.119 (7)	None
Ru^{104}	18.3	0.7 ± 0.2 a	4.5 h	1.15 (100)	M

Ru^{102}(n, γ)Ru^{103}	Determination of Ru with a calculated sensitivity of 0.1 μg; flux = 5 x 10^{11}.	L4
Ru^{104}(n, γ)Ru^{105}	Determination of Ru with a calculated sensitivity of 0.1 μg; flux = 5 x 10^{11}.	L4
	Others: J11, M53, S33.	

Ru^{101}(n, p)Tc^{101}	E_{th} = 0.9 Mev; σ(14.5) = 1.99 mb.	C20 P2
Ru^{96}(n, 2n)Ru^{95}	E_{th} = 13 Mev; σ(14.5) = 0.48 b.	C20 P2

Ru^{96}(n, γ)Ru^{97}	No apparent interference.
Ru^{102}(n, γ)Ru^{103}	Possible interference from Rh^{103}(n, p)Ru^{103} with a Rh matrix; from Pd^{106}(n, α)Ru^{103} with a Pd matrix; from fission of U or Pu.
Ru^{104}(n, γ)Ru^{105}	Possible interference from Pd^{108}(n, α)Ru^{105} with a Pd matrix; from fission of U or Pu.
Ru^{101}(n, p)Tc^{101}	Possible interference from Mo^{100}(n, γ)Mo^{101} $\xrightarrow{\beta^-}$ Tc^{101}; from fission of Th, U, or Pu; possible interference from secondary reaction: Mo^{100}(p, γ)Tc^{101}.
Ru^{96}(n, 2n)Ru^{95}	No apparent interference.

Ru^{96}(n, γ)Ru^{97}	2 x 10^{-3} μg.
Ru^{102}(n, γ)Ru^{103}	2 x 10^{-4} μg.
Ru^{104}(n, γ)Ru^{105}	2 x 10^{-4} μg.

110

$Ru^{100}(p,n)Rh^{100}$	Excitation function from $E_{th}(4.1\ Mev)$ to 6.8 Mev; $E_p > 6.8\ Mev$; $\sigma(6.7) = 0.15\ b.$
$Ru^{101}(p,n)Rh^{101}$	Excitation function from $E_{th}(2.6\ Mev)$ to 6.8 Mev; $E_p > 6.8\ Mev$; $\sigma(6.7) = 0.10\ b.$
$Ru^{102}(p,n)Rh^{102}$	Excitation function from $E_{th}(< 2\ Mev)$ to 6.8 Mev; $E_p > 6.8\ Mev$; $\sigma(6.7) = 0.16\ b.$
$Ru^{104}(p,n)Rh^{104,\ 104m}$	$\sigma(6.7) = 0.13\ b$ and $0.06\ b,$ respectively.

The citation B26 appears to the right of each of the four rows above.

$Ru^{100}(p,n)Rh^{100}$	No apparent interference.
$Ru^{101}(p,n)Rh^{101}$	Possible interference from $Pd^{104}(p,\alpha)Rh^{101}$; from $Pd^{102}(p,2p)Rh^{101}$ or $Pd^{102}(p,pn)Pd^{101} \xrightarrow{\beta^+} Rh^{101}$ at $E > 15\ Mev$.
$Ru^{102}(p,n)Rh^{102}$	Possible interference from $Pd^{105}(p,\alpha)Rh^{102}$; from $Rh^{103}(p,pn)Rh^{102}$ at $E > 15\ Mev$; possible interference from secondary reaction: $Pd^{102}(n,p)Rh^{102}.$
$Ru^{104}(p,n)Rh^{104,\ 104m}$	Possible interference from $Pd^{105}(p,2p)Rh^{104,\ 104m}$ at $E > 15\ Mev$; possible interference from secondary reactions: $Rh^{103}(n,\alpha)Rh^{104,\ 104m}$; $Pd^{104}(n,p)Rh^{104,\ 104m}$; $Ag^{107}(n,\alpha)Rh^{104,\ 104m}.$

$Ru^{100}(p,n)Rh^{100}$	$9 \times 10^{-3}\ \mu g/cm^2$ at 6.7 Mev.
$Ru^{101}(p,n)Rh^{101}$	$5 \times 10^{-2}\ \mu g/cm^2$ at 6.7 Mev.
$Ru^{102}(p,n)Rh^{102}$	$9 \times 10^{-1}\ \mu g/cm^2$ at 6.7 Mev.
$Ru^{104}(p,n)Rh^{104m}$	$4 \times 10^{-3}\ \mu g/cm^2$ at 6.7 Mev.

Rh^{103}	100	150 ± 7			
		12 ± 2 a	4.4 m		IT (99+)
		140 ± 30 a	44 s	2.5 (98.5)	0.56
					1.24
		$R_a = 656^{\dagger}$			$\dagger$ M9

$Rh^{103}(n, \gamma)Rh^{104, 104m}$	Determination of Rh with a portable Ra–Be source; flux $\sim 10^2$.	L11 M33
	Determination of Rh with a calculated sensitivity of 10^{-7} μg; flux $\sim 10^{12}$.	J11

$Rh^{103}(n, \alpha)Tc^{100}$	$\sigma(14.5) = 63$ mb.	P2

$Rh^{103}(n, \gamma)Rh^{104, 104m}$	Possible interference from $Pd^{104}(n, p)Rh^{104, 104m}$ with a Pd matrix; from $Ag^{107}(n, \alpha)Rh^{104, 104m}$ with a Ag matrix; possible interference from self-shielding in comparator samples.
$Rh^{103}(n, \alpha)Tc^{100}$	Possible interference from $Ru^{100}(n, p)Tc^{100}$; possible interference from secondary reaction: $Mo^{100}(p, n)Tc^{100}$.

$Rh^{103}(n, \gamma)Rh^{104m}$	2×10^{-6} μg.

$Rh^{103}(p,n)Pd^{103}$	Excitation function from 3 Mev to 6.8 Mev; $E_{th} < 3$ Mev; $E_p > 6.8$ Mev; $\sigma(6.7) = 0.23$ b.	B26
$Rh^{103}(\alpha,2n)Ag^{105}$	$E_{th} = 16.2$ Mev.	B38
$Rh^{103}(\gamma,n)Rh^{102}$	Excitation function from E_{th}(9.4 Mev) to 25 Mev; $E_p = 16.5$ Mev; $\sigma(16.5) = 0.21$ b.	N3

$Rh^{103}(p,n)Pd^{103}$	Possible interference from $Pd^{104}(p,pn)Pd^{103}$ at $E > 15$ Mev; from $Cd^{106}(p,\alpha)Ag^{103} \xrightarrow{\beta^+} Pd^{103}$; $Pd^{102}(p,\gamma)Ag^{103} \xrightarrow{\beta^+} Pd^{103}$; possible interference from secondary reactions: $Pd^{102}(p,\gamma)Ag^{103} \xrightarrow{\beta^+} Pd^{103}$; $Pd^{102}(n,\alpha)Pd^{103}$; $Cd^{106}(n,\alpha)Pd^{103}$.
$Rh^{103}(\alpha,2n)Ag^{105}$	Possible interference from $Pd^{102}(\alpha,p)Ag^{105}$; possible interference from secondary reactions: $Pd^{104}(p,\gamma)Ag^{105}$ or $Pd^{105}(p,n)Ag^{105}$; $Cd^{108}(p,\alpha)Ag^{105}$.
$Rh^{103}(\gamma,n)Rh^{102}$	No apparent interference from primary reactions; possible interference from secondary reactions: $Pd^{102}(n,p)Rh^{102}$; $Ru^{101}(p,\gamma)Rh^{102}$ or $Ru^{102}(p,n)Rh^{102}$; $Pd^{105}(p,\alpha)Rh^{102}$.

$Rh^{103}(p,n)Pd^{103}$	2×10^{-2} $\mu g/cm^2$ at 6.8 Mev.

Pd^{102}	0.8	4.8 ± 1.5 a	17.0 d	EC (100)	M
Pd^{104}	9.3		s		
Pd^{105}	22.6		s		
Pd^{106}	27.1		21.3 s	None	IT (100)
			∼ 7 x 10^6 y	0.04 (100)	None
Pd^{108}	26.7		4.75 m	None	IT (100)
		10 ± 2 a	13.5 h	1.02 (∼100)	M
Pd^{110}	13.5		5.5 h	(25)	IT (75)
		0.3 ± 0.1 a	22 m	2.2	
		R = 23†			† M9

Pd^{108}(n, γ)Pd^{109}

Determination of Pd in high purity Fe and Al with a sensitivity of 1 x 10^{-3} μg.   G28

Determination of Pd in meteorites with a sensitivity of 1 ppm.   B45   G11

Others: J11, L4, V2.

- -

Pd^{104}(n, p)Rh$^{104 + 104m}$	σ(14.5) = 0.13 b.	P2
Pd^{105}(n, p)Rh^{105}	σ(14.5) = 0.74 b.	P2
Pd^{108}(n, α)Ru^{105}	σ(14) = 2.3 mb.	B30
Pd^{110}(n, α)Ru^{107}	σ(14.5) = 13.8 mb.	P2
Pd^{110}(n, 2n)Pd^{109}	σ(14.5) = 1.95 b.	P2
Pd^{108}(n, np)Rh^{107}	σ(14.5) ≤ 65 mb.	C19

Pd^{102}(n, γ)Pd^{103}

Possible interference from Cd^{106}(n, α)Pd^{103} with a Cd matrix.

Pd^{108}(n, γ)Pd^{109}

Possible interference from Ag^{109}(n, p)Pd^{109} in a Ag matrix; from Cd^{112}(n, α)Pd^{109} in a Cd matrix; from fission of U or Pu.

Pd^{110}(n, γ)Pd^{111}

Possible interference from Cd^{114}(n, α)Pd^{111} with a Cd matrix; from fission of U or Pu.

Pd^{104}(n, p)Rh$^{104, 104m}$

Possible interference from Ag^{107}(n, α)Rh$^{104, 104m}$; from Rh^{103}(n, α)Rh$^{104, 104m}$; possible interference from secondary reaction: Ru^{104}(p, n)Rh$^{104, 104m}$.

Pd^{105}(n, p)Rh^{105}

Possible interference from Ru^{104}(n, γ)Ru^{105} $\xrightarrow{\beta^-}$ Rh^{105}; from fission of Th, U, or Pu; possible interference from secondary reaction: Ru^{104}(p, γ)Rh^{105}.

Pd^{106}(n, p)Rh^{106}

Possible interference from Ag^{106}(n, α)Rh^{106}; from fission of Th, U, or Pu.

Pd^{108}(n, γ)Pd^{109}	1 x 10^{-5} μg.
Pd^{110}(n, γ)Pd^{111}	8 x 10^{-4} μg.
Pd^{110}(n, γ)Pd$^{111, 111m}$ $\xrightarrow{\beta^-}$ Ag^{111}	7 x 10^{-4} μg.

$Pd^{102}(p,n)Ag^{102}$ Thick-target yield at 6.3 Mev = 2.1 x 10^{-6} atom/proton.   E9

$Pd^{104}(p,n)Ag^{104}$ Thick-target yield at 6.3 Mev = 2.6 x 10^{-6} atom/proton; $\sigma(6.3) = 1.8$ mb.   E9

$Pd^{105}(p,n)Ag^{105}$ $\sigma(6.3) = 37$ mb.   E9

$Pd^{106}(p,n)Ag^{106m}$ $\sigma(6.7) = 0.11$ b.   B26

$Pd^{106}(p,n)Ag^{106}$ $\sigma(6.7) = 0.19$ b; thick-target yield at 6.3 Mev > 2.7 x 10^{-6} atom/proton.   B26 E9

$Pd^{108}(p,n)Ag^{108}$ Thick-target yield at 6.3 Mev = 4.5 x 10^{-6} atom/proton; $\sigma(6.3) = 81$ mb.   E9

$Pd^{110}(p,n)Ag^{110m}$ $\sigma(6.7) = 0.09$ b.   B26

$Pd^{110}(p,pn)Pd^{109}$ Excitation function from 11 Mev to 23.5 Mev; $E_{th} < 11$ Mev; $E_p > 23.5$ Mev; $\sigma(23.5) \sim 180$ mb.   C24

$Pd^{110}(d,p)Pd^{111,111m}$ Excitation functions from 50 Mev to 190 Mev; $E_p < 50$ Mev; $\sigma(50) = 15$ mb.   S27

$Pd^{102}(p,n)Ag^{102}$ No apparent interference.

$Pd^{104}(p,n)Ag^{104}$ No apparent interference.

$Pd^{105}(p,n)Ag^{105}$ Possible interference from $Cd^{108}(p,\alpha)Ag^{105}$; from $Cd^{106}(p,2p)Ag^{105}$ or $Cd^{106}(p,pn)Cd^{105} \xrightarrow{\beta^+} Ag^{105}$ at E > 15 Mev.

$Pd^{106}(p,n)Ag^{106,106m}$ Possible interference from $Ag^{107}(p,pn)Ag^{106,106m}$ for E > 12 Mev; possible interference from secondary reaction: $Cd^{106}(n,p)Ag^{106,106m}$.

$Pd^{108}(p,n)Ag^{108}$ Possible interference from $Ag^{109}(p,pn)Ag^{108}$ for E > 15 Mev; from $Cd^{111}(p,\alpha)Ag^{108}$; possible interference from secondary reactions: $Ag^{107}(n,\gamma)Ag^{108}$; $Cd^{108}(n,p)Ag^{108}$.

$Pd^{110}(p,n)Ag^{110m}$ Possible interference from $Cd^{113}(p,\alpha)Ag^{110m}$; from $Cd^{111}(p,2p)Ag^{110m}$ for E > 15 Mev; possible interference from secondary reactions: $Ag^{109}(n,\gamma)Ag^{110m}$; $Cd^{110}(n,p)Ag^{110m}$; $In^{113}(n,\alpha)Ag^{110m}$.

$Pd^{110}(p,pn)Pd^{109}$ No apparent interference from primary reactions for E < 20 Mev; possible interference from secondary reactions: $Ag^{109}(n,p)Pd^{109}$; $Cd^{112}(n,\alpha)Pd^{109}$.

$Pd^{110}(d,p)Pd^{111,111m}$ No apparent interference from primary reactions for E < 20 Mev; possible interference from secondary reaction: $Cd^{114}(n,\alpha)Pd^{111,111m}$.

$Pd^{106}(p,n)Ag^{106m}$ 2 x 10^{-3} $\mu g/cm^2$ at 6.7 Mev.

Ag^{107}	51.35	31 ± 2			
		45 ± 4 a	2.3 m	1.77 (97)	M
				EC (1.6)	
Ag^{109}	48.65	84 ± 7			
		3.2 ± 0.4 a	270 d	M (95)	M
					IT (5)
		113 ± 12 a	24.2 s		

$$R = 466 \pm 70^{\dagger}$$
$$R_a^{107} = 74^{\dagger\dagger}$$
$$R_a^{109} = 1160^{\dagger\dagger}$$

†K23
††M9

$Ag^{107}(n,\gamma)Ag^{108}$

Determination of film exposure by analysis for Ag^{108}.   B19

Determination of Ag with a portable Ra-Be source; flux $\sim 10^2$.   M33

$Ag^{109}(n,\gamma)Ag^{110m}$

Determination of Ag with a portable Ra-Be source; flux $\sim 10^2$.   M33

Determination of film exposure by analysis for Ag^{110}.   B18

Determination of Ag in Al with a sensitivity of 0.9 ppm; flux $\sim 10^{11}$.   B40 B66

Determination of Ag in Si with a sensitivity of 2×10^{-3} ppm; flux $= 2 \times 10^{14}$.   T16

Determination of Ag in Si with a sensitivity of 1×10^{-3} ppm; flux $= 3 \times 10^{12}$.   K2

Others: G28, J11, L4, M55, S32, S33.

- -

$Ag^{109}(n,p)Pd^{109}$

$E_{th} = 0.4$ Mev; average $\sigma(\sim 14.5) = 11.5$ mb.   C20 C39 D15

$Ag^{107}(n,2n)Ag^{106m}$

$E_{th} = 9.5$ Mev; average $\sigma(14.5) = 0.54$ b.   F9 P2 Y1

$Ag^{109}(n,2n)Ag^{108}$

Average $\sigma(14) = 0.6$ b.   F9 P2

$Ag^{107}(n,\gamma)Ag^{108}$

Possible interference from $Cd^{108}(n,p)Ag^{108}$ with a Cd matrix; possible interference from self-shielding in comparator samples.

$Ag^{109}(n,\gamma)Ag^{110m}$

Possible interference from $Cd^{110}(n,p)Ag^{110m}$ with a Cd matrix; from $In^{113}(n,\alpha)Ag^{110m}$ with an In matrix; possible interference from second-order reaction: $Pd^{108}(n,\gamma)Pd^{109} \xrightarrow{\beta^-} Ag^{109}(n,\gamma)Ag^{110m}$; possible interference from self-shielding in comparator samples.

$Ag^{109}(n,p)Pd^{109}$

Possible interference from $Pd^{108}(n,\gamma)Pd^{109}$; from $Cd^{112}(n,\alpha)Pd^{109}$; from fission of Th, U, or Pu.

$Ag^{107}(n,2n)Ag^{106m}$

Possible interference from $Cd^{106}(n,p)Ag^{106m}$; possible interference from secondary reactions: $Pd^{105}(p,\gamma)Ag^{106m}$ or $Pd^{106}(p,n)Ag^{106m}$.

$Ag^{109}(n,2n)Ag^{108}$

Possible interference from $Cd^{108}(n,p)Ag^{108}$; possible interference from secondary reactions: $Pd^{108}(p,n)Ag^{108}$; $Cd^{111}(p,\alpha)Ag^{108}$.

$Ag^{107}(n,\gamma)Ag^{108}$

1×10^{-6} µg.

$Ag^{109}(n,\gamma)Ag^{110m}$

2×10^{-4} µg.

$Ag^{107}(p,n)Cd^{107}$ Excitation function from 3.3 Mev to 6.8 Mev; $E_{th} < 3.3$ Mev; $E_p > 6.8$ Mev; $\sigma(6.7) = 0.14$ b.   B24 B26

$Ag^{109}(p,n)Cd^{109}$ Excitation function from 4.0 Mev to 6.8 Mev; $E_{th} < 4.0$ Mev; $E_p > 6.8$ Mev; $\sigma(6.7) = 95$ mb.   B24

$Ag^{107}(p,pn)Ag^{106m}$ Excitation function from 9 Mev to 23.5 Mev; $E_{th} < 9$ Mev; $E_p > 23.5$ Mev; $\sigma(23.5) \sim 150$ mb.   C24 L24

$Ag^{107}(p,pn)Ag^{106}$ Excitation function from E_{th} (~15 Mev) to 20 Mev; $E_p > 20$ Mev; $\sigma(20) \sim 80$ mb.   L24

$Ag^{107}(d,\alpha2n)Pd^{103}$ Excitation function from E_{th} (~ 20 Mev) to 35 Mev; $E_p \sim 27$ Mev; $\sigma(27) = 16$ mb.   O7

$Ag^{107}(\alpha,n)In^{110,110m}$ Excitation function from E_{th} (~ 12.5 Mev) to 38 Mev; $E_p \sim 17$ Mev; $\sigma(17) = 0.65$ b.   G3 P14

$Ag^{109}(\alpha,n)In^{112}$ Excitation function from 11 Mev to 18 Mev; $E_{th} \sim 6.8$ Mev; $E_p \sim 16$ Mev; $\sigma(16) \sim 0.4$ b.   B29

$Ag^{107}(\alpha,2n)In^{109}$ Excitation function from E_{th} (15.5 Mev) to 38 Mev; $E_p = 29$ Mev; $\sigma(29) = 1.2$ b.   P14 T12

$Ag^{109}(\alpha,2n)In^{111}$ Excitation function from E_{th} (14.5 Mev) to 38 Mev; $E_p \sim 26$ Mev; $\sigma(26) = 1.2$ b.   B29 P14

$Ag^{107}(\alpha,pn)Cd^{109}$ Excitation function from E_{th} (~ 13.5 Mev) to 38 Mev; $E_p = 29$ Mev; $\sigma(29) = 1.3$ b.   P14

$Ag^{109}(\gamma,n)Ag^{108}$ Excitation function from E_{th} (9.05 Mev) to 22 Mev; $E_p = 16.5$ Mev; $\sigma(16.5) = 0.32$ b.   D12 H14

$Ag^{107}(p,n)Cd^{107}$ Possible interference from $Cd^{108}(p,pn)Cd^{107}$ at $E > 15$ Mev with a Cd matrix; possible interference from secondary reactions: $Cd^{106}(n,\gamma)Cd^{107}$; $Cd^{106}(p,\gamma)In^{107} \xrightarrow{\beta^+} Cd^{107}$.

$Ag^{109}(p,n)Cd^{109}$ Possible interference from $Cd^{110}(p,pn)Cd^{109}$ at $E > 15$ Mev; possible interference from secondary reactions: $Cd^{108}(n,\gamma)Cd^{109}$; $Sn^{112}(n,\alpha)Cd^{109}$; $Cd^{108}(p,\gamma)In^{109} \xrightarrow{\beta^+} Cd^{109}$.

$Ag^{107}(p,pn)Ag^{106m}$ Possible interference from $Cd^{106}(p,n)Ag^{106m}$; possible interference from secondary reactions: $Pd^{105}(p,\gamma)Ag^{106m}$; $Cd^{106}(n,p)Ag^{106m}$.

$Ag^{107}(\alpha,n)In^{110,110m}$ Possible interference from $Cd^{108}(\alpha,pn)In^{110,110m}$ at $E > 15$ Mev with a Cd matrix; possible interference from secondary reaction: $Cd^{110}(p,n)In^{110,110m}$.

$Ag^{107}(\alpha,2n)In^{109}$ Possible interference from $Cd^{106}(\alpha,p)In^{109}$ with a Cd matrix; possible interference from secondary reactions: $Cd^{108}(p,\gamma)In^{109}$; $Sn^{112}(p,\alpha)In^{109}$.

$Ag^{109}(\alpha,2n)In^{111}$ Possible interference from $Cd^{108}(\alpha,p)In^{111}$ with a Cd matrix; possible interference from secondary reactions: $Cd^{110}(p,\gamma)In^{111}$ or $Cd^{111}(p,n)In^{111}$; $Sn^{114}(p,\alpha)In^{111}$.

$Ag^{107}(\alpha,pn)Cd^{109}$ Possible interference from $Cd^{106}(\alpha,p)In^{109} \xrightarrow{\beta^+} Cd^{109}$ in a Cd matrix; possible interference from secondary reactions: $Cd^{108}(n,\gamma)Cd^{109}$; $Sn^{112}(n,\alpha)Cd^{109}$; $Cd^{108}(p,\gamma)In^{109} \xrightarrow{\beta^+} Cd^{109}$; $Sn^{112}(p,\alpha)In^{109} \xrightarrow{\beta^+} Cd^{109}$.

$Ag^{109}(\gamma,n)Ag^{108}$ No apparent interference from primary reactions; possible interference from secondary reactions: $Cd^{108}(n,p)Ag^{108}$; $Pd^{108}(p,n)Ag^{108}$; $Cd^{111}(p,\alpha)Ag^{108}$.

$Ag^{107}(p,n)Cd^{107}$ 1×10^{-3} $\mu g/cm^2$ at 6.7 Mev.

Cd^{106}	1.22	1.0 ± 0.5 a	6.7 h 470 d	EC (99+) EC (100)	
Cd^{108}	0.87				
Cd^{110}	12.39	0.2 ± 0.1 a	48.6 m s	None	IT (100)
Cd^{111}	12.75		s		
Cd^{112}	24.07	30 ± 15 mb a	5.1 y s	0.59 (99+)	
Cd^{113}	12.26	$20,000 \pm 300$	s		
Cd^{114}	28.86	0.14 ± 0.03 a 1.1 ± 0.3 a	43 d 53 h	1.16 (98) 1.1 (58) 0.5 (42)	M
Cd^{116}	7.58	1.5 ± 0.3 a	3.0 h ~ 50 m	None	IT (100)

$Cd^{114}(n,\gamma)Cd^{115m}$	Determination of Cd with a calculated sensitivity of 0.05 µg; flux = 5×10^{11}.	L4
$Cd^{114}(n,\gamma)Cd^{115}$	Determination of Cd with a sensitivity of 0.1 µg; flux = 10^{11}.	B42
	Determination of Cd with a sensitivity of 2×10^{-4} ppm; flux = 3×10^{12}.	K2
	Determination of Cd with a sensitivity of 8×10^{-4} ppm; flux = 2×10^{14}.	T16
$Cd^{116}(n,\gamma)Cd^{117}$	Determination of Cd with a calculated sensitivity of 1.0 µg; flux = 5×10^{11}.	L4
	Others: G28, J11, S33	

$Cd^{112}(n,\alpha)Pd^{109}$	$\sigma(14) = (1.35 \pm 0.27)$ mb.	P2
$Cd^{114}(n,\alpha)Pd^{111}$	$\sigma(14) = (0.13 \pm 0.04)$ mb.	P2
$Cd^{114}(n,\alpha)Pd^{111}$	$\sigma(14) = (0.51 \pm 0.13)$ mb.	P2

$Cd^{106}(n,\gamma)Cd^{107}$	No apparent interference from primary or second-order reactions; possible interference from self-shielding in comparator samples.
$Cd^{110}(n,\gamma)Cd^{111m}$	Possible interference from $Sn^{114}(n,\alpha)Cd^{111m}$ with a Sn matrix; possible interference from second-order reaction: $Ag^{109}(n,\gamma)Ag^{110} \xrightarrow{\beta^-} Cd^{110}(n,\gamma)Cd^{111m}$ with a Ag matrix; possible interference from self-shielding in comparator samples.
$Cd^{114}(n,\gamma)Cd^{115,115m}$	Possible interference from $In^{115}(n,p)Cd^{115,115m}$ with an In matrix; from $Sn^{118}(n,\alpha)Cd^{115,115m}$ with a Sn matrix; from fission of U or Pu; possible interference from self-shielding in comparator samples.
$Cd^{116}(n,\gamma)Cd^{117}$	Possible interference from $Sn^{120}(n,\alpha)Cd^{117}$ with a Sn matrix; from fission of U or Pu; possible interference from self-shielding in comparator samples.

$Cd^{114}(n,\gamma)Cd^{115m}$	2×10^{-3} µg.
$Cd^{114}(n,\gamma)Cd^{115}$	1×10^{-4} µg.
$Cd^{116}(n,\gamma)Cd^{117m}$	3×10^{-4} µg.

$Cd^{110}(p,n)In^{110}$ Excitation function from E_{th}(4.5 Mev) to 6.8 Mev; $E_p > 6.8$ Mev; $\sigma(6.7) = 0.16$ b.   B24 B26

$Cd^{111}(p,n)In^{111}$ Excitation function from E_{th}($\sim$ 2.5 Mev) to 6.8 Mev; $E_p > 6.8$ Mev; $\sigma(6.7) = 0.27$ b.   B24 B26

$Cd^{112}(p,n)In^{112m}$ Excitation function from E_{th}($\sim$ 3.2 Mev) to 6.8 Mev; $E_p > 6.8$ Mev; $\sigma(6.7) = 67$ mb.   B24 B26

$Cd^{114}(p,n)In^{114m}$ Excitation function from E_{th}(63.0 Mev) to 6.8 Mev; $E_p > 6.8$ Mev; $\sigma(6.7) = 86$ mb.   B24 B26

$Cd^{116}(p,n)In^{116m}$ $\sigma(6.7) = 0.45$ b.   B26

$Cd^{110}(p,n)In^{110}$ No apparent interference at $E < 20$ Mev.

$Cd^{111}(p,n)In^{111}$ Possible interference from $Sn^{114}(p,\alpha)In^{111}$ in a Sn matrix; from $Sn^{112}(p,2p)In^{111}$ at $E > 15$ Mev in a Sn matrix.

$Cd^{112}(p,n)In^{112,112m}$ Possible interference from $Sn^{115}(p,\alpha)In^{112,112m}$ in a Sn matrix; from $In^{113}(p,pn)In^{112,112m}$ at $E > 15$ Mev; possible interference from secondary reaction: $Sn^{112}(n,p)In^{112,112m}$.

$Cd^{114}(p,n)In^{114,114m}$ Possible interference from $Sn^{117}(p,\alpha)In^{114,114m}$; from $In^{115}(p,pn)In^{114,114m}$ at $E > 15$ Mev; from $Sn^{115}(p,2p)In^{114,114m}$ at $E > 15$ Mev; possible interference from secondary reactions: $In^{113}(n,\gamma)In^{114,114m}$; $Sn^{114}(n,p)In^{114,114m}$.

$Cd^{116}(p,n)In^{116,116m}$ Possible interference from $Sn^{119}(p,\alpha)In^{116,116m}$; from $Sn^{117}(p,2p)In^{116,116m}$ at $E > 15$ Mev; possible interference from secondary reactions: $In^{115}(n,\gamma)In^{116,116m}$; $Sn^{116}(n,p)In^{116,116m}$.

$Cd^{110}(p,n)In^{110}$ 3×10^{-3} $\mu g/cm^2$ at 6.7 Mev.

$Cd^{112}(p,n)In^{112m}$ 3×10^{-3} $\mu g/cm^2$ at 6.7 Mev.

$Cd^{114}(p,n)In^{114m}$ 4×10^{-1} $\mu g/cm^2$ at 6.7 Mev.

$Cd^{116}(p,n)In^{116m}$ 1×10^{-3} $\mu g/cm^2$ at 6.7 Mev.

In^{113}	4.23	56 ± 12 a	50 d	EC (3.5)	IT (96.5)
		2.0 ± 0.6 a	72 s	1.98 (98)	M
In^{115}	95.77	155 ± 15 a	54.0 m	M	M
$(6 \times 10^{14} y)$		52 ± 6 a	13 s		

$$R = 2220 \pm 300^{\dagger}$$
$$R_a^{115} = 2640^{\dagger\dagger}$$

†K23
††M9

$In^{113}(n,\gamma)In^{114m}$ Determination of In in minerals with a sensitivity of 8×10^{-3} µg.   S44

                               Determination of In in Si with a sensitivity of 3×10^{-4} ppm; flux = 3×10^{12}.   C5 K2

$In^{115}(n,\gamma)In^{116m}$ Determination of In with a sensitivity of 0.03 µg; flux = 4×10^{12}.   H43

                               Determination of In with a Ra-Be source; thermal flux $\sim 10^2$.   M33

                               Determination of In using γ-spectrometry.   I3

                               Others: H37, J2, J11, L4, S33, T16, W17.

- -

$In^{115}(n,p)Cd^{115}$ $\sigma(14.5) = 15.5$ mb.   C39

$In^{115}(n,\alpha)Ag^{112}$ Average $\sigma(14.5) = 2.7$ mb.   B31 C39

$In^{113}(n,\gamma)In^{114,114m}$ Possible interference from $Sn^{114}(n,p)In^{114,114m}$ with a Sn matrix; possible interference from self-shielding in comparator samples.

$In^{115}(n,\gamma)In^{116m}$ Possible interference from $Sn^{116}(n,p)In^{116}$ with a Sn matrix; possible interference from self-shielding in comparator samples.

$In^{115}(n,\alpha)Ag^{112}$ Possible interference from $Cd^{112}(n,p)Ag^{112}$; from fission of Th, U, or Pu; possible interference from self-shielding in comparator samples.

$In^{113}(n,\gamma)In^{114m}$ 4×10^{-5} µg.

$In^{113}(n,\gamma)In^{114}$ 4×10^{-4} µg.

$In^{115}(n,\gamma)In^{116m}$ 2×10^{-7} µg.

$In^{113}(p,n)Sn^{113}$ $\sigma(6.7) = 0.20$ b.   B26

$In^{115}(\alpha,n)Sb^{118}$ Relative excitation function from $E_{th}(\sim 11$ Mev) to 34 Mev; $E_p \sim 19$ Mev.   T11

$In^{115}(\alpha,2n)Sb^{117}$ Relative excitation function from $E_{th}(\sim 15$ Mev) to 34 Mev; $E_p \sim 28$ Mev.   T11

$In^{115}(\gamma,\gamma')In^{115m}$ Excitation function from $E_{th}(\sim 0.9$ Mev) to 14 Mev; $E_p = 8$ Mev; average $\sigma(8) = 2.8$ mb.   B50 G12

$In^{115}(\gamma,n)In^{114,114m}$ Excitation function from $E_{th}(9.05$ Mev) to 24 Mev; $E_p = 15$ Mev; $\sigma(15) = 70$ mb and 350 mb,
                                respectively.   G12 M45

$In^{113}(p,n)Sn^{113}$ Possible interference from $Sn^{114}(p,pn)Sn^{113}$ at $E > 15$ Mev with a Sn matrix; possible interference
                                from secondary reaction: $Sn^{112}(n,\gamma)Sn^{113}$.

$In^{115}(\alpha,n)Sb^{118}$ Possible interference from $Sn^{115}(\alpha,p)Sb^{118}$ with a Sn matrix.

$In^{115}(\alpha,2n)Sb^{117}$ Possible interference from $Sn^{115}(\alpha,pn)Sb^{117}$ with a Sn matrix; possible interference from secondary
                                reaction: $Te^{120}(p,\alpha)Sb^{117}$.

$In^{115}(\gamma,\gamma')In^{115m}$ No apparent interference from primary reactions; possible interference from secondary reactions:
                                $Sn^{115}(n,p)In^{115m}$; $Cd^{114}(p,\gamma)In^{115m}$; $Sn^{118}(p,\alpha)In^{115m}$.

$In^{115}(\gamma,n)In^{114,114m}$ Possible interference from $Sn^{115}(\gamma,p)In^{114,114m}$; possible interference from secondary reactions:
                                $Sn^{114}(n,p)In^{114,114m}$; $Cd^{113}(p,\gamma)In^{114,114m}$ or $Cd^{114}(p,n)In^{114,114m}$; $Sn^{117}(p,\alpha)Cd^{114,114m}$.

$In^{113}(p,n)Sn^{113}$ 6 $\mu g/cm^2$ at 6.7 Mev.

121

Sn^{112}	0.95	1.3 ± 0.3 a	119 d	EC (100)	0.392
Sn^{114}	0.65		s		
Sn^{115}	0.34		s		
Sn^{116}	14.24	6 ± 2 mb a	14.0 d	None	IT (100)
Sn^{117}	7.57		s		
Sn^{118}	24.01	10 ± 6 mb a	∼250 d s	None	IT (100)
Sn^{119}	8.58		s		
Sn^{120}	32.97	1 ± 1 mb a	>400 d	0.42	
		0.14 ± 0.03 a	27.5 h	0.38 (100)	None
Sn^{122}	4.71	1.0 ± 0.5 mb a	136 d	1.42 (100)	None
		0.16 ± 0.04 a	40 m	1.26 (100)	0.153
Sn^{124}	5.98	0.2 ± 0.1 a	9.5 m	2.04 (98)	0.326 (99+)
		4 ± 2 mb a	9.4 d	2.37 (95)	M

R = 5.7 ± 0.7† † K23

Sn^{120}(n, γ)Sn^{121}

Determination of Sn in Si with a sensitivity of 7×10^{-4} ppm; flux = 3×10^{12}.   C5

Determination of Sn in Ge with a sensitivity of ∼ 5×10^{-3} ppm; flux = 3×10^{12}.   C5

Determination of Sn in Si with a sensitivity of 6×10^{-3} ppm; flux of 2×10^{14}.   T16

Others: P1, L4, S33.

- -

Sn^{120}(n, γ)Sn^{121} Possible interference from Sb^{121}(n, p)Sn^{121} with an Sb matrix; from Te^{124}(n, α)Sn^{121} with a Te matrix; from fission of U or Pu.

Sn^{122}(n, α)Sn$^{123, 123m}$ Possible interference from Sb^{123}(n, p)Sn$^{123, 123m}$ with an Sb matrix; from Te^{126}(n, α)Sn$^{123, 123m}$ with a Te matrix; from fission of U or Pu.

Sn^{124}(n, γ)Sn$^{125, 125m}$ Possible interference from Te^{128}(n, α)Sn$^{125, 125m}$ with a Te matrix; from fission of U or Pu.

Sn^{120}(n, γ)Sn^{121} 7×10^{-4} μg.

Sn^{122}(n, γ)Sn^{123} 4×10^{-3} μg.

Sn^{124}(n, γ)Sn^{125} m 3×10^{-3} μg.

$Sn^{117}(p,n)Sb^{117}$ — Excitation function from 3 Mev to 6.8 Mev; $E_{th} < 3$ Mev; $E_p > 6.8$ Mev; $\sigma(6.7) = 90$ mb.   B24 B26

$Sn^{118}(p,n)Sb^{118}$ — Excitation function from 3 Mev to 6.8 Mev; $E_{th} < 3$ Mev; $E_p > 6.8$ Mev; $\sigma(6.7) = 75$ mb.   B26

$Sn^{120}(p,n)Sb^{120}$ — Excitation function from E_{th}(3.5 Mev) to 6.8 Mev; $E_p > 6.8$ Mev; $\sigma(6.7) = 0.17$ b.   B24 B26

$Sn^{122}(p,n)Sb^{122}$ — Excitation function from 3 Mev to 6.8 Mev; $E_{th} < 3$ Mev; $E_p > 6.8$ Mev; $\sigma(6.7) = 0.20$ b.   B24 B26

$Sn^{117}(p,n)Sb^{117}$ — Possible interference from $Te^{120}(p,\alpha)Sb^{117}$ with a Te matrix.

$Sn^{118}(p,n)Sb^{118,118m}$ — No apparent interference at $E < 20$ Mev.

$Sn^{120}(p,n)Sb^{120,120m}$ — Possible interference from $Te^{123}(p,\alpha)Sb^{120,120m}$; from $Sb^{121}(p,pn)Sb^{120,120m}$ at $E > 15$ Mev; possible interference from secondary reaction: $Te^{120}(n,p)Sb^{120,120m}$.

$Sn^{122}(p,n)Sb^{122,122m}$ — Possible interference from $Te^{125}(p,\alpha)Sb^{122,122m}$; from $Te^{123}(p,2p)Sb^{122,122m}$ at $E > 15$ Mev; from $Sb^{123}(p,pn)Sb^{122}$ at $E > 15$ Mev; possible interference from secondary reactions: $Sb^{121}(n,\gamma)Sb^{122,122m}$; $Te^{122}(n,p)Sn^{122,122m}$.

$Sn^{117}(p,n)Sb^{117}$ — 8×10^{-3} $\mu g/cm^2$ at 6.7 Mev.

$Sn^{118}(p,n)Sb^{118}$ — 4×10^{-3} $\mu g/cm^2$ at 6.7 Mev.

$Sn^{120}(p,n)Sb^{120}$ — 9×10^{-4} $\mu g/cm^2$ at 6.7 Mev.

$Sn^{122}(p,n)Sb^{122}$ — 8×10^{-2} $\mu g/cm^2$ at 6.7 Mev.

Sb^{121}	57.25	5.9 ± 0.5			
		6.8 ± 1.5 a	3.5 m	None	IT (100)
			2.8 d	1.40 (63)	M
				1.97 (30)	
Sb^{123}	42.75	4.1 ± 0.3			
		30 ± 15 mb a	21 m		
		30 ± 15 mb a	1.3 m		
		2.5 ± 0.5 a	60.9 d	M	M

$$R = 106 \pm 13^{\dagger}$$
$$R_a^{121} = 162^{\dagger\dagger}$$
$$R_a^{123} = \sim 138^{\dagger\dagger}$$

$\dagger$ K23
$\dagger\dagger$ M9

$Sb^{121}(n, \gamma)Sb^{122}$ Determination of Sb in ZrO_2 with a sensitivity of 0.5 ppm.   H40

Determination of Sb in Al; observed interference from self-shielding in comparator samples. P10

Determination of Sb in Si with a sensitivity of 1×10^{-4} ppm; flux = 3×10^{12}. C5 K2

Determination of Sb in Si with a sensitivity of 2×10^{-4} ppm; flux = 2×10^{14}. T16

Determination of Sb in Ge with a sensitivity of $\sim 10^{-5}$ ppm; flux = 3×10^{12}. C5

$Sb^{123}(n, \gamma)Sb^{124}$ Determination of Sb in Al; observed interference from self-shielding in Sb comparator samples. P10

Determination of Sb in liquid metals with a sensitivity of 1×10^{-3} ppm. S32

Others: B40, B66, G28, J11, L4, L23, S33, S39, S71.

$Sb^{121}(n, 2n)Sb^{120}$ $E_{th} = 9.25$ Mev; $\sigma(14.5) = 0.75$ b.   C20 P2

$Sb^{123}(n, 2n)Sb^{122}$ $\sigma(14.5) = 1.25$ b.   P2

$Sb^{121}(n, \gamma)Sb^{122, 122m}$ Possible interference from $Te^{122}(n, p)Sb^{122, 122m}$ with a Te matrix; possible interference from self-shielding in comparator samples.

$Sb^{123}(n, \gamma)Sb^{124}$ Possible interference from $Te^{124}(n, p)Sb^{124}$ with a Te matrix; from $I^{127}(n, \alpha)Sb^{124}$ with an I_2 matrix; possible interference from second-order reaction: $Sn^{122}(n, \alpha)Sn^{123} \xrightarrow{\beta^-} Sb^{123}(n, \gamma)Sb^{124}$ with a Sn matrix; possible interference from self-shielding in comparator samples.

$Sb^{121}(n, 2n)Sb^{120, 120m}$ Possible interference from $Te^{120}(n, p)Sb^{120, 120m}$; possible interference from secondary reactions: $Sn^{119}(p, \gamma)Sb^{120, 120m}$ or $Sn^{120}(p, n)Sb^{120, 120m}$; $Te^{123}(p, \alpha)Sb^{120, 120m}$.

$Sb^{123}(n, 2n)Sb^{122, 122m}$ Possible interference from $Te^{122}(n, p)Sb^{122, 122m}$; possible interference from secondary reactions: $Sn^{122}(p, n)Sb^{122, 122m}$; $Te^{125}(p, \alpha)Sb^{122, 122m}$.

$Sb^{121}(n, \gamma)Sb^{122}$ 9×10^{-6} μg.

$Sb^{123}(n, \gamma)Sb^{124}$ 1×10^{-4} μg.

$Sb^{121}(p,n)Te^{121, 121m}$ $\quad$ $\sigma(6.7) = 0.07$ b and 0.10 b, respectively. $\hfill$ B26

$Sb^{121}(\gamma,n)Sb^{120}$ $\quad$ Excitation function from E_{th} (9.3 Mev) to 25 Mev; $E_p = 15$ Mev; $\sigma(15) = 685$ mb. $\hfill$ K7 K10

$Sb^{123}(\gamma,n)Sb^{122}$ $\quad$ Excitation function from E_{th} (9.3 Mev) to 25 Mev; $E_p = 15$ Mev; $\sigma(15) = 362$ mb. $\hfill$ K7 K10

$Sb^{121}(\gamma,\alpha)In^{117m}$ $\quad$ Excitation function from E_{th} (19 Mev) to 32 Mev; $E_p = 25$ Mev; $\sigma(25) = 65 \pm 15$ μb. $\hfill$ E10

$Sb^{121}(p,n)Te^{121, 121m}$ $\quad$ Possible interference from $Xe^{124}(p,\alpha)I^{121} \xrightarrow{\beta^+} Te^{121, 121m}$ with a Xe matrix; from $Te^{122}(p,pn)Te^{121, 121m}$ at E > 15 Mev; possible interference from secondary reactions: $Te^{120}(n,\gamma)Te^{121, 121m}$; $Xe^{124}(n,\alpha)Te^{121, 121m}$; $Te^{120}(p,\gamma)I^{121} \xrightarrow{\beta^+} Te^{121, 121m}$.

$Sb^{121}(\gamma,n)Sb^{120, 120m}$ $\quad$ No apparent interference from primary reactions; possible interference from secondary reactions: $Te^{120}(n,p)Sb^{120, 120m}$; $Sn^{119}(p,\gamma)Sb^{120, 120m}$ or $Sn^{120}(p,n)Sb^{120, 120m}$; $Te^{123}(p,\alpha)Sb^{120, 120m}$.

$Sb^{123}(\gamma,n)Sb^{122, 122m}$ $\quad$ Possible interference from $Te^{123}(\gamma,p)Sb^{122, 122m}$; possible interference from secondary reactions: $Te^{122}(n,p)Sb^{122, 122m}$; $Sn^{122}(p,n)Sb^{122, 122m}$; $Te^{125}(p,\alpha)Sb^{122, 122m}$.

$Sb^{121}(p,n)Te^{121m}$ $\quad$ 6×10^{-1} μg/cm^2 at 6.7 Mev.

$Sb^{121}(p,n)Te^{121}$ $\quad$ 1×10^{-1} μg/cm^2 at 6.7 Mev.

Te^{120}	0.089	70 ± 70	154 d	None	IT (100)
			17 d	EC (100)	0.575 (87)
					0.506 (13)
Te^{122}	2.46	2.8 ± 0.9			
		1.1 ± 0.5 a	104 d	None	IT (100)
		s			
Te^{123}	0.87	410 ± 30	s		
Te^{124}	4.61	6.8 ± 1.3			
		5 ± 3 a	58 d	None	IT (100)
		s			
Te^{125}	6.99	1.56 ± 0.16	s		
Te^{126}	18.71	0.8 ± 0.3			
		90 ± 20 mb a	105 d		IT (98)
		0.8 ± 0.2 a	9.4 h	0.70 (99)	
Te^{128}	31.79	0.3 ± 0.3			
		15 ± 5 mb a	33.5 d	1.53	IT
		0.13 ± 0.03 a	72 m	M	1.01
					1.46
Te^{130}	34.49	0.5 ± 0.3			
		<8 mb a	30 h	M (78)	IT (22)
		0.22 ± 0.05 a	24.8 m	M	M

R = 106 ± 13† † K23

Te^{126}(n, γ)Te^{127}	Determination of Te in high purity Al and Fe with a sensitivity of 0.5 μg.	G28
	Determination of Te with a calculated sensitivity of 0.1 μg; flux = 5 x 10^{11}.	L4
	Determination of Te with a calculated sensitivity of 0.01 μg; flux ~ 10^{12}.	S33
	Determination of Te with a calculated sensitivity of 10^{-4} μg; flux ~ 10^{13}.	J11
Te^{128}(n, 2n)Te^{127}	σ(14.5) = 0.78 b.	P2
Te^{130}(n, 2n)Te$^{129+129m}$	σ(14.5) = 0.60 b.	P2

Te^{126}(n, γ)Te$^{127, 127m}$	Possible interference from I^{127}(n, p)Te$^{127, 127m}$ with an I matrix; from Xe^{130}(n, α)Te$^{127, 127m}$ with a Xe matrix; from fission of U or Pu.
Te^{128}(n, α)Te$^{129, 129m}$	Possible interference from Xe^{132}(n, α)Te$^{129, 129m}$ with a Xe matrix; from fission of U or Pu.
Te^{130}(n, γ)Te$^{131, 131m}$	Possible interference from Xe^{134}(n, α)Te$^{131, 131m}$ with a Xe matrix; from fission of U or Pu.
Te^{128}(n, 2n)Te$^{127, 127m}$	Possible interference from I^{127}(n, p)Te$^{127, 127m}$; from Xe^{130}(n, α)Te$^{127, 127m}$; from fission of Th, U, or Pu.
Te^{130}(n, 2n)Te$^{129, 129m}$	Possible interference from Xe^{132}(n, α)Te$^{129, 129m}$; from fission of Th, U, or Pu.

Te^{126}(n, γ)Te^{127}	2 x 10^{-4} μg.
Te^{128}(n, γ)Te^{129}	9 x 10^{-4} μg.
Te^{130}(n, γ)Te^{131}	5 x 10^{-4} μg.
Te^{130}(n, γ)Te^{131} $\xrightarrow{\beta^-}$ I^{131}	5 x 10^{-4} μg.

$Te^{124}(p,n)I^{124}$ $\sigma(6.7) = 150$ mb.   B26

$Te^{126}(p,n)I^{126}$ $\sigma(6.7) = 70$ mb.   B26

$Te^{128}(p,n)I^{128}$ Excitation function from $E_{th}(3.2$ Mev) to 6.8 Mev; $E_p > 6.8$ Mev; $\sigma(6.7) = 90$ mb.   B26

$Te^{130}(p,n)I^{130}$ Excitation function from $E_{th}(3.3$ Mev) to 6.8 Mev; $E_p > 6.8$ Mev; $\sigma(6.7) = 95$ mb.   B26

$Te^{124}(p,n)I^{124}$ No apparent interference from primary reactions at E < 20 Mev; possible interference from secondary reaction: $Xe^{124}(n,p)I^{124}$.

$Te^{126}(p,n)I^{126}$ Possible interference from $I^{127}(p,pn)I^{126}$ at E > 15 Mev; from $Xe^{129}(p,\alpha)I^{126}$; possible interference from secondary reaction: $Xe^{126}(n,p)I^{126}$.

$Te^{128}(p,n)I^{128}$ Possible interference from $Xe^{131}(p,\alpha)I^{128}$; from $Xe^{129}(p,2p)I^{128}$ at E > 15 Mev; possible interference from secondary reactions: $I^{127}(n,\alpha)I^{128}$; $Xe^{128}(n,p)I^{128}$.

$Te^{130}(p,n)I^{130}$ Possible interference from $Xe^{131}(p,2p)I^{130}$ at E > 15 Mev; possible interference from secondary reactions: $Xe^{130}(n,p)I^{130}$; $Cs^{133}(n,\alpha)I^{130}$.

$Te^{128}(p,n)I^{128}$ 2×10^{-3} $\mu g/cm^2$ at 6.7 Mev.

$Te^{130}(p,n)I^{130}$ 5×10^{-3} $\mu g/cm^2$ at 6.7 Mev.

I^{127}	100	7.0 ± 0.6			
		5.6 ± 0.3 a	24.99 m	2.12 (76) 1.67 (16)	M
		$R_a = 140^{\dagger}$			$\dagger$M9

$I^{127}(n, \gamma)I^{128}$	Determination of I using a Van de Graaff-Be source with an efficient moderator; sensitivity = 0.7 µg.	A18
	Determination of I in blood using Ra-Be and Van de Graaff-Be sources.	S48
	Determination of I using a Po-Be source and β sensitive emulsions; interference from photo-electrons, compton electrons, and β emitters in the emulsion.	M17
	Others: B60, C41, D2, D3, J11, L4.	

$I^{127}(n, p)Te^{127}$	$\sigma(14.5) = 11.7$ mb.	C39
$I^{127}(n, \alpha)Sb^{124m}$	$\sigma(14.5) = 18.4$ mb.	P2
$I^{127}(n, 2n)I^{126}$	Excitation function from 11 Mev to 18 Mev; $E_{th} = 9.45$ Mev; $E_p = 15$ Mev; $\sigma(15) = 1.3$ b; $\sigma(14.5) = 1.12$ b.	C20 M14 P2

$I^{127}(n, \gamma)I^{128}$	Possible interference from $Xe^{128}(n, p)I^{128}$ with a Xe matrix.
$I^{127}(n, p)Te^{127, 127m}$	Possible interference from $Te^{126}(n, \gamma)Te^{127, 127m}$ or $Te^{128}(n, 2n)Te^{127, 127m}$; from $Xe^{130}(n, \alpha)Te^{127, 127m}$; from fission of Th, U, or Pu.
$I^{127}(n, \alpha)Sb^{124, 124m}$	Possible interference from $Sb^{123}(n, \gamma)Sb^{124, 124m}$; from $Te^{124}(n, p)Sb^{124, 124m}$; possible interference from secondary reaction: $Sn^{124}(p, n)Sb^{124, 124m}$.
$I^{127}(n, 2n)I^{126}$	Possible interference from $Xe^{126}(n, p)I^{126}$ with a Xe matrix; possible interference from secondary reactions: $Te^{125}(p, \gamma)I^{126}$ or $Te^{126}(p, n)I^{126}$; $Xe^{129}(p, \alpha)I^{126}$.

$I^{127}(n, \gamma)I^{128}$	6×10^{-6} µg.

$I^{127}(p,n)Xe^{127}$	$\sigma(6.7) = 44$ mb.	B26
$I^{127}(d,2n)Xe^{127}$	Excitation function from $E_{th}(\sim 3.5$ Mev) to 18 Mev; $E_p = 15$ Mev; $\sigma(15) = 0.7$ b.	B2
$I^{127}(\gamma,n)I^{126}$	Excitation function from $E_{th}(9.1$ Mev to 22 Mev); $E_p = 15.2$ Mev; $\sigma(15.2) = 0.45$ b.	E11 M45
$I^{127}(\gamma,2n)I^{125}$	$\sigma(17.6) = 30 \pm 20$ mb.	E11

$I^{127}(p,n)Xe^{127}$ — Possible interference from $Ba^{130}(p,\alpha)Cs^{127} \xrightarrow{\beta^+} I^{127}$; from $Xe^{128}(p,pn)Xe^{127}$ at $E > 15$ Mev; possible interference from secondary reactions: $Xe^{126}(n,\alpha)Xe^{127}$; $Ba^{130}(n,\alpha)Xe^{127}$; $Xe^{126}(p,\gamma)Cs^{127} \xrightarrow{\beta^+} Xe^{127}$.

$I^{127}(d,2n)Xe^{127}$ — Possible interference from $Xe^{126}(d,p)Xe^{127}$; possible interference from secondary reactions: $Xe^{126}(n,\gamma)Xe^{127}$; $Ba^{130}(n,\alpha)Xe^{127}$; $Xe^{126}(p,\gamma)Cs^{127} \xrightarrow{\beta^+} Xe^{127}$; $Ba^{130}(p,\alpha)Cs^{127} \xrightarrow{\beta^+} Xe^{127}$.

$I^{127}(\gamma,n)I^{126}$ — No apparent interference from primary reactions; possible interference from secondary reactions: $Xe^{126}(n,p)I^{126}$; $Te^{125}(p,\gamma)I^{126}$ or $Te^{126}(p,n)I^{126}$; $Xe^{129}(p,\alpha)I^{126}$.

$I^{127}(p,n)Xe^{127}$ — $2 \times 10^{-1} \mu g/cm^2$ at 6.7 Mev.

Xe^{124}	0.096	74 ± 1	58 s					
			18 h	EC (100)	M			
Xe^{126}	0.090		75 s	none	IT (100)			
			36.4 d	EC (100)	M			
Xe^{128}	1.92	<5	8.0 d s	none	IT (100)			
Xe^{129}	26.44	45 ± 15	s					
Xe^{130}	4.08	<5	12.0 d s	none	IT (100)			
Xe^{131}	21.18	120 ± 15	s					
Xe^{132}	26.89		2.3 d	none	IT (100)			
		0.2 ± 0.1 a	5.27 d	0.347 (100)	0.08	190 ± 90		s
Xe^{134}	10.44		15.6 m	none	IT (100)			
		0.2 ± 0.1 a	9.13 h	0.91 (97)	0.250 (~90)	$(2.72 \pm 0.11) \times 10^{6}$		s
Xe^{136}	8.87	0.15 ± 0.08 a	3.9 m	3.5				

$Xe^{132}(n, \gamma)Xe^{133, 133m}$ Possible interference from $Cs^{133}(n, p)Xe^{133, 133m}$ with a Cs matrix; from $Ba^{136}(n, \alpha)Xe^{133, 133m}$ with a Ba matrix; from fission of U or Pu; possible interference from self-shielding in comparator samples.

$Xe^{134}(n, \gamma)Xe^{135}$ Possible interference from $Ba^{138}(n, \alpha)Xe^{135}$ with a Ba matrix; from fission of U or Pu; possible interference from second-order reaction: $Xe^{135}(n, \gamma)Xe^{136}$; possible interference from self-shielding in comparator samples.

$Xe^{136}(n, \gamma)Xe^{137}$ Possible interference from fission of U or Pu; possible interference from self-shielding in comparator samples.

$Xe^{132}(n, \gamma)Xe^{133}$ 7×10^{-4} µg.

$Xe^{134}(n, \gamma)Xe^{135}$ 2×10^{-3} µg.

Cs^{133} 100 29.0 ± 1.0

                               17 ± 4 mb a   3.2 h   IT ($\sim$99)

                               30 ± 1 a   2.07 y   M   M $134 \pm 12^{*}$a 2.0×10^{6}y

                   (n, α) 0.002 mb$^{* \dagger}$ 12.6-h I^{130}

                        R = $169 \pm 23^{\dagger\dagger}$ $\dagger$M25
                                                                                                                                          $\dagger\dagger$K22

Cs^{133}(n, γ)Cs^{134m} Determination of Cs in liquid metals with a sensitivity of 0.2 ppm; flux $\sim 10^{12}$.   S32

                          Determination of Cs in minerals, rocks, and meteorites with a sensitivity of 0.075 ppm.   C3

                          Determination of Cs in Na-K alloys with a sensitivity of <0.05 ppm.   C4

Cs^{133}(n, γ)Cs^{134} Determination of Cs in sea water with a sensitivity of 0.01 μg.   S43

                          Others: G16 J11 L4 L8 S33.

Cs^{133}(n, α)I^{130} Average σ(14.5) = 1.5 mb.   B30   C39

Cs^{133}(n, γ)$Cs^{134, 134m}$ Possible interference from Ba^{134}(n, p)Cs$^{134, 134m}$; possible interference from self-shielding in

                          comparator samples.

Cs^{133}(n, α)I^{130} Possible interference from Xe^{130}(n, p)I^{130}; possible interference from secondary reaction:

                          Te^{130}(p, n)I^{130}.

Cs^{133}(n, γ)Cs^{134m} 2×10^{-3} μg.

Cs^{133}(n, γ)Cs^{134} 5×10^{-5} μg.

$Cs^{133}(p,n)Ba^{133m}$ $\sigma(6.7) = 43$ mb.   B 26

$Cs^{133}(p,n)Ba^{133, 133m}$ Possible interference from $Ce^{136}(p,\alpha)La^{133} \xrightarrow{\beta^+} Ba^{133, 133m}$ with a Ce matrix; from $Ba^{134}(p,pn)Ba^{133, 133m}$ at $E > 15$ Mev; possible interference from secondary reactions: $Ba^{132}(n,\gamma)Ba^{133, 133m}$; $Ce^{136}(n,\alpha)Ba^{133, 133m}$; $Ba^{132}(p,\gamma)La^{133} \xrightarrow{\beta^+} Ba^{133, 133m}$.

$Cs^{133}(p,n)Ba^{133m}$ $1 \times 10^{-2} \ \mu g/cm^2$ at 6.7 Mev.

Ba^{130}	0.101	10 ± 1	11.5 d	EC (100)	M			
Ba^{132}	0.097	7 ± 2 a	38.8 h	none	IT (100)			
			7.2 y	EC (100)	M			
Ba^{134}	2.42	2 ± 2	28.7 h s	none	IT (100)			
Ba^{135}	6.59	5.8 ± 0.9	s					
Ba^{136}	7.81	0.4 ± 0.4	2.6 m s	none	IT (100)			
Ba^{137}	11.32	5.1 ± 0.4	s					
Ba^{138}	71.66	0.7 ± 0.1						
		0.5 ± 0.1 a	84 m	M		0.163 (26)	4 ± 1a	128 d
		R = 12.6 ± 1.7 †						†K23

Ba^{138}(n, γ)Ba^{139}	Determination of Ba in biological material with a sensitivity of 1.0 μg; flux = 2 x 10^{12}.	H13
	Determination of Ba in human bones with a sensitivity of 1.0 μg; flux = 1 x 10^{12}.	S46
	Determination of Ba in plants and soils.	B35
	Others: B60, J11, L4, S33.	

Ba^{136}(n, p)Cs^{136}	σ(14.5) = 38 mb.	C39
Ba^{138}(n, p)Cs^{138}	E_{th} = 3.1 Mev; average σ(14.5) = 4.3 mb.	C20 C39 P2

Ba^{130}(n, γ)Ba^{131}	No apparent interference.
Ba^{132}(n, γ)Ba$^{133, 133m}$	Possible interference from Ce^{136}(n, α)Ba$^{133, 133m}$ with a Ce matrix.
Ba^{138}(n, γ)Ba^{139}	Possible interference from La^{139}(n, p)Ba^{139} with a La matrix; from Ce^{142}(n, α)Ba^{139} with a Ce matrix; from fission of U or Pu.
Ba^{138}(n, p)Cs^{138}	Possible interference from fission of Th, U, or Pu.

Ba^{130}(n, γ)Ba^{131}	4 x 10^{-3} μg.
Ba^{136}(n, γ)Ba^{137m}	2 x 10^{-3} μg.
Ba^{138}(n, γ)Ba^{139}	1 x 10^{-4} μg.

Ba^{136}(p, n)La^{136} E_{th} = 4.1 Mev; σ(6.7) = 0.10 b.   B26

Ba^{136}(p, n)La^{136} No apparent interference from primary reactions at E <20 Mev; possible interference from secondary
                              reaction: Ce^{136}(n, p)La^{136}.

Ba^{136}(p, n)La^{136} 8 x 10^{-3} μg/cm^2 at 6.7 Mev.

La^{138}	0.089		s				
$(1.1 \times 10^{11}y)$							
La^{139}	99.911	8.2 ± 0.8 a	40.2 h	M	M	3.1 ± 1.0 a	3.8 h
		$R = 11^{\dagger}$					† M9

$La^{139}(n,\gamma)La^{140}$	Determination of La with a calculated sensitivity of 2×10^{-3} μg; flux $= 5 \times 10^{11}$.	L4
	Determination of La with a calculated sensitivity of 10^{-4} μg; flux $\sim 10^{12}$.	S33
	Determination of La with a calculated sensitivity of 10^{-4} μg; flux $\sim 10^{12}$.	J11
	Determination of La in high purity Al.	A4

$La^{139}(n,p)Ba^{139}$	$E_{th} = 2.1$ Mev; $\bar{\sigma}(14.5) = 4$ mb.	C20 C39 P2
$La^{139}(n,\alpha)Cs^{136}$	$\sigma(14.5) = 1.9$ mb.	C39

$La^{139}(n,\gamma)La^{140}$	Possible interference from $Ce^{140}(n,p)La^{140}$ in a Ce matrix; from fission of U or Pu; possible interference from second-order reaction: $Ba^{138}(n,\gamma)Ba^{139} \xrightarrow{\beta^-} La^{139}(n,\gamma)La^{140}$.
$La^{139}(n,p)Ba^{139}$	Possible interference from $Ba^{138}(n,\gamma)Ba^{139}$; from $Ce^{142}(n,\alpha)Ba^{139}$.

$La^{139}(n,\gamma)La^{140}$	5×10^{-6} μg.

$La^{139}(p,n)Ce^{139}$ Excitation function from E_{th} (2.1 Mev) to 6.8 Mev; E_p > 6.8 Mev; $\sigma(6.7)$ = 24 mb.   B26

$La^{139}(p,n)Ce^{139}$ Possible interference from $Nd^{142}(p,\alpha)Pr^{139} \xrightarrow{\beta^+} Ce^{139}$; from $Ce^{140}(p,pn)Ce^{139}$ at E > 15 Mev; possible interference from secondary reactions: $Ce^{138}(n,\gamma)Ce^{139}$; $Nd^{142}(n,\alpha)Ce^{139}$; $Ce^{138}(p,\gamma)Pr^{139} \xrightarrow{\beta^+} Ce^{139}$.

$La^{139}(p,n)Ce^{139}$ 2 $\mu g/cm^2$ at 6.7 Mev.

Ce^{136}	0.19	25 ± 25					
		0.6 ± 0.2 a	34.5 h		IT (99+)		
		6.3 ± 1.5 a	8.7 h	EC (100)			
Ce^{138}	0.26	9 ± 6					
		7 ± 5 mb a	55 s		IT (100)		
		0.6 ± 0.3 a	140 d	EC (100)	0.165		
Ce^{140}	88.48	0.66 ± 0.06					
		0.31 ± 0.10 a	33.1 d	0.44 (70)	0.142		
				0.58 (30)			
Ce^{142}	11.07	1.0 ± 0.2					
$(5 \times 10^{15}$ y$)$		0.95 ± 0.05 a	33 h	M	M	$6.0 \pm 0.7^*$ a	285 d

$Ce^{140}(n,\gamma)Ce^{141}$	Determination of Ce in La with a sensitivity of 300 ppm without chemical separation.	K27
$Ce^{142}(n,\gamma)Ce^{143}$	Determination of Ce with a sensitivity of 0.08 μg.	C32
	Others: G28, J11, L4, S33.	

$Ce^{140}(n,p)La^{140}$	$\sigma(14.5) = 12$ mb.	C39
$Ce^{142}(n,p)La^{142}$	$\sigma(14.5) = 9.4$ mb.	C39
$Ce^{140}(n,\alpha)Ba^{137m}$	Average $\sigma(14.5) = 9.5$ mb.	C39 P2
$Ce^{142}(n,np)La^{141}$	$\sigma(14.5) = 18$ mb.	C19

$Ce^{140}(n,\gamma)Ce^{141}$ Possible interference from $Pr^{141}(n,p)Ce^{141}$ with a Pr matrix; from $Nd^{144}(n,\alpha)Ce^{141}$ with a Nd matrix; from fission of U or Pu; possible interference from second-order reaction: $La^{139}(n,\gamma)La^{140} \xrightarrow{\beta^+} Ce^{140}(n,\gamma)Ce^{141}$.

$Ce^{142}(n,\gamma)Ce^{143}$ Possible interference from $Nd^{146}(n,\alpha)Ce^{143}$ with a Nd matrix; from fission of U or Pu.

$Ce^{140}(n,\alpha)Ba^{137m}$ Possible interference from $Ba^{136}(n,\gamma)Ba^{137m}$ or $Ba^{138}(n,2n)Ba^{137m}$; from fission of Th, U, or Pu.

$Ce^{140}(n,\gamma)Ce^{141}$	3×10^{-4} μg.
$Ce^{142}(n,\gamma)Ce^{143}$	4×10^{-4} μg.

$Ce^{140}(p,n)Pr^{140}$ $\sigma(6.7) = 54$ mb.   B26

$Ce^{142}(p,n)Pr^{142}$ $\sigma(6.7) = 57$ mb.   B26

$Ce^{140}(p,n)Pr^{140}$ Possible interference from $Nd^{143}(p,\alpha)Pr^{140}$; from $Pr^{141}(p,pn)Pr^{140}$ at E > 15 Mev.

$Ce^{142}(p,n)Pr^{142}$ Possible interference from $Nd^{145}(p,\alpha)Pr^{142}$; possible interference from secondary reactions: $Pr^{141}(n,\gamma)Pr^{142}$; $Nd^{142}(n,p)Pr^{142}$.

$Ce^{140}(p,n)Pr^{140}$ 1×10^{-3} $\mu g/cm^2$ at 6.7 Mev.

$Ce^{142}(p,n)Pr^{142}$ 4×10^{-2} $\mu g/cm^2$ at 6.7 Mev.

139

Pr^{141} 100 11.6 ± 0.6

10 ± 3 a   19.2 h   2.17 (92)   1.57 (44) $18 \pm 3^{*}$a   13.7 d
0.59 (8)

$R_a^{141} = 11.3^{\dagger}$

† M9

$Pr^{141}(n, \gamma)Pr^{142}$

Determination of Pr in high purity Fe and Al with a sensitivity of 3×10^{-4} μg.   G28

Determination of Pr with a calculated sensitivity of 2×10^{-3} μg; flux = 5×10^{11}.   L4

Determination of Pr with a calculated sensitivity of 10^{-4} μg; flux ~ 10^{12}.   S33

Determination of Pr with a calculated sensitivity of 10^{-5} μg; flux ~ 10^{12}.   J11

- -

$Pr^{141}(n, 2n)Pr^{140}$ E_{th} = 9.4 Mev; $\sigma(14.5)$ = 2.06 b.   C20 P2

$Pr^{141}(n, \gamma)Pr^{142}$ Possible interference from $Nd^{142}(n, p)Pr^{142}$ with a Nd matrix.

$Pr^{141}(n, 2n)Pr^{140}$ No apparent interference from primary reactions at E < 20 Mev; possible interference from secondary reactions: $Ce^{140}(p, n)Pr^{140}$; $Nd^{143}(p, \alpha)Pr^{140}$.

$Pr^{141}(n, \gamma)Pr^{142}$ 4×10^{-6} μg.

$Pr^{141}(p,n)Nd^{141}$ $\sigma(6.7) = 16$ mb.   B26

$Pr^{141}(p,n)Nd^{141}$ Possible interference from $Sm^{144}(p,\alpha)Pm^{141} \xrightarrow{\beta^+} Nd^{141}$; from $Nd^{142}(p,pn)Nd^{141}$ at
                                 $E > 15$ Mev; possible interference from secondary reaction: $Sm^{144}(n,\alpha)Nd^{141}$.

$Pr^{141}(p,n)Nd^{141}$ 4×10^{-3} $\mu g/cm^2$ at 6.7 Mev.

Nd^{142}	27.13	18 ± 2	s		
Nd^{143}	12.20	324 ± 10	s		
Nd^{144} (5 x 10^{15} y)	23.87	5.0 ± 0.6	s		
Nd^{145}	8.30	60 ± 6	s		
Nd^{146}	17.18	10 ± 1			
		1.8 ± 0.6 a	11.1 d	M	M
Nd^{148}	5.72	3.4 ± 1.0			
		3.7 ± 1.2 a	2.0 h	M	M
Nd^{150}	5.60	3.0 ± 1.5	15 m	1.93	M

R = 40† † M9

Nd^{146}(n, γ)Nd^{147}	Determination of Nd with a calculated sensitivity of 0.1 μg; flux = 5 x 10^{11}.	L4
Nd^{148}(n, γ)Nd^{149}	Determination of Nd with a calculated sensitivity of 0.02 μg; flux ∼ 10^{12}.	S33
	Determination of Nd with a calculated sensitivity of 10^{-4} μg; flux ∼ 10^{12}.	J11
	Determination of Nd with a sensitivity of 0.1 μg; flux = 5 x 10^{11}.	L4
Nd^{142}(n, p)Pr^{142}	σ (14.5) = 13.5 mb.	C39
Nd^{143}(n, p)Pr^{143}	σ (14.5) = 11.5 mb.	C39
Nd^{146}(n, α)Ce^{143}	σ (14.5) = 2.6 mb.	C39

Nd^{146}(n, γ)Nd^{147}	Possible interference from Sm^{150}(n, α)Nd^{147} with a Sm matrix; from fission of U or Pu; possible interference from self-shielding in comparator samples.
Nd^{148}(n, γ)Nd^{149}	Possible interference from Sm^{152}(n, α)Nd^{149} with a Sm matrix; from fission of U or Pu; possible interference from self-shielding in comparator samples.
Nd^{150}(n, γ)Nd^{151}	Possible interference from Sm^{154}(n, α)Nd^{151} with a Sm matrix; possible interference from self-shielding in comparator samples.

Nd^{146}(n, γ)Nd^{147}	2 x 10^{-4} μg.
Nd^{148}(n, γ)Nd^{149}	2 x 10^{-4} μg.
Nd^{150}(n, γ)Nd^{151} $\xrightarrow{\beta^-}$ Pm^{151}	2 x 10^{-4} μg.

Pm^{147} (2.64 y)	60 ± 20 a	5.3 d

$Nd^{148}(p,n)Pm^{148m}$ $\sigma(6.7) = 36$ mb.   B26

$Nd^{148}(p,n)Pm^{148,148m}$ Possible interference from $Sm^{149}(p,2p)Pm^{148,148m}$ at $E > 15$ Mev; possible interference from secondary reactions: $Eu^{151}(n,\alpha)Pm^{148,148m}$; $Sm^{148}(n,p)Pm^{148,148m}$.

$Nd^{148}(p,n)Pm^{148}$ 7 $\mu g/cm^2$ at 6.7 Mev.

Sm^{144}	3.16	<2 a	340 d	EC (100)	0.485 0.061	
Sm^{147} (1.3 x 10^{11}y)	15.07	87 ± 60	s			
Sm^{148}	11.27		s			
Sm^{149}	13.84	40,800 ± 900 66,000 ± 3000*	s			
Sm^{150}	7.47		93 y	0.076		10,000±2000*
Sm^{152}	26.63	224 ± 7 140 ± 40 a	47.1 h	M	M	
Sm^{154}	22.53	5.5 ± 1.1 a	23.5 m	1.8 (100)	0.105 0.246	

$$R = 1790 \pm 270^{\dagger}$$

$$R_a^{152} > 1750^{\dagger\dagger}$$

† K23
†† M9

Sm^{152}(n, γ)Sm^{153}	Determination of Sm in the presence of Dy and Eu with a sensitivity of 0.01 μg.	L11
	Determination of Sm in high purity Fe and Al with a sensitivity of 1 x 10^{-4} μg.	G28
Sm^{154}(n, γ)Sm^{155}	Determination of Sm in the presence of other rare earths with a Ra-Be source.	M34
	Others: J11, L4, S33	

Sm^{152}(n, α)Nd^{149}	σ(14.5) = 8.9 mb.	P2
Sm^{154}(n, 2n)Sm^{153}	σ(14.5) = 0.225 b.	P2

Sm^{152}(n, γ)Sm^{153}	Possible interference from Eu^{153}(n, p)Sm^{153} with an Eu matrix; from Gd^{156}(n, α)Sm^{153} with a Gd matrix; from fission of U or Pu; possible interference from self-shielding in comparator samples.
Sm^{154}(n, γ)Sm^{155}	Possible interference from Gd^{158}(n, α)Sm^{155} with a Gd matrix; from fission of U or Pu; possible interference from self-shielding in comparator samples.
Sm^{152}(n, α)Nd^{149}	Possible interference from Nd^{148}(n, γ)Nd^{149} or Nd^{150}(n, 2n)Nd^{149}; from fission of Th, U, or Pu.
Sm^{154}(n, 2n)Sm^{153}	Possible interference from Eu^{153}(n, p)Sm^{153}; from Gd^{156}(n, α)Sm^{153}; from fission of Th, U, or Pu.

Sm^{152}(n, γ)Sm^{153}	1 x 10^{-6} μg.
Sm^{154}(n, γ)Sm^{155}	3 x 10^{-5} μg.

Eu^{151}	47.77	7700 ± 80					
		$1400 \pm 300^{*}$ a	9.2 h	1.88 EC (25)	M		
			12.7 y	M (27) EC (73)	M	$5500 \pm 1500^{*}$ a	s
Eu^{153}	52.23	450 ± 20					
		$420 \pm 100^{*}$ a	16 y	M	M	$1500 \pm 400^{*}$ a	1.7 y
		$R_a^{153} = 950^{\dagger}$					$\dagger$ M9

$Eu^{151}(n,\gamma)Eu^{152m}$	Determination of Eu in the presence of Sm and Dy with a sensitivity of 0.01 µg.	L11
$Eu^{151}(n,\gamma)Eu^{152}$	Determination of Eu in the presence of other rare earths with a Ra-Be source; sensitivity = 1.0 µg.	M34
	Others: H31, J11, L4, S33.	

$Eu^{151}(n,\gamma)Eu^{152, 152m}$	Possible interference from $Gd^{152}(n,p)Eu^{152, 152m}$ with a Gd matrix; possible interference from second-order reaction: $Eu^{152}(n,\gamma)Eu^{153}$; possible interference from self-shielding in comparator samples.

$Eu^{151}(n,\gamma)Eu^{152m}$	6×10^{-8} µg.
$Eu^{153}(n,\gamma)Eu^{154}$	5×10^{-5} µg.

Gd^{152}	0.20	< 125 a	236 d	EC (100)	M
Gd^{154}	2.15		s		
Gd^{155}	14.73	$61,000 \pm 5,000$ $70,000 \pm 20,000^{*}$	s		
Gd^{156}	20.47		s		
Gd^{157}	15.68	$240,000 \pm 12,000$ $160,000 \pm 60,000^{*}$	s		
Gd^{158}	24.87	4 ± 2 a	18.0 h	0.95 ($\sim$80) 0.60 ($\sim$20)	M
Gd^{160}	21.90	0.8 ± 0.3 a	3.6 m	1.5	M
		$R = 67 \pm 8^{\dagger}$			$\dagger$ K23

$Gd^{160}(n, \gamma)Gd^{161}$	Determination of Gd with a calculated sensitivity of 0.02 µg; flux = 5×10^{11}.	L4
	Determination of Gd with a calculated sensitivity of 10^{-3} µg; flux $\sim 10^{12}$.	S33
	Determination of Gd with a calculated sensitivity of 10^{-5} µg; flux $\sim 10^{12}$.	J11

$Gd^{157}(n, p)Eu^{157}$	$\sigma(14.5) = 11.3$ mb.	C39
$Gd^{156}(n, \alpha)Sm^{153}$	$\sigma(14.5) = 3.2$ mb.	C39
$Gd^{160}(n, 2n)Gd^{159}$	$\sigma(14.5) = 1.47$ b.	P2

$Gd^{158}(n, \gamma)Gd^{159}$	Possible interference from $Tb^{159}(n, p)Gd^{159}$ with a Tb matrix; from $Dy^{162}(n, \alpha)Gd^{159}$ with a Dy matrix; from fission of U or Pu; possible interference from self-shielding in comparator samples.
$Gd^{160}(n, \gamma)Gd^{161}$	Possible interference from $Dy^{164}(n, \alpha)Gd^{161}$ with a Gd matrix; from fission of U or Pu; possible interference from self-shielding in comparator samples.
$Gd^{160}(n, 2n)Gd^{159}$	Possible interference from $Tb^{159}(n, p)Gd^{159}$; from $Dy^{162}(n, \alpha)Gd^{159}$; from fission of Th, U, or Pu.

$Gd^{158}(n, \gamma)Gd^{159}$	4×10^{-5} µg.
$Gd^{160}(n, \gamma)Gd^{161}$	2×10^{-4} µg.
$Gd^{160}(n, \gamma)Gd^{161} \xrightarrow{\beta^{-}} Tb^{161}$	2×10^{-4} µg.

Gd^{156}(p, n)Tb^{156m} $\sigma(6.7) = 36$ mb.   B26

Gd^{156}(p, n)Tb$^{156, 156m}$ No apparent interference from primary reactions at E < 20 Mev; possible interference from secondary reaction: Dy^{156}(n, p)Tb$^{156, 156m}$.

Gd^{156}(p, n)Tb^{156} 1×10^{-2} μg/cm^2 at 6.7 Mev.

Tb^{159}	100	46 ± 4						
		> 22 a		73 d	M	M	$525 \pm 100^{*}$ a	7.09 d

$Tb^{159}(n, \gamma)Tb^{160}$ Determination of Tb with a calculated sensitivity of 4×10^{-3} μg; flux $= 5 \times 10^{11}$.   L4

Determination of Tb with a calculated sensitivity of 10^{-4} μg; flux $\sim 10^{12}$.   S33

Determination of Tb with a calculated sensitivity of 10^{-5} μg; flux $\sim 10^{12}$.   J11

- -

$Tb^{159}(n, \gamma)Tb^{160}$ Possible interference from $Dy^{160}(n, p)Tb^{160}$ with a Dy matrix; possible interference from self-shielding in comparator samples.

$Tb^{159}(n, \gamma)Tb^{160}$ 4×10^{-6} μg.

Dy^{156}	0.052		8.2 h	EC (100)	M		
Dy^{158}	0.090		134 d	EC (100)	0.058		
Dy^{160}	2.298		s				
Dy^{161}	18.88		s				
Dy^{162}	25.53		s				
Dy^{163}	24.97		s				
Dy^{164}	28.18	510 ± 20 a	1.25 m		IT		
		$2100 \pm 300^{*}$ a	139 m	M	M	$5000 \pm 2000^{*}$ a	82 h

$Dy^{164}(n, \gamma)Dy^{165m}$	Determination of Dy using a Ra-Be source.	M33 M34
$Dy^{164}(n, \gamma)Dy^{165}$	Determination of Dy in rare earth oxides with a sensitivity of < 100 ppm.	H30
	Determination of Dy in the presence of Eu and Sm with a sensitivity of 0.01 μg.	L11
	Determination of Dy in pure Ho_2O_3 with a sensitivity of 11%.	P6
	Determination of Dy in the presence of other rare earths using a Ra-Be source.	M34
	Others: G15, J11, L4, L10, S33.	

$Dy^{162}(n, \alpha)Gd^{159}$	$\sigma(14.5) = 3.56$ mb.	C39

$Dy^{164}(n, \gamma)Dy^{165, 165m}$	Possible interference from $Ho^{165}(n, p)Dy^{165, 165m}$ with a Ho matrix; from $Er^{168}(n, \alpha)Dy^{165}$ with an Er matrix; possible interference from self-shielding in comparator samples.

$Dy^{164}(n, \gamma)Dy^{165m}$	3×10^{-7} μg.
$Dy^{164}(n, \gamma)Dy^{165}$	8×10^{-8} μg.

Ho^{165}	100	64 ± 3			
		60 ± 12 a	27.3 h	M	M
			> 30 y	M	M

Ho^{165}(n, γ)Ho^{166}	Determination of Ho in the presence of other rare earths with a Ra–Be source; thermal neutron flux ∼ 10^2.	M34
	Determination of Ho in high purity Fe and Al with a sensitivity of 6 x 10^{-5} μg.	G28
	Others: J11, L4, S33.	

Ho^{165}(n, γ)Ho^{166}	Possible interference from Er^{166}(n, p)Ho^{166} with an Er matrix; from Tm^{169}(n, α)Ho^{166} with a Tm matrix; possible interference from second-order reaction: Dy^{164}(n, γ)Dy^{165} $\xrightarrow{\beta^-}$ Ho^{165}(n, γ)Ho^{166}; possible interference from self-shielding in comparator samples.

Ho^{165}(n, γ)Ho^{166}	7 x 10^{-7} μg.

Er^{162}	0.136		75 m	EC	0.43	
					1.10	
Er^{164}	1.56		10 h	EC	1.1	
Er^{166}	33.4		2.5 s			
			s			
Er^{167}	22.9		s			
Er^{168}	27.1	2.0 ± 0.4 a	9.4 d	0.34		
Er^{170}	14.9	9 ± 2 a	7.8 h	1.11 (93)	M	

Er^{170}(n, γ)Er^{171}	Determination of Er with a calculated sensitivity of 0.02 μg; flux = 5 x 10^{11}.	L4
	Determination of Er with a calculated sensitivity of 10^{-3} μg; flux ∼ 10^{12}.	S33
	Determination of Er with a calculated sensitivity of 10^{-5} μg; flux ∼ 10^{12}.	J11

Er^{168}(n, γ)Er^{169}	Possible interference from Tm^{169}(n, p)Er^{169} with a Tm matrix; from Yb^{172}(n, α)Er^{169} with an Yb matrix; possible interference from self-shielding in comparator samples.
Er^{170}(n, γ)Er^{171}	Possible interference from Yb^{174}(n, α)Er^{171} with an Yb matrix; possible interference from self-shielding in comparator samples.

Er^{168}(n, γ)Er^{169}	1 x 10^{-4} μg.
Er^{170}(n, γ)Er^{171}	3 x 10^{-5} μg.

Tm^{169}	100	127 ± 4					
		130 ± 30 a	129 d	0.968 (76)	0.084	150±20* a	1.9 y
				0.884 (24)			

Tm^{169}(n, γ)Tm^{170} Determination of Tm in Er with a sensitivity of 10 ppm.   K16

Determination of Tm with a calculated sensitivity of 2 x 10^{-3} μg; flux = 5 x 10^{11}.   L4

Determination of Tm with a calculated sensitivity of 10^{-4} μg; flux ~ 10^{12}.   S33

Determination of Tm with a calculated sensitivity of 10^{-5} μg; flux ~ 10^{12}.   J11

Tm^{169}(n, γ)Tm^{170} Possible interference from Yb^{170}(n, p)Tm^{170} with an Yb matrix; possible interference from second-order reactions: Tm^{170}(n, γ)Tm^{171}; Er^{168}(n, γ)Er^{169} $\xrightarrow{\beta^-}$ Tm^{169}(n, γ)Tm^{170}; possible interference from self-shielding in comparator samples.

Tm^{169}(n, γ)Tm^{170} 2 x 10^{-6} μg.

Tm^{169}(p, 3n)Yb^{167} Relative excitation function from E$_{th}$(19.5 Mev) to 27 Mev; E$_p$ > 27 Mev.   H11

Tm^{169}(p, 3n)Yb^{167} Possible interference from Yb^{168}(p, pn)Yb^{167}.

Yb^{168}	0.140	11,000 ± 3000* a	32 d	EC (100)	M
Yb^{170}	3.03		s		
Yb^{171}	14.31		s		
Yb^{172}	21.82		s		
Yb^{173}	16.13		s		
Yb^{174}	31.84	60 ± 40 a	4.1 d	M	M
Yb^{176}	12.73	5.5 ± 1.0 a	1.9 h	1.30 (88)	M

Yb^{174}(n, γ)Yb^{175}	Determination of Yb in Er.	K16
	Determination of Yb with a calculated sensitivity of 10^{-3} μg; flux = 5 x 10^{11}.	L4
	Determination of Yb with a calculated sensitivity of 10^{-4} μg; flux ~ 10^{12}.	S33
	Determination of Yb with a calculated sensitivity of 10^{-5} μg; flux ~ 10^{12}.	J11

Yb^{168}(n, γ)Yb^{169}	No apparent interference from primary or second-order reactions; possible interference from self-shielding in comparator samples.
Yb^{174}(n, γ)Yb^{175}	Possible interference from Lu^{175}(n, p)Yb^{175} with a Lu matrix; from Hf^{178}(n, α)Yb^{175} with a Hf matrix; possible interference from self-shielding in comparator samples.
Yb^{176}(n, γ)Yb^{177}	Possible interference from Hf^{189}(n, α)Yb^{177} with a Hf matrix; possible interference from self-shielding in comparator samples.

Yb^{168}(n, γ)Yb^{169}	6 x 10^{-6} μg.
Yb^{174}(n, γ)Yb^{175}	2 x 10^{-6} μg.
Yb^{176}(n, γ)Yb^{177}	7 x 10^{-5} μg.
Yb^{176}(n, γ)Yb^{177} --$\xrightarrow{\beta^-}$-- Lu^{177}	7 x 10^{-5} μg.

Lu^{175}	97.40	35 ± 15 a	3.7 h	1.1 1.2 s	0.089
Lu^{176} $(2.4 \times 10^{10} y)$	2.60	4000 ± 800 a	6.8 d	0.497 (90)	M

$R = 720^{\dagger}$ † M9

$Lu^{175}(n, \gamma)Lu^{176m}$ Determination of Lu with a calculated sensitivity of 10^{-3} µg; flux = 5 x 10^{11}.   L4

$Lu^{176}(n, \gamma)Lu^{177}$ Determination of Lu in Er using ion exchange separation techniques with a sensitivity of 10 ppm.   K16

Determination of Lu with a sensitivity of 10^{-4} µg; flux = 10^{12}.   C32

Determination of Lu with a sensitivity of 3×10^{-4} µg; flux = 5 x 10^{11}.   L4

Others: J11, S33

- -

$Lu^{175}(n, p)Yb^{175}$ $\sigma(14.5) = 3.4$ mb.   C39

$Lu^{175}(n, \gamma)Lu^{176m}$ Possible interference from $Hf^{176}(n, p)Lu^{176m}$ with a Hf matrix; possible interference from self-shielding in comparator samples.

$Lu^{176}(n, \gamma)Lu^{177}$ Possible interference from $Yb^{176}(n, \gamma)Yb^{177} \xrightarrow{\beta^{-}} Lu^{177}$; from $Hf^{177}(n, p)Lu^{177}$ or $Hf^{180}(n, \alpha)Yb^{177} \xrightarrow{\beta^{-}} Lu^{177}$ with a Hf matrix; from $Ta^{180}(n, \alpha)Lu^{177}$ with a Ta matrix; possible interference from self-shielding in comparator samples.

$Lu^{175}(n, \gamma)Lu^{176m}$ 1×10^{-6} µg.

$Lu^{176}(n, \gamma)Lu^{177}$ 5×10^{-7} µg.

Lu$^{175}(\gamma,n)$Lu^{174} Excitation function from E_{th}(7.77 Mev) to 23 Mev; E_p = 16 Mev; $\sigma(16)$ = 225 mb.   K19

Lu$^{175}(\gamma,n)$Lu^{174} No apparent interference from primary reactions; possible interference from secondary reactions: Hf^{174}(n, p)Lu^{174}; Yb^{173}(p, γ)Lu^{174} or Yb^{174}(p, n)Lu^{174}; Hf^{177}(p, α)Lu^{174}.

Hf^{174}	0.18	1500 ± 1000	70 d	EC (100)	M
Hf^{176}	5.15	15 ± 15	s		
Hf^{177}	18.39	380 ± 30	4.8 s s		
Hf^{178}	27.08	75 ± 10	19 s s		
Hf^{179}	13.78	65 ± 15	5.5 h s	none	IT (100)
Hf^{180}	35.44	14 ± 5 10 ± 3 a	44.6 d	0.408	M

$$R = 1470 \pm 200^{\dagger}$$

$$R_a^{180} = 21.8^{\dagger\dagger}$$

† K23
†† M9

$Hf^{178}(n,\gamma)Hf^{179m}$	Determination of Hf in Zr using gross counting techniques with a sensitivity of 0.1 ppm; flux = 3×10^{9}.	L12
	Determination of Hf in Zr using gross γ counting techniques; sensitivity = 7 ppm; flux = 6.5×10^{13}; observed interference from Na.	L11 M4
$Hf^{179}(n,\gamma)Hf^{180m}$	Determination of Hf in Zr with a sensitivity of 10 ppm; flux = 6.5×10^{13}.	M4
$Hf^{180}(n,\gamma)Hf^{181}$	Determination of Hf in Zr with a sensitivity of 10 ppm; flux = 6.5×10^{13}.	M4
	Others: A19, G28, J11, L4, M53, S33.	

- -

$Hf^{178}(n,\alpha)Yb^{175}$	$\sigma(14.5) = 2.0$ mb.	C39

$Hf^{174}(n,\gamma)Hf^{175}$	No apparent interference from primary or second-order reactions; possible interference from self-shielding in comparator samples.
$Hf^{178}(n,\gamma)Hf^{179m}$	Possible interference from $W^{182}(n,\alpha)Hf^{179m}$ with a W matrix; possible interference from self-shielding in comparator samples.
$Hf^{180}(n,\gamma)Hf^{181,181m}$	Possible interference from $Ta^{181}(n,p)Hf^{181,181m}$ with a Ta matrix; from $W^{184}(n,\alpha)Hf^{181}$ with a W matrix; possible interference from self-shielding in comparator samples.

$Hf^{174}(n,\gamma)Hf^{175}$	8×10^{-5} μg.
$Hf^{180}(n,\gamma)Hf^{181}$	4×10^{-5} μg.

Ta^{180}	0.012			0.33 s s				
Ta^{181}	100	21 ± 1 30 ± 10 mb a 19 ± 7 a	16.5 m 115 d	M	IT (95) M	$17,000 \pm 2000^{*}$ a	5.0 d

$$R = 474 \pm 62^{\dagger}$$

$$R_a^{181} = 590^{\dagger\dagger}$$

† K23
†† M9

$Ta^{181}(n, \gamma)Ta^{182m}$ Non-destructive determination of Ta in Ta ores using Ra-Be and RaD-Be sources with
a sensitivity of ~ 10 mg.   E6

$Ta^{181}(n, \gamma)Ta^{182}$ Determination of Ta in Si with a sensitivity of 3×10^{-3} ppm; flux = 2×10^{14}.   T16

Determination of Ta in Nb minerals using γ-spectrometry with a sensitivity of 300 ppm.   B22 K26 L18 M41

Determination of Ta in Si using γ spectrometry with a sensitivity of 8 ppm;
flux = 3.4×10^{12}.   M47 M48

Others: G28, J11, L4, S33.

$Ta^{181}(n, 2n)Ta^{180m}$ $\sigma(14.5) = 0.87$ b.   P2

$Ta^{181}(n, \gamma)Ta^{182, 182m}$ Possible interference from $W^{182}(n, p)Ta^{182}$ with a W matrix; from $Re^{185}(n, \alpha)Ta^{182}$;
possible interference from second-order reactions: $Ta^{182}(n, \gamma)Ta^{183}$; $Hf^{180}(n, \gamma)Hf^{181} \xrightarrow{\beta^-} Ta^{181}(n, \gamma)Ta^{182}$;
possible interference from self-shielding in comparator samples.

$Ta^{181}(n, 2n)Ta^{180m}$ Possible interference from $W^{180}(n, p)Ta^{180m}$ with a W matrix; possible interference from secondary
reaction: $Hf^{180}(p, n)Ta^{180m}$.

$Ta^{181}(n, \gamma)Ta^{182m}$ 2×10^{-3} μg.

$Ta^{181}(n, \gamma)Ta^{182}$ 2×10^{-5} μg.

$Ta^{181}(p, pn)Ta^{180m}$ Excitation function from $\sim$ 13 Mev to 23.5 Mev; $E_p > 23.5$ Mev; $\sigma(23.5) \sim$ 100 mb.   C24

$Ta^{181}(d, p)Ta^{182}$ Excitation function from $E_{th}(\sim$ 6 Mev) to 15 Mev; $E_p \sim$ 13.5 Mev; $\sigma(13.5) \sim$ 0.9 b; thick-target yield at 15 Mev = 5×10^5 dps/μa-hr.   S65 S66

$Ta^{181}(\gamma, n)Ta^{180m}$ Excitation function from $E_{th}(7.6$ Mev) to 21 Mev; $E_p \sim$ 14 Mev; $\sigma(14) \sim$ 0.6 b; $\sigma(17.6) = 0.32$ b.   H7 H14 H18 K7 P3

$Ta^{181}(\gamma, 2n)Ta^{179}$ Excitation function from $E_{th}(14$ Mev) to 22 Mev; $E_p \sim$ 17 Mev; $\sigma(17) \sim$ 0.23 b.   W8

$Ta^{181}(p, pn)Ta^{180m}$ Possible interference from $Hf^{180}(p, n)Ta^{180m}$; from $W^{183}(p, \alpha)Ta^{180m}$; possible interference from secondary reaction: $W^{180}(n, p)Ta^{180m}$.

$Ta^{181}(d, p)Ta^{182}$ Possible interference from $Hf^{180}(d, \gamma)Ta^{182}$; from $W^{184}(d, \alpha)Ta^{182}$; possible interference from secondary reactions: $W^{182}(n, p)Ta^{182}$; $Re^{185}(n, \alpha)Ta^{182}$.

$Ta^{181}(\gamma, n)Ta^{180m}$ No apparent interference from primary reactions; possible interference from secondary reactions: $W^{180}(n, p)Ta^{180m}$; $Hf^{179}(p, \gamma)Ta^{180m}$ or $Hf^{180}(p, n)Ta^{180m}$; $W^{183}(p, \alpha)Ta^{180m}$.

$Ta^{181}(d, p)Ta^{182}$ 4×10^{-2} μg/cm^2 at 13.5 Mev.

W^{180}	0.14	60 ± 60					
		10 ± 10 a	145 d	EC (100)			
W^{182}	26.4	20 ± 2	5.5 s				
			s				
W^{183}	14.4	11 ± 1					
			s				
W^{184}	30.6	2.0 ± 0.3					
			1.62 m		IT		
		2.1 ± 0.6 a	75.8 d	0.430 (100)	None		
W^{186}	28.4	35 ± 3					
		34 ± 7 a	24 h	M	M	90 ± 40 a	69.5 d

$$R = 290 \pm 35 \,^{\dagger}$$

$$R_a^{186} = 355 \,^{\dagger\dagger}$$

†K23

††M9

$W^{186}(n,\gamma)W^{187}$ — Determination of W in Si without chemistry using γ spectrometry with a sensitivity of 0.6 ppm; flux = 3.4×10^{12}.   M47 M48

Determination of W in Ti with a calculated sensitivity of 6 ppm; flux = 10^{12}.   B44

Others: G28, J11, L4, M53, S33.

- -

$W^{184}(n,p)Ta^{184}$ — $\sigma(14.5) = 4.75$ mb.   C39

$W^{186}(n,p)Ta^{186}$ — $\sigma(14.5) = 2.9$ mb.   C39

$W^{186}(n,np)Ta^{185}$ — $\sigma(14.5) \leq 1.6$ mb.   C19

$W^{184}(n,\gamma)W^{185, 185m}$ — Possible interference from $Re^{185}(n,p)W^{185, 185m}$; from $Os^{188}(n,\alpha)W^{185, 185m}$ with an Os matrix; possible interference from self-shielding in comparator samples.

$W^{186}(n,\gamma)W^{187}$ — Possible interference from $Re^{187}(n,p)W^{187}$; from $Os^{190}(n,\alpha)W^{187}$ with an Os matrix; possible interference from second-order reaction: $W^{187}(n,\gamma)W^{188}$; possible interference from self-shielding in comparator samples.

$W^{184}(n,\gamma)W^{185}$ — 3×10^{-4} μg.

$W^{186}(n,\gamma)W^{187}$ — 5×10^{-6} μg.

Re^{185}	37.07	104 ± 8	89 h	1.07 (70) 0.93 (22) EC (8)	M		
Re^{187} $(5 \times 10^{10} y)$	62.93	66 ± 5					
		75 ± 15 a	18.7 m 16.7 h	None 2.1 (79) 1.96 (20)	IT M	<2 a	150 d

$$R_a^{185} = 1160^{\dagger}$$

$$R_a^{187} = 305^{\dagger}$$

† M9

$Re^{185}(n,\gamma)Re^{186}$	Determination of the relative abundance of Re in nature.	B45 B46 G10
$Re^{187}(n,\gamma)Re^{188}$	Determination of the relative abundance of Re in nature.	B45 B46 H26 G10
	Others: J11, L4, S33	

- -

$Re^{187}(n,p)W^{187}$	$\sigma(14.5) = 3.9$ mb.	C39
$Re^{187}(n,\alpha)Ta^{184}$	$\sigma(14.5) = 0.9$ mb.	C39

$Re^{185}(n,\gamma)Re^{186}$	Possible interference from $Os^{186}(n,p)Re^{186}$ with an Os matrix.
$Re^{187}(n,\gamma)Re^{188}$	Possible interference from $Os^{188}(n,p)Re^{188}$ with an Os matrix; from $Ir^{191}(n,\alpha)Re^{188}$ with an Ir matrix; possible interference from second-order reaction: $W^{186}(n,\gamma)W^{187} \xrightarrow{\beta^-} Re^{187}(n,\gamma)Re^{188}$.

$Re^{185}(n,\gamma)Re^{186}$	1×10^{-6} μg.
$Re^{187}(n,\gamma)Re^{188}$	1×10^{-6} μg.

Os^{184}	0.018	<200 a	93.6 d	EC (100)	M		
Os^{186}	1.59		39 h s				
Os^{187}	1.64		s				
Os^{188}	13.3		5.7 h s	None	IT		
Os^{189}	16.1		9.5 m s	None	IT		
Os^{190}	26.4		14 h	None	IT (100)		
		8 ± 3 a	16 d	0.143 (100)			
Os^{192}	41.0	1.6 ± 0.4 a	31 h	M	M	600 ± 200 a	~700 d

R = 180 ± 20†

† K23

Os^{190}(n, γ)Os^{191}	Determination of Os with a calculated sensitivity of 0.02 μg; flux = 5 x 10^{11}.	L4
Os^{192}(n, γ)Os^{193}	Determination of Os with a calculated sensitivity of 0.03 μg; flux = 5 x 10^{11}.	L4
	Others: J11, M53, S33.	

- -

Os^{190}(n, α)W^{187}	σ (14.5) = 0.57 mb.	C39

Os^{190}(n, γ)Os^{191}	Possible interference from Ir^{191}(n, p)Os^{191} with an Ir matrix; from Pt^{194}(n, α)Os^{191} with a Pt matrix; possible interference from self-shielding in comparator samples.
Os^{192}(n, γ)Os^{193}	Possible interference from Ir^{193}(n, p)Os^{193} with an Ir matrix; from Pt^{196}(n, α)Os^{193} with a Pt matrix; possible interference from second-order reaction: Os^{193}(n, γ)Os^{194}; possible interference from self-shielding in comparator samples.

Os^{190}(n, γ)Os$^{191, 191m}$	3 x 10^{-5} μg.
Os^{192}(n, γ)Os^{193}	8 x 10^{-5} μg.

Ir^{191}	38.5	260 ± 100 a	1.4 m		IT (99+)			
		700 ± 200 a	74.5 d	M	M	700 ± 200	s	
				EC (3.5)				
Ir^{193}	61.5	130 ± 30 a	19 h	M	M			

R = 2000 ± 490†

$R_a^{191} = 3500^{\dagger\dagger}$

$R_a^{193} = 1370^{\dagger\dagger}$

$\dagger$ K23
$\dagger\dagger$ M9

Ir^{191}(n, γ)Ir^{192m}	Determination of Ir with a portable Ra-Be source; thermal flux $\sim 10^2$.	M33
Ir^{191}(n, γ)Ir^{192}	Determination of Ir with a calculated sensitivity of 4×10^{-4} μg; flux = 5×10^{11}.	L4
Ir^{193}(n, γ)Ir^{194}	Determination of Ir with a calculated sensitivity of 10^{-5} μg; flux $\sim 10^{12}$.	S33
	Determination of Ir with a calculated sensitivity of 10^{-7} μg; flux $\sim 10^{12}$.	J11
	Determination of Ir with a calculated sensitivity of 3×10^{-4} μg; flux = 5×10^{11}.	L4

Ir^{193}(n, p)Os^{193}	σ(14.5) = 2.7 mb.	C39
Ir^{191}(n, α)Re^{188}	σ(14.5) = 2.4 mb.	C39

Ir^{191}(n, γ)Ir$^{192, 192m}$ — Possible interference from Pt^{192}(n, p)Ir$^{192, 192m}$ with a Pt matrix; possible interference from second-order reaction: Os^{190}(n, γ)Os^{191} $\xrightarrow{\beta^-}$ Ir^{191}(n, γ)Ir$^{192, 192m}$; possible interference from self-shielding in comparator samples.

Ir^{193}(n, γ)Ir^{194} — Possible interference from Pt^{194}(n, p)Ir^{194} with a Pt matrix; from Au^{197}(n, α)Ir^{194} with a Au matrix; possible interference from second-order reaction: Os^{192}(n, γ)Os^{193} $\xrightarrow{\beta^-}$ Ir^{193}(n, γ)Ir^{194}; possible interference from self-shielding in comparator samples.

Ir^{191}(n, γ)Ir^{192m}	5×10^{-7} μg.
Ir^{191}(n, γ)Ir^{192}	8×10^{-7} μg.
Ir^{193}(n, γ)Ir^{194}	7×10^{-7} μg.

Pt^{190} $(5.9 \times 10^{11}y)$	0.012	150 ± 150	3.0 d s	EC (100)	M		
Pt^{192}	0.78	8 ± 8 90 ± 40 a	4.3 d >74 d	None EC	IT (100)		
Pt^{194}	32.8	1.2 ± 0.9	3.5 d s	None	IT (100)		
Pt^{195}	33.7	27 ± 2	s				
Pt^{196}	25.4	0.7 ± 0.7 0.8 ± 0.1 a	78 m 18 h	None M	IT (100) M		
Pt^{198}	7.2	4.0 ± 0.5 3.9 ± 0.8 a	31 m	M	M	15 ± 10	11.5 h
		R = 69[†]					[†] M9

$Pt^{192}(n,\gamma)Pt^{193m}$　　Determination of Pt with a calculated sensitivity of 0.1 μg; flux = 5×10^{11}. 　　L4

$Pt^{196}(n,\gamma)Pt^{197}$　　Determination of Pt in Si with a sensitivity of 9×10^{-4} ppm; flux = 2×10^{14}. 　　T16

Determination of Pt with a calculated sensitivity of 0.02 μg; flux = 5×10^{11}. 　　L4

Others: J11, S33.

$Pt^{194}(n,p)Ir^{194}$　　$\sigma(14.5) = 3.9$ mb. 　　C39

$Pt^{195}(n,p)Ir^{195}$　　$\sigma(14.5) = 2.9$ mb. 　　C39

$Pt^{198}(n,2n)Pt^{197}$　　$\sigma(14.5) = 2.77$ b. 　　P2

$Pt^{190}(n,\gamma)Pt^{191}$　　No apparent interference.

$Pt^{192}(n,\gamma)Pt^{193m}$　　Possible interference from $Hg^{196}(n,\alpha)Pt^{193m}$ with a Hg matrix.

$Pt^{194}(n,\gamma)Pt^{195m}$　　Possible interference from $Hg^{198}(n,\alpha)Pt^{195m}$ with a Hg matrix; possible interference from second-order reaction: $Ir^{193}(n,\gamma)Ir^{194} \xrightarrow{\beta^-} Pt^{194}(n,\gamma)Pt^{195m}$.

$Pt^{196}(n,\gamma)Pt^{197}$　　Possible interference from $Au^{197}(n,p)Pt^{197}$ with a Au matrix; from $Hg^{200}(n,\alpha)Pt^{197}$ with a Hg matrix.

$Pt^{198}(n,2n)Pt^{197}$　　Possible interference from $Au^{197}(n,p)Pt^{197}$; from $Hg^{200}(n,\alpha)Pt^{197}$.

$Pt^{196}(n,\gamma)Pt^{197}$　　3×10^{-4} μg.

$Pt^{198}(n,\gamma)Pt^{199}$　　2×10^{-4} μg.

$Pt^{198}(n,\gamma)Pt^{199} \xrightarrow{\beta^-} Au^{199}$　　2×10^{-4} μg.

$Pt^{198}(d,p)Pt^{199}$ Excitation function from 50 Mev to 190 Mev; E_p < 50 Mev; $\sigma(50)$ = 30 mb.   S27

$Pt^{198}(d,p)Pt^{199}$ No apparent interference from primary reactions at E < 20 Mev; possible interference
                                from secondary reaction: $Hg^{202}(n,\alpha)Pt^{199}$.

Au^{197}	100	98.8 ± 0.3					
		96 ± 10 a	2.70 d	0.96 (98.6)	0.412 ($\sim$95)	26,000$\pm$1,200 a	3.14 d
		$R_a = 1558^{\dagger}$					$\dagger$ M9

$Au^{197}(n, \gamma)Au^{198}$	Determination of Au in Si with a sensitivity of 5×10^{-5} ppm; flux = 2×10^{14}.	T16
	Determination of Au in biological material with a sensitivity of 1×10^{-4} µg; flux = 1×10^{12}.	G29
	Determination of Au in meteorites with a sensitivity of 1 ppm.	G11
	Determination of Au in sea water with a sensitivity of 400 µg; flux $\sim 10^{12}$.	H50
	Others: F12, G10, J11, L4, M56, S33, T18, V2.	

$Au^{197}(n, p)Pt^{197}$	$\sigma(14.5) = 2.42$ mb.	C39
$Au^{197}(n, \alpha)Ir^{194}$	$\sigma(14.5) = 0.43$ mb.	C39
$Au^{197}(n, 2n)Au^{196}$	$\sigma(14.5) = 1.72$ b.	P2

$Au^{197}(n, \gamma)Au^{198}$ Possible interference from $Hg^{198}(n, p)Au^{198}$ with a Hg matrix; possible interference from second-order reactions: $Pt^{196}(n, \gamma)Pt^{197} \xrightarrow{\beta^-} Au^{197}(n, \gamma)Au^{198}$; $Au^{198}(n, \gamma)Au^{199}$; possible interference from self-shielding in comparator samples.

$Au^{197}(n, 2n)Au^{196}$ Possible interference from $Hg^{196}(n, p)Au^{196}$ with a Hg matrix; possible interference from secondary reactions: $Pt^{196}(p, n)Au^{196}$; $Hg^{199}(p, \alpha)Au^{196}$.

$Au^{197}(n, \gamma)Au^{198}$ 5×10^{-7} µg.

$Au^{197}(d,p)Au^{198}$ Excitation function from E_{th}($\sim$ 5.5 Mev) to 9 Mev; $E_p >$ 9 Mev; $\sigma(9) \sim$ 0.2 b.   P4

$Au^{197}(\gamma,n)Au^{196}$ Excitation function from E_{th}(8.0 Mev) to 21 Mev; $E_p \sim$ 14.5 Mev; average $\sigma(14.5) \sim$ 0.6 b.   H14   M45

$Au^{197}(d,p)Au^{198}$ Possible interference from $Pt^{198}(d,2n)Au^{198}$; from $Hg^{198}(d,2p)Au^{198}$ or $Hg^{200}(d,\alpha)Au^{198}$;
possible interference from secondary reactions: $Hg^{198}(n,p)Au^{198}$; $Pt^{198}(p,n)Au^{198}$;
$Hg^{201}(p,\alpha)Au^{198}$.

$Au^{197}(\gamma,n)Au^{196,196m}$ No apparent interference from primary reactions; possible interference from secondary reactions:
$Hg^{196}(n,p)Au^{196,196m}$; $Pt^{195}(p,\gamma)Au^{196,196m}$ or $Pt^{196}(p,n)Au^{196,196m}$; $Hg^{199}(p,\alpha)Au^{196,196m}$.

$Au^{197}(d,p)Au^{198}$ 5×10^{-3} $\mu g/cm^2$ at 9 Mev.

177

Hg^{196}	0.146	$3100 \pm 1000^*$	24 h	EC (3)	IT (97)
			65 h	EC (100)	M
Hg^{198}	10.02		42 m s	None	IT (100)
Hg^{199}	16.84	$2500 \pm 800^*$	s		
Hg^{200}	23.13	$<60^*$	s		
Hg^{201}	13.22	$<60^*$	s		
Hg^{202}	29.80	3.8 ± 0.8 a	47 d	0.208	0.279
Hg^{204}	6.85	0.43 ± 0.10	5.5 m	1.8	0.203

$R = 72.4 \pm 8.0^\dagger$ $\dagger$ K23

$Hg^{202}(n,\gamma)Hg^{203}$ Determination of Hg in high purity Fe and Al with a sensitivity of 4×10^{-3} µg.   G28

Determination of Hg in Si with a sensitivity of 3×10^{-3} ppm; flux = 2×10^{14}.   T16

$Hg^{204}(n,\gamma)Hg^{205}$ Determination of Hg in liquid metals with a sensitivity of 0.5 ppm.   S32

Others: J11, L4, L23, S33.

- -

$Hg^{200}(n,p)Au^{200}$ $\sigma(14.5) = 3.63$ mb.   C39

$Hg^{201}(n,p)Au^{201}$ $\sigma(14.5) = 2.12$ mb.   C39

$Hg^{200}(n,\alpha)Pt^{197}$ $\sigma(14.5) = 1.77$ mb.   C39

$Hg^{202}(n,\alpha)Pt^{199}$ $\sigma(14.5) = 1.01$ mb.   C39

$Hg^{196}(n,\gamma)Hg^{197, 197m}$ No apparent interference from primary or second-order reactions; possible interference from self-shielding in comparator samples.

$Hg^{202}(n,\gamma)Hg^{203}$ Possible interference from $Tl^{203}(n,p)Hg^{203}$ with a Tl matrix; from $Pb^{206}(n,\alpha)Hg^{203}$ with a Pb matrix; possible interference from self-shielding in comparator samples.

$Hg^{204}(n,\gamma)Hg^{205}$ Possible interference from $Tl^{205}(n,p)Hg^{205}$ with a Tl matrix; from $Pb^{208}(n,\alpha)Hg^{205}$ with a Pb matrix; possible interference from self-shielding in comparator samples.

$Hg^{196}(n,\gamma)Hg^{197, 197m}$ 2×10^{-5} µg.

$Hg^{202}(n,\gamma)Hg^{203}$ 1×10^{-4} µg.

$Hg^{204}(n,\gamma)Hg^{205}$ 2×10^{-3} µg.

Tl^{203}	29.50	11.4 ± 0.9				
		8 ± 3 a	3.56 y	0.764 (~98)	None	
				EC (2)		
		(n, p) 0.025 mb*†	48-d Hg^{203}			
Tl^{205}	70.50	0.80 ± 0.08				
		0.10 ± 0.03 a	4.19 m	1.51	None	

$$R_a^{203} = 129^{\dagger\dagger}$$

$$R_a^{205} = 0.5^{\dagger\dagger}$$

† M37

†† M9

$Tl^{203}(n, \gamma)Tl^{204}$ Determination of Tl in meteorites with a sensitivity of 0.1 ppb; flux ~ 5 x 10^{13}.   R21

Determination of Tl in KI with a sensitivity of 0.1 µg.   D8

Determination of Tl in Si with a sensitivity of 8 x 10^{-3} ppm; flux = 3 x 10^{12}.   C5 K2

Others: J11, L4, S33.

$Tl^{205}(n, p)Hg^{205}$ $\overline{\sigma}(14.5) = 4.9$ mb.   C39 P2

$Tl^{203}(n, \alpha)Au^{200}$ $\sigma(14.5) = 0.37$ mb.   C39

$Tl^{203}(n, 2n)Tl^{202}$ Relative excitation function from 11 Mev to 19 Mev; $E_{th} < 12$ Mev; σ for Ra-Be

neutrons = 0.59 ± 0.07 b.   L16 M13

$Tl^{203}(n, \gamma)Tl^{204}$ Possible interference from $Pb^{204}(n, p)Tl^{204}$ with a Pb matrix; possible interference

from second-order reaction: $Hg^{202}(n, \gamma)Hg^{203} \xrightarrow{\beta^-} Tl^{203}(n, \gamma)Tl^{204}$.

$Tl^{205}(n, \gamma)Tl^{206}$ Possible interference from $Pb^{206}(n, p)Tl^{206}$ with a Pb matrix; from $Bi^{209}(n, \alpha)Tl^{206}$

with a Bi matrix.

$Tl^{205}(n, p)Hg^{205}$ Possible interference from $Pb^{208}(n, \alpha)Hg^{205}$; from $Hg^{204}(n, \gamma)Hg^{205}$.

$Tl^{203}(n, 2n)Tl^{202}$ Possible interference from $Pb^{204}(n, 3n)Pb^{202m} \xrightarrow{K} Tl^{202}$; possible interference from

secondary reactions: $Hg^{201}(p, \gamma)Tl^{202}$ or $Hg^{202}(p, n)Tl^{202}$.

$Tl^{203}(n, \gamma)Tl^{204}$ 1 x 10^{-3} µg.

$Tl^{205}(n, \gamma)Tl^{206}$ 8 x 10^{-4} µg.

Tl^{205}(γ, α)Au^{201} Excitation function from E$_{th}$(19 Mev) to 32 Mev; E$_p$ = 25 Mev; σ(25) = 95 $\pm$ 15 μb.   E10

Pb^{204}	1.48	0.8 ± 0.6			
		0.7 ± 0.2*a	5 x 10^7 y	EC	
Pb^{206}	23.6	25 ± 5 mb	0.80 s		IT
			s		
Pb^{207}	22.6	0.70 ± 0.03	s		
Pb^{208}	52.3	<30 mb			
		0.6 ± 0.2 mb a	3.30 h	0.635	None
		R = 0.1†			† M9

Pb^{208}(n, γ)Pb^{209}	Determination of Pb in meteorites with a sensitivity of 8 x 10^{-2} ppm; flux ~ 5 x 10^{13}.	R21
	Determination of Pb with a calculated sensitivity of 10^{-3} μg.	J11
	Determination of Pb with a calculated sensitivity of 1 μg.	M47
Pb^{204}(n, 2n)Pb^{203}	Determination of Pb in meteorites using reactor neutrons with a sensitivity of 2 ppb; thermal flux ~ 5 x 10^{13}.	R21

Pb^{208}(n, p)Tl^{208}	σ(14.5) = 0.96 mb.	P2
Pb^{208}(n, α)Hg^{205}	σ(14.5) = 1.58 mb.	C39

Pb^{208}(n, γ)Pb^{209}	Possible interference from Bi^{209}(n, p)Pb^{209} with a Bi matrix.
Pb^{208}(n, p)Tl^{208}	No apparent interference.

Pb^{208}(n, γ)Pb^{209}	0.2 μg.

$Pb^{206}(p,n)Bi^{206}$ Excitation function from E_{th}(7 Mev) to 85 Mev; E_p = 12.7 Mev; $\sigma(12.7)$ = 0.23 b.   B17

$Pb^{206}(p,2n)Bi^{205}$ Excitation function from E_{th}(12 Mev) to 85 Mev; E_p = 22 Mev; $\sigma(22)$ = 1.03 b.   B17

$Pb^{207}(p,2n)Bi^{206}$ Excitation function from E_{th}(12 Mev) to 85 Mev; E_p = 20.9 Mev; $\sigma(20.9)$ = 0.95 b.   B17

$Pb^{206}(p,3n)Bi^{204}$ Excitation function from E_{th}(21 Mev) to 85 Mev; E_p = 30 Mev; $\sigma(30)$ = 0.9 b.   B17

$Pb^{207}(p,3n)Bi^{205}$ Excitation function from E_{th}(20 Mev) to 85 Mev; E_p = 30.7 Mev; $\sigma(30.7)$ = 0.94 b.   B17

$Pb^{208}(p,3n)Bi^{206}$ Excitation function from E_{th}(19 Mev) to 85 Mev; E_p = 30.8 Mev; $\sigma(30.8)$ = 0.98 b.   B17

$Pb(\alpha,)Po^{210}$ Excitation function from E_{th}($\sim$ 18 Mev) to 50 Mev; $E_p \sim$ 30.5 Mev; $\sigma(30.5)$ = 0.55 b.   J11

$Pb(\alpha,)Po^{209}$ Excitation function from E_{th}($\sim$ 18 Mev) to 50 Mev; $E_p \sim$ 39 Mev; $\sigma(39)$ = 0.67 b.   J11

$Pb(\alpha,)Po^{208}$ Excitation function from E_{th}($\sim$ 18 Mev) to 50 Mev; E_p > 50 Mev; $\sigma(48)$ = 0.76 b.   J11

$Pb^{206}(p,n)Bi^{206}$ No apparent interference from primary reactions at E < 27 Mev.

$Pb^{206}(p,2n)Bi^{205}$ No apparent interference from primary reactions at E < 30 Mev.

$Pb^{207}(p,2n)Bi^{206}$ No apparent interference from primary reactions at E < 27 Mev.

$Pb^{207}(p,3n)Bi^{205}$ No apparent interference from primary reactions at E < 30 Mev.

$Pb^{208}(p,3n)Bi^{206}$ No apparent interference from primary reactions at E < 27 Mev.

$Pb(\alpha,)Po^{210}$ No apparent interference at E < 30 Mev.

$Pb(\alpha,)Po^{209}$ No apparent interference from primary reactions at E < 30 Mev; possible interference from secondary reaction: $Bi^{209}(p,n)Po^{209}$.

$Pb(\alpha,)Po^{208}$ No apparent interference from primary reactions at E < 30 Mev; possible interference from secondary reaction: $Bi^{209}(p,2n)Po^{208}$.

$Pb^{206}(p,n)Bi^{206}$ 5×10^{-2} $\mu g/cm^2$ at 12.7 Mev.

$Pb^{207}(p,2n)Bi^{206}$ 1×10^{-2} $\mu g/cm^2$ at 20.9 Mev.

Bi^{209}	100	34 ± 2 mb		1.155 (~100)	None	
		19 ± 2 mb a	5.01 d			
		14 mb a	2.6 x 10^6 y			
		R = 0.5††				
		R$_a$ = 76 ± 8 mb†				† C30
						†† M9

Bi^{209}(n, γ)Bi^{210m} Determination of Bi in meteorites with a sensitivity of 2 ppb; flux ~ 5 x 10^{13}; determined that naturally occurring Bi^{210m} did not interfere.   R21

Determination of Bi in Si with a sensitivity of 0.01 ppm; flux = 3 x 10^{12}.   K2

Determination of Bi in Si with a sensitivity of 1.5 x 10^{-3} ppm; flux = 2 x 10^{14}.   T16

Determination of Bi in Ge with a sensitivity of 0.03 ppm; flux = 3 x 10^{12}.   C5

Determination of Bi in high purity Fe and Al with a sensitivity of 0.1 µg.   G28

Others: J11, L4, S33.

- -

Bi^{209}(n, p)Pb^{209} σ(14.5) = 1.33 mb.   C39

Bi^{209}(n, α)Tl^{206} Average σ(14.5) = 0.77 mb.   C39 P2

Bi^{209}(n, γ)Bi^{210m} No apparent interference from primary or second-order reactions; possible interference from naturally occurring Bi^{210m}.

Bi^{209}(n, α)Tl^{206} Possible interference from Tl^{205}(n, γ)Tl^{206}; from Pb^{206}(n, p)Tl^{206}.

Bi^{209}(n, γ)Bi^{210m} 3 x 10^{-3} µg.

$Bi^{209}(p,n)Po^{209}$ Excitation function from 6.0 Mev to 10.7 Mev; $E_{th} < 6$ Mev; $E_p > 10.7$ Mev; $\sigma(10.7) = 0.16$ b.   A14

$Bi^{209}(p,2n)Po^{208}$ Excitation function from $E_{th}(9.65$ Mev) to 340 Mev; $E_p \sim 19$ Mev; $\sigma(19) = 1.0$ b.   A14 B17 K4
         Thick-target yield at 22 Mev = 9.8 mc/ma-hr.   M15

$Bi^{209}(p,3n)Po^{207}$ Excitation function from $E_{th}(\sim 17$ Mev) to 85 Mev; $E_p \sim 29$ Mev; $\sigma(29) = 0.82$ b.   B17

$Bi^{209}(d,n)Po^{210}$ Excitation function from 5.8 Mev to 21.5 Mev; $E_{th} \sim 5.2$ Mev; $E_p = 12$ Mev; $\sigma(12) \sim 25$ mb.   K14 R17

$Bi^{209}(d,p)Bi^{210m}$ Excitation function from 6.3 Mev to 21.5 Mev; $E_{th} < 6$ Mev; $E_p = 12.5$ Mev; $\sigma(12.5) = 0.12$ b.   K14 R17

$Bi^{209}(d,3n)Po^{208}$ Excitation function from $E_{th}(12.0$ Mev) to 21.5 Mev; $E_p > 21.5$ Mev; $\sigma(21.5) \sim 1$ b.   K14 R17

$Bi^{209}(\alpha,2n)At^{211}$ Excitation function from 20 Mev to 40 Mev; $E_{th} < 20$ Mev; $E_p \sim 31$ Mev; $\sigma(31) = 0.9$ b.   K14 R17

$Bi^{209}(\gamma,n)Bi^{208}$ Excitation function from $E_{th}(7.4$ Mev) to ~ 17 Mev; $E_p \sim 13.5$ Mev; $\sigma(13.5) \sim 0.45$ b.   H7

$Bi^{209}(p,n)Po^{209}$ No apparent interference.

$Bi^{209}(p,2n)Po^{208}$ No apparent interference.

$Bi^{209}(p,3n)Po^{207}$ No apparent interference.

$Bi^{209}(d,n)Po^{210}$ Possible interference from $Pb^{208}(d,\gamma)Bi^{210m} \xrightarrow{\beta^-} Po^{210}$; possible interference from naturally occurring Po^{210}.

$Bi^{209}(d,p)Bi^{210,210m}$ Possible interference from $Pb^{208}(d,\gamma)Bi^{210,210m}$; possible interference from naturally occurring Bi^{210m}.

$Bi^{209}(d,3n)Po^{208}$ No apparent interference.

$Bi^{209}(\alpha,2n)At^{211}$ No apparent interference.

$Bi^{209}(d,n)Po^{210}$ 4×10^{-1} $\mu g/cm^2$ at 12.5 Mev.

$Bi^{209}(d,p)Bi^{210m}$ 2×10^{-2} $\mu g/cm^2$ at 12.5 Mev.

Z = 84   POLONIUM

No stable isotopes.

Z = 85   ASTATINE

No stable isotopes.

Z = 86   RADON

No stable isotopes.

Z = 87   FRANCIUM

No stable isotopes.

Z = 88   RADIUM

Ra^{226} 20 ± 3 a   41.2 m
(1620 y)   (f)< 0.1 mb

Z = 89   ACTINIUM

No stable isotopes.

ASTATINE   Z = 85

RADON   Z = 86

FRANCIUM   Z = 87

RADIUM   Z = 88

ACTINIUM   Z = 89

Th^{232}	100	7.56 ± 0.15					
$(1.39 \times 10^{10}$y)		7.33 ± 0.12 a	22.4 m	1.23	M	$1400 \pm 200^{*}$a	24.1 d
						(f) $15 \pm 2^{*}$	
		(f) 0.2 mb					
		$R = 61.8 \pm 12.0^{\dagger}$					
		$R_a = 69.2^{\dagger\dagger}$					$\dagger$ K23
							$\dagger\dagger$ M9

$Th^{232}(n, \gamma)Th^{233}$	Determination of Th in minerals with a sensitivity of 0.1 μg; flux $\sim 10^{12}$.	J9
	Determination of Th in meteorites with a sensitivity of 0.02 ppm.	B10 B55
	Determination of Th in high purity Al.	A4
	Determination of Th with a sensitivity of ~ 10 ppm; flux $\sim 10^{11}$.	L3
	Others: B60, L10, S33.	

$Th^{232}(n, 2n)Th^{231}$	$\bar{\sigma}$ for U^{235} fission neutrons = 12.4 ± 0.6 mb.	P7
	$\dfrac{\bar{\sigma}\,(n, \gamma)}{\bar{\sigma}\,(n, 2n)}$ for U^{235} fission neutrons = 1.3 ± 0.3.	H20

$Th^{232}(n, \gamma)Th^{233}$	Possible interference from $U^{236}(n, \alpha)Th^{233}$ with a U matrix; possible interference from second-order reaction: $Th^{233}(n, \gamma)Th^{234}$; possible interference from self-shielding in comparator samples.

$Th^{232}(n, \gamma)Th^{233}$	9×10^{-6} μg.
$Th^{232}(n, \gamma)Th^{233} \xrightarrow{\beta^{-}} Pa^{233}$	5×10^{-6} μg.

Pa^{231}	200 ± 15 a	1.31 d	M	M	$760 \pm 100^{*}$a	27.0 d
$(3.4 \times 10^{4}$y)					(f) 700 ± 100	

$Th^{232}(p,n)Pa^{232}$	Excitation function from $E_{th}(\sim 5\ Mev)$ to 32 Mev; $E_p = 15\ Mev$; $\sigma(15) = 13.1\ mb$.	T14 T15
$Th^{232}(p,3n)Pa^{230}$	Excitation function from $E_{th}(\sim 18\ Mev)$ to 32 Mev; $E_p = 26\ Mev$; $\sigma(26) = 0.40\ b$.	T14 T15
$Th^{232}(d,p)Th^{233}$	Excitation function from 6.5 Mev to 190 Mev; $E_{th} < 6.5\ Mev$; $E_p = 13\ Mev$; $\sigma(13) = 0.17\ b$.	P2 S27
$Th^{232}(d,2n)Pa^{232}$	Excitation function from $E_{th}(9\ Mev)$ to 190 Mev; $E_p \sim 10\ Mev$; $\sigma(10) = 0.15\ b$.	C36
$Th^{232}(d,4n)Pa^{230}$	Excitation function from $E_{th}(16\ Mev)$ to 190 Mev; $E_p \sim 23\ Mev$; $\sigma(23) = 0.16\ b$.	C36
$Th^{232}(\gamma,n)Th^{231}$	Excitation function from $E_{th}(\sim 6\ Mev)$ to 23 Mev; $E_p = 14.2\ Mev$; $\sigma(14.2) = 0.99\ b$.	K11

$Th^{232}(p,n)Pa^{232}$	Possible interference from $U^{235}(p,\alpha)Pa^{232}$.
$Th^{232}(p,3n)Pa^{230}$	No apparent interference at $E < 30\ Mev$.
$Th^{232}(d,p)Th^{233}$	No apparent interference at $E < 25\ Mev$.
$Th^{232}(d,2n)Pa^{232}$	Possible interference from $U^{234}(d,\alpha)Pa^{232}$ with a U matrix; possible interference from secondary reaction: $U^{235}(p,\alpha)Pa^{232}$.
$Th^{232}(d,4n)Pa^{230}$	No apparent interference at $E < 25\ Mev$.
$Th^{232}(\gamma,n)Th^{231}$	Possible interference from $U^{235}(\gamma,\alpha)Th^{231}$.

$Th^{232}(p,n)Pa^{232}$	$5 \times 10^{-2}\ \mu g/cm^2$ at 15 Mev.
$Th^{232}(d,p)Th^{233}$	$6 \times 10^{-4}\ \mu g/cm^2$ at 13 Mev.

U^{233}
$(1.62 \times 10^5 \text{y})$ 581 ± 7
                   52 ± 2 a 2.48×10^5 y
                (f) 527 ± 4

U^{234} 0.0057 97 ± 5
$(2.48 \times 10^5 \text{y})$ 90 ± 30 a   26.5 m   None   IT (100)
                (f)≤ 0.65 7.1×10^8 y

U^{235} 0.714 694 ± 8
$(7.1 \times 10^8 \text{y})$ 107 ± 5 a 2.39×10^7 y
                (f) 582 ± 6

U^{236}
$(2.39 \times 10^7 \text{y})$ 7 ± 2
                   6 ± 1 a   6.75 d   0.248 (96)   M

U^{238} 99.3 2.71 ± 0.02
$(4.51 \times 10^9 \text{y})$ 2.74 ± 0.06 a   23.54 m   1.21 (100)   0.073 22 ± 5 a   14.1 h
                (f)< 0.5 mb   (f) 14 ± 3

$R_f^{235} = 271$[†††]

$R_a^{236} = 257 \pm 22$[††]

$R_a^{238} = 282$[†††]

                                                        [†] K23
                                                        [††] C1

$R(\text{nat}) = 106 \pm 13$[†]   [†††] M9

$U(n,)$	Determination of U^{235} by gross γ counting before and after activation with a Ra-Be source with an efficient moderator; assay independent of enrichment.	H42 W4
$U^{238}(n, \gamma)U^{239}$	Determination of U by assay for Np^{239} with a sensitivity of 0.3 µg; flux $\sim 10^{12}$.	M10
	Determination of U in Al by assay for U^{239} with a sensitivity of 0.04 ppm.	M2
$U^{233}(n, f)$	Determination of U^{233} in Al by assay for Ba^{139} or Ba^{140} with a sensitivity of 0.5 ppm; flux $\sim 8 \times 10^{12}$.	M3
$U^{235}(n, f)$	Determination of U^{235} by analysis for Ba^{140} with a sensitivity of 2.5×10^{-3} µg; flux $= 10^{12}$.	S28
	Determination of U in sea water by fission counting during irradiation; sensitivity $= 3 \times 10^{-5}$ ppm.	H12 S56
	Determination of U^{235} in highly depleted U by analysis for Ba^{140} after irradiation with RaC-Be (E_{max} = 0.69 Mev) neutrons; sensitivity = 5 ppm; by fission counting, with a sensitivity of 5 ppm.	M8
	Determination of U^{235} by assay for Te^{132} with a sensitivity of 50 µg; flux $= 10^{10}$; chemical separation of Te deferred until short-lived Te isotopes decayed.	F7
	Determination of U^{235} in U using special assay techniques for Ba^{140} with a precision of 2% at a confidence level of 3σ.	S17 S18
	Others: A4, B59, F1, G28, H9, J11, L10, M16, R2, R20, R21, S26, S33.	

$U^{238}(n, 2n)U^{237}$	Excitation function from 6 Mev to 16 Mev; $E_{th} < 6$ Mev; $E_p \sim 10$ Mev; $\sigma(10) \sim 1.5$ b.	K33

$U^{238}(n, \gamma)U^{239}$	No apparent interference from primary reactions with assay for U^{239}; possible interference from $Pu^{239}(n, p)Np^{239}$ with assay for Np^{239}; possible interference from self-shielding in comparator samples.
$U^{235}(n, f)Z^A$	Possible interference from fission of U^{233}, Pu^{239}, or Th^{232}; nuclide to be assayed should be selected to avoid interference from (n, γ), (n, p), (n, α), or $(n, 2n)$ reactions; Ba^{140} and Te^{132} are apparently free from interfering reactions; possible interference from self-shielding in comparator samples.

$U^{238}(n, \gamma)U^{239}$	2×10^{-5} µg.
$U^{238}(n, \gamma)U^{239} \xrightarrow{\beta^-} Np^{239}$	2×10^{-5} µg.

$U^{238}(d,p)U^{239}$ Excitation function from 6 Mev to 190 Mev; $E_{th} < 6$ Mev; $E_p = 13$ Mev; $\sigma(13) = 0.20$ b.   S27

$U^{238}(d,2n)Np^{238}$ Excitation function from $E_{th}(8.5$ Mev) to 190 Mev; $E_p \sim 12$ Mev; $\sigma(12) = 58$ mb.   C36

$U^{238}(d,4n)Np^{236}$ Excitation function from $E_{th}(17.5$ Mev) to 190 Mev; $E_p \sim 28$ Mev; $\sigma(28) = 38$ mb.   C36

$U^{238}(\alpha,\alpha n)U^{237}$ Excitation function from 22 Mev to 46 Mev; $E_{th} < 22$ Mev; $E_p = 45$ Mev; $\sigma(45) = 0.15$ b.   R9

$U^{233}(\gamma,n)U^{232}$ Excitation function from 7 Mev to 23 Mev; $E_{th} \sim 7.0$ Mev; $E_p = 14$ Mev; $\sigma(14) = 1.67$ b.   K11

$U^{238}(\gamma,n)U^{237}$ Excitation function from 6 Mev to 23 Mev; $E_{th} \sim 6.0$ Mev; $E_p = 15.2$ Mev; $\sigma(15.2) = 1.29$ b.   D14 K11

$U^{238}(d,p)U^{239}$ No apparent interference.

$U^{238}(d,2n)Np^{238}$ No apparent interference.

$U^{238}(d,4n)Np^{236}$ No apparent interference.

$U^{238}(\alpha,\alpha n)U^{237}$ No apparent interference.

$U^{238}(\gamma,n)U^{237}$ No apparent interference.

$U^{238}(d,p)U^{239}$ 5×10^{-4} $\mu g/cm^2$ at 13 Mev.

Np^{237}
$(2.2 \times 10^6 \, y)$
     170 ± 5
     $169 \pm 6 \, a$ 2.10 d   M   M

$Np^{237}(n,p)U^{237}$ $\sigma(14.5) = 1.3$ mb.   C39

Pu^{239}
$(2.44 \times 10^4 \, y)$
     1026 ± 13
     $315 \pm 16 \, a$ $6.58 \times 10^3 \, y$ $250 \pm 40 \, a$ 13.2 y

----

$Pu^{239}(n,p)Np^{239}$ $\sigma(14.5) = 3.0$ mb.   C39

$Pu^{239}(n,\gamma)Pu^{240}$ No apparent interference from primary reactions; possible interference from second-order reaction: $Pu^{240}(n,\gamma)Pu^{241}$; possible interference from self-shielding in comparator samples.

$Pu^{239}(n,f)$ See $U^{235}(n,f)$.

PLUTONIUM   Z = 94

$Pu^{239}(\gamma, n)Pu^{238}$ Excitation function from E_{th}(6 Mev) to 23 Mev; E_p = 13.6 Mev; σ(13.6) = 1.58 b.   K11

$Pu^{239}(\gamma, n)Pu^{238}$ No apparent interference.

GLOSSARY

1. **Activation**: The production of radionuclides by nuclear reactions.
2. **Activation product**: The radionuclide formed by a nuclear reaction.
3. **Alpha particle**: A particle having a mass of four and a charge of two; a helium nucleus.
4. **Beta radiation**: An electron ejected from the nucleus during the decay of a radionuclide; electrons having negative charge are frequently called negatrons; those with positive charge, positrons.
5. **Bremsstrahlung**: The electromagnetic radiation emitted during acceleration of electrons in the coulombic fields of atomic nuclei.
6. **Carrier**: A measurable quantity of an element which facilitates the chemical isolation of the tracer quantities of the radioactive isotopes of that element.
7. **Charged particle**: An atomic particle having some or all of its electrons removed; e.g., protons, deuterons, alphas.
8. **Cross-section**: The probability of occurrence of a reaction between two particles or between a particle and a nucleus.
9. **Cross-section, macroscopic**: The probability of occurrence of a reaction between a particle and a target having a specified atomic density.
10. **Deuteron**: A nuclear particle having the mass number two and a unit charge.
11. **Electron capture**: A mode of decay of a radionuclide in which an orbital electron is assimilated into the nucleus; the net nuclear transformation is a unit decrease in nuclear charge with constant mass number.
12. **Excitation function**: The variation of the cross-section for a nuclear reaction with the energy of the particle inducing the reaction.
13. **Flux perturbation**: The suppression or enhancement of the neutron flux external to a sample which has a large macroscopic cross-section for the neutron absorption.
14. **Gamma radiation**: Electromagnetic radiation emitted during decay of a radionuclide.
15. **Isomer**: One of several states of a nuclide which differ in excitation energy.
16. **Isomeric transition**: A mode of decay of an isomer in which either a quantum of electromagnetic radiation or a conversion electron is emitted during transition to an isomer having a lower energy level.
17. **Isotope**: One of several atomic species of an element which differ only in the number of neutrons in their nuclei.
18. **Matrix element**: The principal constituent of a sample; any constituent which has a concentration large with respect to a given trace element.
19. **Neutron**: A nuclear particle having the mass number unity and zero charge.
20. **Neutron, fast**: A neutron with large kinetic energy ($> \sim 0.1$ Mev).
21. **Neutron, resonance**: A neutron having a kinetic energy intermediate between those of thermal and fast neutrons. Many nuclei show one or more resonance absorptions in this energy region.
22. **Neutron, thermal**: A neutron having a kinetic energy such that it is in thermal equilibrium with its environment, the corres-

---

* The definitions presented here reflect the usage of the terms in this handbook and are not necessarily of general applicability.

ponding velocity is 2200 meters/sec at room temperature.

23. **Nondestructive analysis**: Analysis of a sample without permanent alteration of its properties.

24. **Nuclear particle**: A particle which induces a nuclear reaction or is created by one.

25. **Nuclide**: An atomic species characterized by the number of protons and neutrons in its nucleus and its energy content.

26. **Photon**: A quantum, or unit, of electromagnetic radiation, specifically of sufficient energy to induce a nuclear reaction.

27. **Proton**: A nuclear particle having the mass number one and a unit charge.

28. **Reaction, competing**: A nuclear reaction which yields an activation product isotopic with the activation product of interest.

29. **Reaction, interfering**: A nuclear reaction in a sample constituent other than the trace element of interest which yields the same activation product.

30. **Reaction, nuclear**: The process in which a nuclear particle interacts with the nucleus of an atom to produce a different atom and a second particle.

31. **Reaction, primary**: A nuclear reaction induced in an original sample constituent by the principal irradiating particles.

32. **Reaction, secondary**: A nuclear reaction induced in an original sample constituent by particles created during primary nuclear reactions.

33. **Reaction, second-order**: A nuclear reaction induced in primary reaction products by the principal irradiating particles.

34. **Resonance integral**: The effective cross-section of a nuclide for resonance neutrons.

35. **Sample**: The object or specimen to be analyzed.

36. **Self-shielding**: The suppression of the neutron flux within a specimen due to a large absorption cross-section.

37. **Sensitivity**: The limit of detection for an element in a given analysis.

38. **Sensitivity, standard**: The minimum detectable quantity for an element under a standard set of irradiation and measurement conditions. (See page 17 for the standard conditions used in the Tabulation.

39. **Target nuclide**: The isotope of the trace element of interest which undergoes the activation reaction.

40. **Trace element**: A constituent of a sample which is present in small concentrations, usually < 1 milligram per gram of matrix.

41. **Triton**: A nuclear particle having the mass number three and a unit charge.

PART II: EXAMPLES OF NUCLEAR REACTIONS

It is customary to specify a nuclear reaction by the charge and mass number of each reactant and each product, e.g.,

$$y^{(i)^a} + Y^{(M)^A} = Z^{(N)^B} + z^{(j)^b} \qquad (16)$$

where

i = the irradiating particle
M = the target nuclide
j = the secondary particle
N = the activation product nuclide
Y and Z = the atomic numbers of the target and activation product nuclides, respectively
A and B = the mass numbers of the target and activation product nuclides, respectively
y and z = the nuclear charges of the irradiating and secondary particles, respectively
a and b = the mass numbers of the irradiating and secondary particles, respectively

Equation (16) is usually written in the form

$$M^A (i, j) N^B \qquad (17)$$

since the subscripts are redundant when i, j, M, and N are the symbols for the elements.

Several reactions in the form of equation (16) are now illustrated.

(n, γ)	$_0(n)^1 + {}_Z(M)^A = {}_Z(N)^{A+1} + {}_0(\gamma)^0$
(n, p)	$_0(n)^1 + {}_Z(M)^A = {}_{Z-1}(N)^A + {}_1(p)^1$
(p, α)	$_1(p)^1 + {}_Z(M)^A = {}_{Z-1}(N)^{A-3} + {}_2(\alpha)^4$
$(d, 2n)$	$_1(d)^2 + {}_Z(M)^A = {}_{Z+1}(N)^A + 2\,{}_0(n)^1$
(γ, n)	$_0(\gamma)^0 + {}_Z(M)^A = {}_Z(N)^{A-1} + {}_0(n)^1$

Examples of reactions which interfere with the more commonly used activation reactions may be shown in the following manner.

Principal reaction:

$$Z^A(\text{n},\gamma)Z^{A+1}$$

Primary interference:

$$Z+1^A(\text{n},\text{p})Z^{A+1}$$
$$Z+2^{A+1}(\text{n},\text{p})Z+1^{A+1} \, {-}{-}\!\overset{\beta^+}{-}\!{-} \, Z^{A+1}$$

Primary interference:

$$Z+2^{A+4}(\text{n},\alpha)Z^{A+1}$$
$$Z+1^{A+4}(\text{n},\alpha)Z-1^{A+1} \, {-}{-}\!\overset{\beta^-}{-}\!{-} \, Z^{A+1}$$

Second-order interference:

$$Z-1^{A-1}(\text{n},\gamma)Z-1^A \, {-}{-}\!\overset{\beta^-}{-}\!{-} \, Z^A(\text{n},\gamma)Z^{A+1}$$

Second-order interference:

$$Z^A(\text{n},\gamma)Z^{A+1}(\text{n},\gamma)Z^{A+2}$$

Principal reaction: $\qquad Z^A(\text{n},\text{p})Z-1^A$

Primary interference: $\quad Z+1^{A+3}(\text{n},\alpha)Z-1^A$

Secondary interference: $Z-2^A(\text{p},\text{n})Z-1^A$

Principal reaction: $\qquad Z^A(\text{p},\text{n})Z+1^A$

Primary interference: $\quad Z+2^{A+3}(\text{p},\alpha)Z+1^A$

Secondary interference: $Z+3^{A+3}(\text{n},\alpha)Z+1^A$

Secondary interference: $Z+2^A(\text{n},\text{p})Z+1^A$

Finally, examples of competing reactions frequently encountered with the (n,γ) activation process are given.

Principal reaction: $\qquad Z^A(\text{n},\gamma)Z^{A+1}$

Competing reaction: $\quad Z^{A-2}(\text{n},\gamma)Z^{A-1}$

Competing reaction: $\quad Z+1^{A-1}(\text{n},\text{p})Z^{A-1}$

Competing reaction: $\quad Z+2^{A+2}(\text{n},\alpha)Z^{A-1}$

BIBLIOGRAPHY

A1   R. L. Aamodt, B. Peterson, and R. Phillips, Phys. Rev. 88, 739 (1953).

A2   B. M. Abraham, H. E. Flotow, and R. D. Carlson, Anal. Chem. 29, 1058 (1957).

A3   F. Ajzenberg and T. Lauritsen, Rev. Mod. Phys. 27, 77 (1955).

A4   P. Albert, Ann. Chim. (Paris) 1, 827 (1956).

A5   P. Albert, M. Caron, and G. Chaudron, Compt. rend. 233, 1108 (1951).

A6   P. Albert, M. Caron, and G. Chaudron, Compt. rend. 236, 1030 (1953).

A7   P. Albert, G. Chaudron, and P. Sue, Bull. soc. chim. France, 11 Journee Microanal. C97 (1953).

A8   L. Allen, Jr., W. A. Biggers, R. J. Prestwood, and R. K. Smith, Phys. Rev. 107, 1363 (1957).

A9   E. A. Alperovitch and J. M. Miller, Nature 176, 68 (1955).

A10   G. Ambrosino and P. Pindrus, Rev. met. 50, 136 (1953).

A11   E. Anders, R. N. Sensarma, and P. H. Kato, J. Chem. Phys. 24, 622 (1956).

A12   O. U. Anders, USAEC Report No. AECU-3513 (1957).

A13   O. U. Anders and W. W. Meinke, Progress Report No. 4, Project No. 7, USAEC Contract No. AT(11-1)-70, University of Michigan, Ann Arbor, 1955.

A14   C. G. Andre, J. R. Huizenga, J. F. Mech, W. J. Romler, E. G. Rouh, and S. R. Rocklin, Phys. Rev. 101, 645 (1956).

A15   Anon., Nucleonics 15, No. 12, 70 (1957).

A16   Anon,, Nucleonics 15, No. 11, 170 (1957).

A17   G. J. Atchison and W. H. Beamer, Anal. Chem. 24, 1812 (1952).

A18   G. J. Atchison and W. H. Beamer, Anal. Chem. 28, 237 (1956).

A19   A. H. W. Aten, Jr., Ned. Tijdschr. Natuurk.10, 257 (1943).

A20   A. H. W. Aten, Jr., Anal. Chim. Acta. 2, 492 (1948).

A21   P. Axel and J. P. Fox, Phy. Rev. 102, 400 (1956).

B1   C. L. Bailey, M. Phillips, and J. H. Williams, Phys. Rev. 62, 80 (1942).

B2   S. J. Balestrini, Phys. Rev. 95, 1502 (1954).

B3   M. Bancie-Grillot and E. Grillot, Compt. rend. 237, 171 (1953).

B4   W. C. Barber, W. C. George, and D. D. Reagan, Phys. Rev. 98, 73 (1955).

B5   R. Barjon, D. Magnac-Valette, and J. Schmouker, Compt. rend. 242, 896 (1956).

B6   F. O. Bartell, A. C. Helmholtz, S. D. Softky, and D. B. Stewart, Phys. Rev. 80, 1006 (1951).

B7   F. O. Bartell and S. Softky, Phys. Rev. 84, 463 (1951).

B8   R. Basile, J. Hure, P. Leveque, and C. Schuhl, Compt. rend. 239, 422 (1954).

B9   R. Basile and C. Schuhl, Compt. rend. 240, 2399 (1955).

B10   G. L. Bate, J. R. Huizenga, and H. A. Potratz, Science 126, 612 (1957).

B11   L. C. Bate and G. W. Leddicotte, USAEC Report No. CF-57-1-116 (1957).

B12   R. E. Batzel and G. H. Coleman, Phys. Rev. 93, 280 (1954).

B13   R. E. Batzel and G. H. Coleman, USAEC Report No. LRL-72 (1953).

B14   R. E. Batzel, W. W. T. Crane, and G. D. O'Kelley, Phys. Rev. 91, 939 (1953).

B15   J. G. Bayly, F. Brown, G. R. Hall, and A. J. Walter, J. Inorg. Nuclear Chem. 5, 259 (1958).

B16   R. L. Becker and H. H. Barschall, Phys. Rev. 102, 1384 (1956).

B17   R. E. Bell and H. M. Skarsgard, Can. J. Phys. 34, 745 (1956).

B18   I. B. Berlman, Nucleonics 11, No. 2, 70 (1953).

B19   I. B. Berlman, H. F. Lucas, and H. A. May, Rev. Sci. Instr. 24, 396 (1953).

B20   A. I. Berman, Am. J. Phys. 22, 277 (1954).

B21   A. I. Berman and K. L. Brown, Phys. Rev. 96, 83 (1954).

B22   J. Beydon and C. Fisher, Anal. Chim. Acta. 8, 538 (1953).

B23   A. Blanzet, M. Quesson, J. L. Soule, and G. Thouzeau, Bull. soc. chim. France, 1956, p. 317.

B24   J. P. Blaser, F. Boehm, P. Marmier, and D. C. Peaslee, Helv. Phys. Acta. 24, 3 (1951).

B25   J. P. Blaser, F. Boehm, P. Marmier, P. Prieswerk, and P. Scherrer, Helv. Phys. Acta. 22, 598 (1949).

B26   J. P. Blaser, F. Boehm, P. Marmier, and P. Scherrer, Helv. Phys. Acta. 24, 441 (1951).

B27   J. P. Blaser, F. Boehm, P. Marmier, and P. Scherrer, Helv. Phys. Acta. $\underline{24}$, 465 (1951).

B28   J. P. Blaser, P. Marmier, and M. Sembert, Helv. Phys. Acta. $\underline{25}$, 442 (1952).

B29   E. Bleuler, A. Stebbins, and D. Tendam, Phys. Rev. $\underline{90}$, 460 (1953).

B30   H. G. Blosser, C. D. Goodman, and T. H. Handley, Phys. Rev. $\underline{110}$, 531 (1958).

B31   H. G. Blosser, C. D. Goodman, T. H. Handley, and M. L. Randolph, Phys. Rev. $\underline{100}$, 429 (1955).

B32   W. Bollmann and W. Zunti, Helv. Phys. Acta. $\underline{24}$, 517 (1951).

B33   T. W. Bonner, Proc. Intern. Conf. on the Peaceful Uses of Atomic Energy, U. N., New York, 1956, Vol. IV, Paper 578.

B34   H. J. M. Bowen, J. Nuclear Energy $\underline{3}$, 18 (1956).

B35   H. J. M. Bowen and T. A. Dymond, Proc. Roy. Soc. $\underline{B\ 144}$, 355 (1955).

B36   G. E. Boyd, Anal. Chem. $\underline{21}$, 335 (1949).

B37   G. E. Boyd and Q. V. Larson, J. Phys. Chem. $\underline{60}$, 707 (1956).

B38   H. L. Bradt and O. J. Tendam. Phys. Rev. $\underline{72}$, 1117 (1947).

B39   J. E. Brolley, Jr., J. L. Fowler, and K. L. Schlacks, Phys. Rev. $\underline{88}$, 618 (1952).

B40   W. A. Brooksbank, USAEC Report No. ORNL-2226 (1956).

B41   W. A. Brooksbank and G. W. Leddicotte, J. Phys. Chem. $\underline{57}$, 819 (1953).

B42   W. A. Brooksbank, G. W. Leddicotte, and H. A. Mahlman, J. Phys. Chem. $\underline{57}$, 815 (1953).

B43   W. A. Brooksbank, G. W. Leddicotte, H. A. Mahlman, and J. E. Strain, USAEC Report No. CF-56-7-106 (1956).

B44   W. A. Brooksbank, G. W. Leddicotte, and S. A. Reynolds, Anal. Chem. $\underline{28}$, 1033 (1956).

B45   H. Brown and E. Goldberg, Science $\underline{109}$, 347 (1949).

B46   H. Brown and E. Goldberg, Phys. Rev. $\underline{76}$, 1260 (1949).

B47   R. M. Brugger, T. W. Bonner, and J. B. Marion, Phys. Rev. $\underline{100}$, 84 (1955).

B48   J. H. Buck, Phys. Rev. $\underline{54}$, 1025 (1938).

B49   W. H. Burgus, G. A. Cowan, J. W. Handley, W. Hess, M. L. Stevenson, T. Shull, and H. F. York, Phys. Rev. $\underline{95}$, 750 (1954).

B50   J. L. Burkhardt, E. J. Winhold, and T. H. Dupree, Phys. Rev. $\underline{100}$, 199 (1955).

B51   E. A. Burrill and A. J. Gale, "Activation Analysis with Van de Graaff Neutron Sources", High Voltage Engineering Corp., Cambridge, 1954.

B52   W. A. Butler and G. M. Almy, Phys. Rev. $\underline{91}$, 58 (1953).

B53   P. R. Byerly, Jr., and W. E. Stephens, Phys. Rev. $\underline{83}$, 54 (1951).

C1   M. J. Cabell, T. A. Eastwood, and P. J. Campion, J. Nuclear Energy $\underline{7}$, 81 (1958).

C2   M. J. Cabell and A. A. Smales, Research (London) $\underline{9}$, 214 (1956).

C3   M. J. Cabell and A. A. Smales, Analyst $\underline{82}$, 390 (1957).

C4   M. J. Cabell and A. Thomas, Brit. Atomic Energy Research Establishment Report No. AERE-C/R-1725 (1955).

C5   J. P. Cali, private communication (1958).

C6   J. P. Cali, L. F. Lowe, E. M. Reilly, and H. D. Thompson, Air Force Cambridge Research Center Report No. ERD-CRRC-TM-57-103 (1957).

C7   A. A. Caretto and E. O. Wiig, Phys. Rev. $\underline{103}$, 236 (1956).

C8   J. H. Carver, R. D. Edge, and D. H. Wilkinson, Phys. Rev. $\underline{89}$, 658 (1953).

C9   G. A. Chackett, K. F. Chackett, P. Reasbeck, J. L. Symonds, and J. Warren, Proc. Phys. Soc. (London) $\underline{A69}$, 43 (1956).

C10   R. A. Charpie, D. J. Hughes, D. J. Littler, and M. Trocheris, ed., "Progress in Nuclear Energy: Series II", McGraw-Hill Book Co., N. Y., 1956.

C11   J. W. Chastain, USAEC Report No. TID-7013 (1957).

C12   G. Chaudron, Bull. soc. chim. France, 1954, p. 419.

C13   W. W. Chupp and E. M. McMillan, Phys. Rev. $\underline{72}$, 873 (1947).

C14   E. T. Clarke, Phys. Rev. $\underline{71}$, 187 (1947).

C15   E. T. Clarke and J. W. Irvine, Jr., Phys. Rev. $\underline{66}$, 231 (1944).

C16   E. T. Clarke and J. W. Irvine, Jr., Phys. Rev. $\underline{69}$, 680 (1946).

C17   H. M. Clark and D. E. Neil, USAEC Report No. AECU-3144 (1955).

C18   H. M. Clark and R. T. Overman,   USAEC Report No. MDDC-1329 (1947).

C19   A. V. Cohen, S. B. Hyder, and P. H. White,   Nuclear Phys. 1, 278 (1956).

C20   B. L. Cohen,   Phys. Rev. 81, 184 (1951).

C21   B. L. Cohen,   Phys. Rev. 102, 453 (1956).

C22   B. L. Cohen and T. H. Handley,   Phys. Rev. 93, 514 (1954).

C23   B. L. Cohen and E. Newman,   Phys. Rev. 99, 718 (1955).

C24   B. L. Cohen, E. Newman, R. A. Charpie, and T. H. Handley,   Phys. Rev. 94, 620 (1954).

C25   B. L. Cohen, E. Newman, and T. H. Handley,   Phys. Rev. 99, 723 (1955).

C26   B. L. Cohen, H. L. Reynolds, and A. Zucker,   Phys. Rev. 96, 1617 (1954).

C27   R. E. Connolly and M. B. LeBoeuf,   Anal. Chem. 25, 1095 (1953).

C28   L. G. Cook and K. D. Shafer,   Can. J. Chem. 32, 94 (1954).

C29   J. H. Coon,   Phys. Rev. 75, 1355 (1949).

C30   P. N. Cooper,   Brit. Atomic Energy Research Establishment Report No. AERE-R/M-93 (1956).

C31   J. M. Cork and J. Halpern,   Phys. Rev. 57, 667 (1940).

C32   F. W. Cornish,   Brit. Atomic Energy Research Establishment Report No. AERE-C/R-1224 (1953).

C33   J. F. Cosgrove and G. H. Morrison,   Anal. Chem. 29, 1017 (1957).

C34   W. E. Crandall, G. P. Millburne, and W. Birnbaum,   Phys. Rev. 101, 329 (1956).

C35   W. E. Crandall, G. P. Millburne, R. V. Pyle, and W. Birnbaum,   Phys. Rev. 101, 329 (1956).

C36   W. W. T. Crane and G. M. Iddings,   USAEC Report No. MTA-48 (1953).

C37   I. Curie,   J. phys. radium 13, 497 (1952).

C38   I. Curie,   Bull. soc. chim. France, 11 Journee Microanal. C 95 (1953).

D1   P. Daudel,   Anal. Chim. Acta. 5, 426 (1951).

D2   P. Daudel,   Compt. rend. 218, 234 (1944).

D3   P. Daudel,   Rev. sci. 84, 462 (1946).

D4   M. V. Davis and D. T. Hauser,   Nucleonics 16, No. 3, 87 (1958).

D5   A. K. De,   J. Sci. Ind. Research (India) 16A, 337 (1957).

D6   A. K. De and W. W. Meinke,   Anal. Chem. 30, 1474 (1958).

D7   J. DeBiesse, J. Challansonnet, and G. Neyret,   Compt. rend. 232, 602 (1951).

D8   C. J. Delbecq, L. E. Glendennin, and P. H. Yuster,   Anal. Chem. 25, 350 (1953).

D9   L. A. Delsasso, L. N. Ridenour, R. Sherr, and M. G. White,   Phys. Rev. 55, 113 (1939).

D10   E. der Mateosian and M. Goldhaber,   Phys. Rev. 108, 766 (1957).

D11   W. A. Dewar and J. M. A. Lenihan,   Scot. Med. J. 1, 236 (1956).

D12   B. C. Diven and G. M. Almy,   Phys. Rev. 80, 407 (1950).

D13   R. Druyan, T. C. Mitchell, and E. R. King,   J. Lab. Clin. Med. 52, 304 (1958).

D14   R. B. Duffield and J. R. Huizenga,   Phys. Rev. 89, 1042 (1953).

D15   B. G. Dzantiev, U. N. Levkovskii, and A. D. Malievskii,   Soviet Phys. (Doklady) 2, 135 (1957).

E1   T. A. Eastwood,   Canadian Atomic Energy Report No. CI-193 (1952).

E2   R. D. Edge,   Nuclear Phys. 2, 485 (1956).

E3   L. C. Edwards,   Intern. J. Appl. Radiation Isotopes 1, 184 (1956).

E4   P. A. Egelstaff and B. T. Taylor,   Nature 166, 825 (1950).

E5   C. E. Eggenberger and P. Marmier,   Helv. Phys. Acta. 24, 323 (1951).

E6   G. G. Eicholz,   Nucleonics 10, No. 12, 58 (1952).

E7   D. E. Emhizer, J. V. Fitzgerald, R. E. Jones, and K. M. Laing,   J. Am. Ceram. Soc. 34, 388 (1951).

E8   P. M. Endt and J. C. Kluyver,   Rev. Mod. Phys. 26, 95 (1954).

E9   T. Enns,   Phys. Rev. 56, 872 (1939).

E10   P. Erdos, P. Scherrer, and P. Stoll,   Helv. Phys. Acta. 30, 639 (1957).

E11   J. Ero and L. Keszthelyi,   Nuclear Phys. 2, 371 (1956).

F1   J. Facchini and L. Orsoni,   Nuovo cimento 6, 241 (1949).

F2   R. A. Faires, J. E. Johnston, and R. J. Millett,   Nucleonics 12, No. 10, 48 (1954).

F3   H. Faraggi, R. Bernas, and A. Bonnet,   Compt. rend. 235, 425 (1952).

F4   N. Faull,   Brit. Atomic Energy Research Establishment Report No. AERE-R/R-1919 (1956).

F5   G. A. Ferguson, J. Halpern, R. Nathans, and P. F. Yergin,   Phys. Rev. 95, 776 (1954).

F6   R. W. Fink,   USAEC Report No. ORO-165 (1957).

F7   C. Fisher and J. Beydon,   Bull. soc. chim. France, 11 Journee Microanal. C102 (1953).

F8   I. Fogelstrom-Fineman, O. Holm-Hansen, B. M. Tolbert, and M. Calvin,   Intern. J. Appl. Radiation Isotopes 2, 280 (1957).

F9   S. G. Forbes,   Phys. Rev. 88, 1309 (1952).

F10   L. M. Foster and C. D. Gaitanis,   Anal. Chem. 27, 1342 (1955).

F11   J. L. Fowler and J. E. Brolley,   Rev. Mod. Phys. 28, 103 (1956).

F12   M. S. Freedman,   J. Chem. Phys. 20, 1040 (1952).

F13   G. Freier, E. E. Lambi, and J. H. Williams,   Phys. Rev. 75, 901 (1949).

F14   E. C. Freiling,   Nucleonics 14, No. 8, 65 (1956).

F15   G. Friedlander and J. W. Kennedy,   "Introduction to Radiochemistry", John Wiley and Sons, Inc., New York, 1949, p. 107 ff.

F16   E. G. Fuller,   Phys. Rev. 96, 1306 (1954).

G1   A. M. Gaudin and J. H. Pannel,   Anal. Chem. 23, 1261 (1951).

G2   R. C. Geiger and R. C. Plumb,   Nucleonics 14, No. 2, 30 (1956).

G3   S. N. Ghoshal,   Phys. Rev. 73, 417 (1948).

G4   S. N. Ghoshal,   Phys. Rev. 80, 939 (1950).

G5   D. Gibbons, B. A. Loveridge, and R. J. Millett,   Brit. Atomic Energy Research Establishment Report No. AERE-I/R-2208 (1957).

G6   J. H. Gibbons, R. L. Macklin, and H. W. Schmitt,   Phys. Rev. 100, 167 (1955).

G7   R. C. Gibbs and K. Way,   "A Directory to Nuclear Data Tabulations", National Academy of Science-National Research Council, Washington, 1958.

G8   H. Glatti, O. Seipple, and P. Stoll,   Helv. Phys. Acta. 25, 491 (1952).

G9   R. Gold,   Nucleonics 15, No. 7, 111 (1957).

G10   E. D. Goldberg and H. Brown,   Anal. Chem. 22, 308 (1950).

G11   E. Goldberg, A. Uchiyama, and H. Brown,   Geochim. et Cosmochim. Acta. 2, 1 (1951).

G12   J. Goldemberg and L. Katz,   Phys. Rev. 90, 308 (1953).

G13   J. Goldemberg and L. Katz,   Can. J. Phys. 32, 49 (1954).

G14   J. Goldemberg and L. Katz,   Phys. Rev. 95, 471 (1954).

G15   B. Goldschmidt and O. Djourkovitch,   Bull. soc. chim. France 6, 718 (1939).

G16   B. M. Gordon, L. Friedman, and G. Edwards,   Geochim. et Cosmochim. Acta. 12, 470 (1957).

G17   C. L. Gordon,   Anal. Chem. 21, 96 (1949).

G18   C. L. Gordon,   Anal. Chem. 23, 81 (1951).

G19   C. L. Gordon,   Anal. Chem. 26, 176 (1954).

G20   H. Gotte and J. A. Hattemer,   Z. Naturforsch. 10b, 343 (1955).

G21   E. R. Graves and R. W. Davis,   Phys. Rev. 97, 1205 (1955).

G22   L. H. Greenberg, J. G. V. Taylor, and R. N. H. Haslam,   Phys. Rev. 95, 1540 (1954).

G23   H. Griffon and J. Barbaud,   Compt. rend. 23, 1455 (1951).

G24   E. Grillot,   Compt. rend. 234, 1775 (1952).

G25   B. Grimeland,   Nuovo cimento (10) 2, 1336 (1955).

G26   J. A. Grundl, R. L. Henkel, and B. L. Perkins,   Phys. Rev. 109, 425 (1958).

G27   S. R. Gunn, H. G. Hicks, H. B. Levy, and P. C. Stevenson,   Phys. Rev. 107, 1642 (1957).

H1   C. P. Haigh,   Nature 172, 359 (1953).

H2   R. K. Haling, R. A. Peck, Jr., and H. P. Eubank,   Phys. Rev. 106, 971 (1957).

H3   K. L. Hall,   USAEC Report No. AECU-3126 (1955).

H4   T. A. Hall,   Nucleonics 12, No. 3, 34 (1954).

H5   N. A. Hallden,   Nucleonics 13, No. 6, 78 (1955).

H6   I. Halpern,   Phys. Rev. 76, 248 (1949).

H7   J. Halpern, R. Nathans, and A. K. Mann,   Phys. Rev. 88, 679 (1952).

H8   J. Halperin, R. W. Stoughton, C. V. Ellison, and D. E. Ferguson,   Nuclear Sci. and Eng. 1, 1 (1956).

H9   H. Hamaguchi, G. W. Reed, and A. L. Turkevich,   Geochim. et Cosmochim. Acta. 12, 337 (1957).

H10   R. P. Hamlen and W. S. Koski,   USAEC Report No. MCC-1023-TR-117 (1955).

H11   T. H. Handley and E. L. Olson,   Phys. Rev. 94, 968 (1954).

H12   W. W. Happ and J. L. Horwood,   Science 115, 622 (1952).

H13   G. E. Harrison and W. H. A. Raymond,   J. Nuclear Energy 1, 290 (1955).

H14   W. H. Hartley, W. E. Stephens, and E. J. Winhold,   Phys. Rev. 104, 178 (1956).

H15   R. N. H. Haslam, H. E. Johns, and R. J. Horsley,   Phys. Rev. 82, 270 (1951).

H16   R. N. H. Haslam, W. N. Roberts, and D. S. Robb,   Can. J. Phys. 32, 361 (1954).

H17   R. N. H. Haslam and H. M. Skarsgard,   Phys. Rev. 81, 479 (1951).

H18   R. N. H. Haslam, L. A. Smith, and J. G. V. Taylor,   Phys. Rev. 84, 840 (1951).

H19   R. N. H. Haslam, R. G. Summers-Gill, and E. H. Crosby,   Can. J. Phys. 30, 257 (1952).

H20   R. A. Hasse, P. Kafalas, and R. R. Heinrich,   J. Nuclear Energy 7, 205 (1958).

H21   W. Heckrotte and P. Wolff,   Phys. Rev. 73, 264 (1948).

H22   R. E. Heft and W. F. Libby,   Phys. Rev. 100, 799 (1955).

H23   W. Herr,   Angew. Chem. 64, 679 (1952).

H24   W. Herr,   Z. Naturforsch. 8a, 305 (1953).

H25   W. Herr,   Arch. Eisenhuttenw. 26, 523 (1953).

H26   W. Herr,   Z. Naturforsch. 9a, 907 (1954).

H27   W. Herr,   Angew. Chem. 67, 823 (1955).

H28   W. Herr and E. Merz,   Z. Naturforsch. 10a, 613 (1955).

H29   W. N. Hess,   USAEC Report No. UCRL-3839 (1957).

H30   G. Hevesy and H. Levi,   Kgl. Danske Videnskab. Selskab, Math.-fys. Medd. 14, No. 5 (1936).

H31   G. Hevesy and H. Levi,   Kgl. Danske Videnskab. Selskab, Math.-fys. Medd. 15, No. 11 (1938).

H32   H. G. Hicks, P. C. Stevenson, and W. E. Nervik,   Phys. Rev. 102, 1390 (1956).

H33   N. M. Hintz,   Phys. Rev. 83, 185 (1951).

H34   N. M. Hintz and N. F. Ramsay,   Phys. Rev. 88, 19 (1952).

H35   J. M. Hollander, I. Perlman, and G. T. Seaborg,   Rev. Mod. Phys. 25, 469 (1953).

H36   R. J. Horsley, R. N. H. Haslam, and H. E. Johns,   Phys. Rev. 87, 756 (1952).

H37   J. Hoste and H. van den Berghe,   Mikrochim. Acta., 1956, p. 797.

H38   H. A. Howe,   Phys. Rev. 109, 2083 (1958).

H39   J. E. Hudgens, Jr.,   Anal. Chem. 24, 1704 (1952).

H40   J. E. Hudgens, Jr., and P. J. Cali,   Anal. Chem. 24, 171 (1952).

H41   J. E. Hudgens, Jr., and H. J. Dabagian,   Nucleonics 10, No. 5, 25 (1952).

H42   J. E. Hudgens, Jr., and R. C. Meyer,   USAEC Report No. NBL-126 (1956).

H43   J. E. Hudgens, Jr., and L. C. Nelson,   Anal. Chem. 24, 1472 (1952).

H44   J. E. Hudgens, Jr., L. C. Nelson, R. C. Meyer, and G. Zyskowski,   USAEC Report No. NBL-102 (1954).

H45   D. J. Hughes,   Nucleonics 11, No. 2, 30 (1953).

H46   D. J. Hughes,   "Pile Neutron Research", Addison Wesley Publishing Co., Cambridge, 1953.

H47   D. J. Hughes and J. A. Harvey,   USAEC Report No. BNL-325 (1955).

H48   D. J. Hughes and R. B. Schwartz,   USAEC Report No. BNL-325, Supp. No. 1 (1957).

H49   D. J. Hughes and R. B. Schwartz,   USAEC Report No. BNL-325, 2nd Edition (1958).

H50   R. W. Hummel,   Analyst 82, 483 (1957).

H51   R. W. Hummel and A. A. Smales,   Analyst 81, 110 (1956).

H52   P. Hurlimann and P. Huber,   Helv. Phys. Acta. 28, 33 (1955).

I1   P. Iredale, Brit. Atomic Energy Research Establishment Report No. AERE-EL/M-96 (1956).

I2   J. W. Irvine, Jr., and E. T. Clarke, J. Chem. Phys. 16, 686 (1948).

I3   H. Irving, J. van R. Smit, and L. Salmon, Analyst 82, 549 (1957).

J1   J. V. Jakovlev, Proc. Intern. Conf. on the Peaceful Uses of Atomic Energy, U. N., New York, 1956, Vol. XV, Paper 632.

J2   J. A. James and D. H. Richards, Nature 175, 769 (1955).

J3   J. A. James and D. H. Richards, Nature 176, 1026 (1955).

J4   J. A. James and D. H. Richards, Anal. Chim. Acta. 15, 118 (1956).

J5   J. A. James and D. H. Richards, Nature 177, 1230 (1956).

J6   R. A. James, Phys. Rev. 93, 288 (1954).

J7   N. Jarmie, Phys. Rev. 98, 41 (1955).

J8   N. Jarmie and J. D. Seagraves, eds., USAEC Report No. LA-2014 (1957).

J9   E. N. Jenkins, Analyst 80, 301 (1955).

J10   E. N. Jenkins and A. A. Smales, Quart. Review (London) 10, 83 (1956).

J11   R. E. Jervis, Canadian Atomic Energy Report No. AECL-301 (1956).

J12   S. A. E. Johansson, Phys. Rev. 97, 1186 (1955).

J13   W. John, Jr., Phys. Rev. 103, 704 (1956).

J14   H. E. Johns, R. J. Horsley, R. N. H. Haslam, and A. Quinton, Phys. Rev. 84, 856 (1951).

K1   P. Kafalas and J. W. Irvine, Jr., Phys. Rev. 104, 703 (1956).

K2   A. Kant, J. P. Cali, and H. D. Thompson, Anal. Chem. 28, 1867 (1956).

K3   L. Kaplan and K. E. Wilzbach, Anal. Chem. 26, 1797 (1954).

K4   D. G. Karraker, USAEC Report No. UCRL-1202 (1951).

K5   L. Katz, R. G. Baker, and R. Montalbetti, Can. J. Phys. 31, 250 (1953).

K6   L. Katz and A. G. W. Cameron, Phys. Rev. 84, 1115 (1951).

K7   L. Katz and A. G. W. Cameron, Can. J. Phys. 29, 518 (1951).

K8   L. Katz, R. N. H. Haslam, J. Goldemberg, and J. G. V. Taylor, Can. J. Phys. 32, 580 (1954).

K9   L. Katz, R. N. H. Haslam, R. J. Horsley, and A. G. W. Cameron, Phys. Rev. 95, 464 (1954).

K10   L. Katz, H. E. Johns, R. G. Baker, R. N. H. Haslam, and R. A. Douglas, Phys. Rev. 82, 271 (1951).

K11   L. Katz, K. G. McNeill, M. LeBlanc, and F. Brown, Can. J. Phys. 35, 470 (1957).

K12   L. Katz, L. Pease, and H. Moody, Can. J. Phys. 30, 476 (1952).

K13   L. Katz and A. S. Penfold, Phys. Rev. 81, 815 (1951).

K14   E. L. Kelly and E. Segre, Phys. Rev. 75, 999 (1949).

K15   T. J. Kennette and H. G. Thode, J. Inorg. Nuclear Chem. 5, 253 (1958).

K16   B. H. Ketelle and G. E. Boyd, J. Amer. Chem. Soc. 69, 2800 (1947).

K17   R. D. Keynes and P. R. Lewis, Nature 165, 809 (1950).

K18   C. A. Kienberger, R. E. Greene, and F. S. Voss, USAEC Report No. K-1042 (1953).

K19   H. J. King and L. Katz, Can. J. Phys. 36, 415 (1958).

K20   A. W. Kirby, G. R. Grove, and D. L. Timma, Phys. Rev. 102, 1140 (1956).

K21   J. Kleinberg, ed., USAEC Report No. LA-1721 (Rev.) (1955).

K22   E. D. Klema and A. O. Hanson, Phys. Rev. 73, 106 (1948).

K23   U. B. Klimentov and V. M. Gryazev, Atomnaya Energiya 3, 507 (1957).

K24   R. C. Koch, Ph. D. Thesis, University of Chicago, (1955).

K25   A. Kohn, Rev. met. 48, 219 (1951).

K26   A. Kohn, Compt. rend. 236, 1419 (1953).

K27   H. W. Kohn and E. R. Tomkins, USAEC Report No. ORNL-390 (1949).

K28   M. E. Kohn-Abrest, Ann. fals. et fraudes 49, 407 (1956).

K29   R. S. Krishnan, Nature 148, 407 (1941).

K30   V. E. Krohn, Jr., and E. F. Shrader, Phys. Rev. 87, 685 (1952).

K31   I. Kumabe, E. Takekoshi, H. Ogata, Y. Tsuneoka, and S. Oki, J. Phys. Soc. Japan 13, 129 (1958).

L1   G. W. Leddicotte,   Nucleonics 14, No. 5, 46 (1956).

L2   G. W. Leddicotte,   Nucleonics 14, No. 5, 47 (1956).

L3   G. W. Leddicotte and H. A. Mahlman,   Proc. Intern. Conf. on the Peaceful Uses of Atomic Energy, U. N., New York, 1956, Vol. VIII, Paper 250.

L4   G. W. Leddicotte and S. A. Reynolds,   Nucleonics 8, No. 3, 62 (1951).

L5   G. W. Leddicotte and S. A. Reynolds,   USAEC Report No. CF-52-12-155 (1952).

L6   G. W. Leddicotte and S. A. Reynolds,   USAEC Report No. AECD-3489 (1953).

L7   G. W. Leddicotte and S. A. Reynolds,   ASTM Bull. No. 188, 29 (1953).

L8   G. W. Leddicotte and S. A. Reynolds,   USAEC Report No. ORNL-1623 (1954).

L9   G. W. Leddicotte and S. A. Reynolds,   USAEC Report No. CF-55-11-20 (1955).

L10   G. W. Leddicotte and S. A. Reynolds,   USAEC Report No. CF-56-7-106 (1956).

L11   P. Leveque,   Proc. Intern. Conf. on the Peaceful Uses of Atomic Energy, U. N., New York, 1956, Vol. XV, Paper 342.

L12   P. Leveque and H. Goenvec,   Bull. soc. chim. France, 1955, p. 1213.

L13   W. B. Lewis,   Nucleonics 12, No. 10, 30 (1954).

L14   M. Lindner and R. N. Osborne,   Phys. Rev. 91, 342 (1953).

L15   M. Lindner and R. N. Osborne,   Phys. Rev. 91, 1501 (1953).

L16   K. Lintner,   Acta. Phys. Aus. 3, 352 (1950).

L17   R. S. Livingston and A. L. Boch,   USAEC Report No. ORNL-1196 (1956).

L18   J. V. P. Long,   Brit. Atomic Energy Report No. CRL-AE-60 (1950).

L19   B. A. Loveridge and A. A. Smales,   "Methods of Biochemical Analysis", Interscience, New York, 1957, Vol. 5, p. 225.

M1   M. H. MacGregor,   Nucleonics 15, No. 11, 176 (1957).

M2   W. D. Mackintosh and R. E. Jervis,   Canadian Atomic Energy Report No. AECL-481 (1957).

M3   W. D. Mackintosh and R. E. Jervis,   Canadian Atomic Energy Report No. AECL-483 (1957).

M4   W. D. Mackintosh and R. E. Jervis,   Anal. Chem. 30, 1180 (1958).

M5   R. L. Macklin and H. E. Banta,   Phys. Rev. 97, 753 (1955).

M6   R. L. Macklin and J. H. Gibbons,   Phys. Rev. 109, 105 (1958).

M7   R. L. Macklin, N. H. Lazar, and W. S. Lyon,   Phys. Rev. 107, 504 (1957).

M8   R. L. Macklin and J. H. Lykins,   J. Chem. Phys. 19, 844 (1951).

M9   R. L. Macklin and H. S. Pomerance,   "Progress in Nuclear Energy: Series I", McGraw-Hill Book Co., New York, 1956, p. 179.

M10   H. A. Mahlman and G. W. Leddicotte,   Anal. Chem. 27, 823 (1955).

M11   J. B. Marion, R. M. Brugger, and R. A. Chapman,   Phys. Rev. 101, 247 (1956).

M12   H. C. Martin,   Phys. Rev. 93, 498 (1954).

M13   H. C. Martin and B. C. Diven,   Phys. Rev. 86, 565 (1952).

M14   H. C. Martin and R. E. Taschek,   Phys. Rev. 89, 1302 (1953).

M15   J. A. Martin, R. S. Livingston, R. L. Murray, and M. Rankin,   Nucleonics 13, No. 3, 28 (1955).

M16   S. May and P. Leveque,   UNESCO Intern. Conf. on Radioisotopes in Scientific Research, Paris, 1957, Paper 49.

M17   G. Mayr,   Nucleonics 12, No. 5, 58 (1954).

M18   G. Mayr, H. D. Brunner, and M. Brucer,   Nucleonics 11, No. 10, 21 (1953).

M19   J. J. G. McCue and W. M. Preston,   Phys. Rev. 84, 1150 (1951).

M20   W. R. McDonell and A. S. Newton,   Nucleonics 10, No. 1, 62 (1952).

M21   H. A. C. McKay,   Brit. Atomic Energy Research Establishment Report No. AERE-C/M-23 (1949).

M22   G. E. McMurtrie and D. P. Crawford,   Phys. Rev. 77, 840 (1950).

M23   P. McPherson, E. Pederson, and L. Katz,   Can. J. Phys. 32, 593 (1954).

M24   J. W. Meadows,   Phys. Rev. 91, 885 (1953).

M25   J. W. Meadows, Phys. Rev. 98, 744 (1955).

M26   J. W. Meadows, R. M. Diamond, and R. A. Sharp, Phys. Rev. 102, 190 (1956).

M27   J. W. Meadows and R. B. Holt, Phys. Rev. 83, 47 (1951).

M28   J. W. Meadows and R. B. Holt, Phys. Rev. 83, 1257 (1951).

M29   W. W. Meinke, USAEC Report No. UCRL-432 (1949).

M30   W. W. Meinke, Science 121, 177 (1955).

M31   W. W. Meinke, Anal. Chem. 28, 736 (1956).

M32   W. W. Meinke, Anal. Chem. 30, 686 (1958).

M33   W. W. Meinke and R. E. Anderson, Anal. Chem. 25, 778 (1953).

M34   W. W. Meinke and R. E. Anderson, Anal. Chem. 26, 907 (1954).

M35   W. W. Meinke and R. S. Maddock, Anal. Chem. 29, 1171 (1957).

M36   W. W. Meinke, G. C. Wick, and G. T. Seaborg, J. Inorg. Nuclear Chem. 3, 69 (1956).

M37   C. E. Mellish, J. A. Payne, and R. L. Otlet, UNESCO Intern. Conf. on Radioisotopes in Scientific Research, Paris, 1957, Paper 189.

M38   W. F. Merritt, P. J. Campion, and R. G. Hawkings, Can. J. Phys. 35, 16 (1957).

M39   F. Metzger, F. Adler, and P. Huber, Helv. Phys. Acta. 21, 278 (1948).

M40   R. Michon, Ann. fals. et fraudes 49, 284 (1956).

M41   G. W. C. Milner and A. A. Smales, Analyst 79, 425 (1954).

M42   J. A. Miskel and A. C. Wahl, Phys. Rev. 84, 700 (1951).

M43   A. Moljk, R. W. P. Drever, and S. C. Curran, Nucleonics 13, No. 2, 44 (1955).

M44   R. Montalbetti and L. Katz, Can. J. Phys. 31, 798 (1953).

M45   R. Montalbetti, L. Katz, and J. Goldemberg, Phys. Rev. 91, 659 (1953).

M46   D. F. C. Morris and F. M. Brewer, Geochim. et Cosmochim. Acta. 5, 134 (1954).

M47   G. H. Morrison, Applied Spectroscopy 10, No. 2, 71 (1956).

M48   G. H. Morrison and J. F. Cosgrove, Anal. Chem. 27, 810 (1955).

M49   G. H. Morrison and J. F. Cosgrove, Anal. Chem. 28, 320 (1956).

N1   H. Nabholz, P. Stoll, and H. Waffler, Phys. Rev. 86, 1043 (1952).

N2   R. Nathans and J. Halpern, Phys. Rev. 92, 940 (1953).

N3   R. Nathans and J. Halpern, Phys. Rev. 93, 437 (1954).

N4   R. Nathans and P. F. Yergin, Phys. Rev. 98, 1296 (1955).

N5   H. W. Newson, Phys. Rev. 48, 855 (1935).

N6   H. W. Newson, Phys. Rev. 51, 620 (1937).

O1   E. Odeblad, Acta. Radiol. 42, 391 (1954).

O2   E. Odeblad, Acta. Radiol. 45, 396 (1956).

O3   E. Odeblad and G. Nati, Acta. Radiol. 43, 249 (1955).

O4   E. Odeblad and S. Odeblad, Anal. Chim. Acta. 15, 114 (1956).

O5   E. Odeblad, B. Westin, and K. G. Malmfors, Acta. Radiol. 49, 137 (1958).

O6   S. Oleska, USAEC Report No. BNL-3341 (1955).

O7   L. Ornstein, R. Kropveld, and A. H. Wopstra, Physica 19, 915 (1953).

O8   R. G. Osmond and A. A. Smales, Anal. Chim. Acta. 10, 117 (1954).

P1   W. K. H. Panofsky and R. Phillips, Phys. Rev. 74, 1732 (1948).

P2   E. B. Paul and R. L. Clarke, Can. J. Phys. 31, 267 (1953).

P3   J. Pauly, Compt. rend. 238, 80 (1954).

P4   D. C. Peaslee, Phys. Rev. 74, 1001 (1948).

P5   A. S. Penfold and B. M. Spicer, Phys. Rev. 100, 1377 (1955).

P6   G. Phillips and F. W. Cornish, Brit. Atomic Energy Research Establishment Report No. AERE-C/R-1276 (1953).

P7   J. A. Phillips, J. Nuclear Energy 7, 215 (1958).

P8   E. Picciotto and M. van Styvandael,   Compt. rend. $\underline{232}$, 855 (1951).

P9   R. C. Plumb,   Nucleonics $\underline{14}$, No. 5, 48 (1956).

P10   R. C. Plumb and J. E. Lewis,   Nucleonics $\underline{13}$, No. 8, 42 (1955).

P11   R. C. Plumb and R. H. Silverman,   Nucleonics $\underline{12}$, No. 12, 29 (1954).

P12   J. J. Point,   UNESCO Intern. Conf. on Radioisotopes in Scientific Research, Paris, 1957, Paper 48.

P13   D. Popovic,   Nuovo cimento (9) $\underline{12}$, 143 (1954).

P14   K. G. Porges,   Phys. Rev. $\underline{101}$, 225 (1956).

P15   I. L. Preiss,   USAEC Report No. ORO-164 (1957).

P16   R. J. Prestwood,   Phys. Rev. $\underline{98}$, 47 (1955).

R1   T. C. Randle, J. M. Dickson, and J. M. Cassells,   Phil. Mag. $\underline{42}$, 665 (1951).

R2   G. W. Reed and A. L. Turkevich,   Nature (London) $\underline{176}$, 794 (1955).

R3   L. Reiffel and C. A. Stone,   J. Lab. Clin. Med. $\underline{49}$, 286 (1957).

R4   F. L. Ribe,   Phys. Rev. $\underline{103}$, 741 (1956).

R5   H. T. Richards and R. V. Smith,   Phys. Rev. $\underline{74}$, 1870 (1948).

R6   H. T. Richards, R. V. Smith, and C. P. Browne,   Phys. Rev. $\underline{80}$, 524 (1950).

R7   W. Riezler,   Z. Naturforsch. 4a, 545 (1949).

R8   S. O. Ring and L. M. Litz,   USAEC Report No. LRL-108 (1954).

R9   S. E. Ritsema,   USAEC Report No. UCRL-3266 (1956).

R10   C. J. Rodden,   Ann. Rev. Nuclear Sci. $\underline{1}$, 343 (1952).

R11   H. Rose,   J. Nuclear Energy $\underline{5}$, 4 (1957).

R12   A. H. Rosenfeld, R. A. Swanson, and S. D. Warshaw,   Phys. Rev. $\underline{103}$, 413 (1956).

R13   J. C. Roy, P. J. Berry, and L. P. Roy,   Can. J. Chem. $\underline{36}$, 731 (1958).

R14   L. P. Roy and J. C. Roy,   Can. J. Phys. $\underline{35}$, 1215 (1957).

R15   S. Rubin, T. O. Passell, and L. E. Bailey,   Anal. Chem. $\underline{29}$, 736 (1957).

R16   W. J. Rubinson,   J. Chem. Phys. $\underline{17}$, 542 (1949).

S1   R. Sagane,   Phys. Rev. $\underline{85}$, 926 (1952).

S2   R. Sagane, M. Eguchi, and J. Shigeta,   J. Phys. Math. Soc. Japan $\underline{16}$, 383 (1942).

S3   N. Saito,   Japan Analyst $\underline{4}$, 254 (1955).

S4   N. K. Sala and L. K. Rangan,   Indian J. Phys. $\underline{30}$, 80 (1956).

S5   L. Salmon,   Brit. Atomic Energy Research Establishment Report No. AERE-C/M-154 (1952).

S6   L. Salmon,   Brit. Atomic Energy Research Establishment Report No. AERE-C/R-1324 (1954).

S7   L. Salmon,   Brit. Atomic Energy Research Establishment Report No. AERE-C/M-323 (1957).

S8   D. C. Salter and L. Bird,   Phil. Mag. (7) $\underline{44}$, 1305 (1953).

S9   J. E. Sanders,   Atomics $\underline{5}$, 78 (1954).

S10   E. V. Sayre, A. Murrenhoff, and C. F. Weick,   USAEC Report No. BNL-508 (1958).

S11   U. Schindewolf,   Angew. Chem. $\underline{70}$, 181 (1958).

S12   K. Schmeiser and D. Jerchel,   Angew. Chem. $\underline{65}$, 490 (1953).

S13   K. Schmeiser and D. Jerchel,   Angew. Chem. $\underline{65}$, 366 (1955).

S14   R. B. Schwartz, J. W. Corbett, and W. W. Watson,   Phys. Rev. $\underline{101}$, 1370 (1956).

S15   M. B. Scott, A. O. Hanson, and D. W. Kerst,   Phys. Rev. $\underline{100}$, 209 (1955).

S16   G. T. Seaborg and J. J. Livingood,   J. Amer. Chem. Soc. $\underline{60}$, 1784 (1938).

S17   A. P. Seyfang,   Analyst $\underline{80}$, 74 (1955).

S18   A. P. Seyfang and A. A. Smales,   Analyst $\underline{78}$, 394 (1953).

S19   R. A. Sharp, R. M. Diamond, and G. Wilkinson,   Phys. Rev. $\underline{101}$, 1493 (1956).

S20   R. K. Sheline, R. B. Holtzman, and C. Y. Fan,   Phys. Rev. $\underline{83}$, 919 (1951).

S21   R. K. Sheline and N. R. Johnson,   Phys. Rev. $\underline{89}$, 520 (1953).

S22   R. Sher and J. J. Floyd,   Phys. Rev. $\underline{102}$, 242 (1956).

S23   R. Sher, J. Halpern, and A. K. Mann,   Phys. Rev. $\underline{84}$, 387 (1951).

S24   G. F. Shipman and O. I. Milner,   Anal. Chem. 30, 210 (1958).

S25   E. S. Shire, J. R. Wormold, G. Lindsay-Jones, A. Linder, and A. G. Stanley,   Phil. Mag. (7) 44, 1197 (1953).

S26   S. F. Singer,   U.S. Office of Naval Research Report No. ONRL-76-52 (1952).

S27   L. M. Slater,   USAEC Report No. UCRL-2441 (1954).

S28   A. A. Smales,   Analyst 77, 778 (1952).

S29   A. A. Smales,   Atomics 4, No. 3, 55 (1953).

S30   A. A. Smales,   J. Electronics 1, 327 (1955).

S31   A. A. Smales,   Geochim. et Cosmochim. Acta. 8, 300 (1955).

S32   A. A. Smales,   Proc. Intern. Conference on the Peaceful Uses of Atomic Energy, U.N., New York, 1956,
       Vol. IX, Paper 766.

S33   A. A. Smales,   Proc. Intern. Conference on the Peaceful Uses of Atomic Energy, U.N., New York, 1956,
       Vol. XV, Paper 770.

S34   A. A. Smales and L. O. Brown,   Brit. Atomic Energy Research Establishment Report No. AERE-E/R-439 (1949).

S35   A. A. Smales and B. A. Loveridge,   Anal. Chim. Acta. 13, 566 (1955).

S36   A. A. Smales and D. Mapper,   Brit. Atomic Energy Research Establishment Report No. AERE-C/R-607 (1950).

S37   A. A. Smales and D. Mapper,   Brit. Atomic Energy Research Establishment Report No. AERE-C/R-2392 (1950).

S38   A. A. Smales, D. Mapper, and H. J. Wood,   Analyst 82, 75 (1957).

S39   A. A. Smales, D. Mapper, H. J. Wood, and L. Salmon,   Brit. Atomic Energy Research Establishment
       Report No. AERE-C/R-2254 (1957).

S40   A. A. Smales and B. D. Pate,   Analyst 77, 188 (1952).

S41   A. A. Smales and B. D. Pate,   Analyst 77, 195 (1952).

S42   A. A. Smales and B. D. Pate,   Anal. Chem. 24, 717 (1952).

S43   A. A. Smales and L. Salmon,   Analyst 80, 37 (1955).

S44   A. A. Smales, J. van R. Smit, and H. Irving,   Analyst 82, 539 (1957).

S45   G. W. Smith and D. R. Farmelo,   Nucleonics 16, No. 2, 80 (1958).

S46   E. M. Sowden and S. R. Stitch,   Biochem. J. 67, 104 (1957).

S47   R. P. Spencer, T. G. Mitchell, and E. R. King,   J. Lab. Clin. Med. 50, 646 (1957).

S48   R. P. Spencer, T. G. Mitchell, and E. R. King,   Intern. J. Appl. Radiation Isotopes 3, 104 (1958).

S49   B. M. Spicer,   Phys. Rev. 100, 791 (1955).

S50   B. M. Spicer,   Australian J. Phys. 10, 326 (1957).

S51   B. M. Spicer and A. S. Penfold,   Phys. Rev. 100, 1375 (1955).

S52   G. H. Stafford and L. H. Stein,   Nature 172, 1103 (1953).

S53   J. R. Stehn and E. R. Clancy,   "Chart of the Nuclides" (Rev.), General Electric Co., Schenectady, 1956.

S54   W. E. Stephens and M. N. Lewis,   Phys. Rev. 69, 43 (1946).

S55   W. E. Stephens, J. Halpern, and R. Sher,   Phys. Rev. 82, 511 (1951).

S56   D. C. Stewart and W. C. Bentley,   Science 120, 50 (1954).

S57   D. Strominger, J. M. Hollander, and G. T. Seaborg,   Rev. Mod. Phys. 30, 585 (1958).

S58   P. Sue,   Bull. soc. chim. France D9, 1951.

S59   P. Sue,   Compt. rend. 237, 1696 (1953).

S60   P. Sue,   Compt. rend. 240, 88 (1955).

S61   P. Sue,   Compt. rend. 242, 770 (1956).

S62   P. Sue and P. Albert,   Compt. rend. 242, 2461 (1950).

S63   W. H Sullivan,   "Trilinear Chart of the Nuclides", U. S. Government Printing Office, Washington, 1957.

S64   R. G. Summers-Gill, R. N. H. Haslam, and L. Katz,   Can. J. Phys. 31, 70 (1953).

S65   K. H. Sun, F. A. Pecjak, R. A. Charpie, and J. F. Nechaj,   Phys. Rev. 82, 459 (1951).

S66   K. H. Sun, F. A. Pecjak, and J. F. Nechaj,   Phys. Rev. 78, 338 (1950).

S67   A. Szalay and E. Csongor,   Phys. Rev. 74, 1063 (1948).

S68   G. Szekely,   Anal. Chem. 26, 1500 (1954).

T1   J. Talbot, P. Albert, M. Caron, and G. Chaudron,   Rev. met. 50, 817 (1953).

T2   F. L. Talbott and N. P. Heydenburg,   Phys. Rev. 90, 186 (1953).

T3   H. E. Tatel and J. M. Cork,   Phys. Rev. 71, 159 (1947).

T4   H. L. Taylor, O. Lonsjo, and T. W. Bonner,   Phys. Rev. $\underline{100}$, 174 (1955).

T5   J. G. V. Taylor and R. N. H. Haslam,   Phys. Rev. $\underline{87}$, 1138 (1952).

T6   J. G. V. Taylor, L. B. Robinson, and R. N. H. Haslam,   Can. J. Phys. $\underline{32}$, 238 (1954).

T7   T. I. Taylor and W. W. Havens, Jr.,   Nucleonics $\underline{5}$, No. 6, 4 (1949).

T8   T. I. Taylor and W. W. Havens, Jr.,   Nucleonics $\underline{6}$, No. 2, 66 (1950).

T9   T. I. Taylor and W. W. Havens, Jr.,   Nucleonics $\underline{6}$, No. 4, 54 (1950).

T10 T. I. Taylor and W. W. Havens, Jr.,   in W. G. Berl, ed., <u>Physical Methods in Chemical Analysis</u>, Academic Press, New York, 1956, Vol. 3, p. 539.

T11 G. M. Temmer,   Phys. Rev. $\underline{76}$, 424 (1949).

T12 D. J. Tendam and H. L. Bradt,   Phys. Rev. $\underline{72}$, 1118 (1947).

T13 J. Terrell and D. M. Holm,   Phys. Rev. $\underline{109}$, 2031 (1958).

T14 H. A. Tewes,   Phys. Rev. $\underline{98}$, 25 (1955).

T15 H. A. Tewes and R. A. James,   Phys. Rev. $\underline{88}$, 860 (1952).

T16 B. A. Thompson, B. M. Strause, and M. B. LeBoeuf, Anal. Chem. $\underline{30}$, 1023 (1958).

T17 E. W. Titterton and T. A. Brinkley,   Proc. Phys. Soc. $\underline{66A}$, 579 (1953).

T18 C. A. Tobias and R. W. Dunn,   Science $\underline{109}$, 109 (1949).

T19 M. E. Toms and W. E. Stephens,   Phys. Rev. $\underline{82}$, 709 (1951).

T20 S. E. Turner,   Anal. Chem. $\underline{28}$, 1457 (1956).

V1   E. A. Vincent and A. A. Smales,   Geochim. et Cosmochim. Acta. $\underline{9}$, 154 (1956).

V2   M. von Ardenne and F. Bernhard,   Z. Physik $\underline{122}$, 740 (1944).

W1   A. C. Wahl,   J. Chem. Phys. $\underline{21}$, 182 (1953).

W2   D. Walker, W. T. Link, and W. I. B. Smith,   Proc. Phys. Soc. (London) $\underline{A65}$, 861 (1952).

W3   R. L. Walker,   Phys. Rev. $\underline{76}$, 244 (1949).

W4   H. Wanke and E. U. Monse,   Z. Naturforsch. $\underline{10a}$, 667 (1955).

W5   H. J. Watters and J. F. Fagan, Jr.,   Phys. Rev. $\underline{92}$, 1248 (1953).

W6   K. Way, ed.,   "Nuclear Data Cards", National Research Council, (1955 ff).

W7   V. F. Weisskopf and D. H. Ewing,   Phys. Rev. $\underline{57}$, 472 (1940).

W8   E. A. Whalin and A. O. Hanson,   Phys. Rev. $\underline{89}$, 324 (1953).

W9   A. F. Wickersham, Jr.,   Phys. Rev. $\underline{107}$, 1050 (1957).

W10 J. W. G. Wignall,   Australian J. Phys. $\underline{8}$, 310 (1955).

W11 D. H. Wilkinson,   Phys. Rev. $\underline{100}$, 32 (1955).

W12 C. F. Williamson, E. L. Hudspeth, I. L. Morgan, and R. G. Moore,   Phys. Rev. $\underline{110}$, 139 (1958).

W13 F. P. W. Winteringham,   Analyst $\underline{75}$, 627 (1950).

W14 O. Wolczek,   Postepy Fiz. $\underline{5}$, 89 (1954).

W15 R. L. Wolfgang and G. Friedlander,   Phys. Rev. $\underline{96}$, 190 (1954).

W16 R. L. Wolfgang and W. F. Libby,   Phys. Rev. $\underline{85}$, 437 (1952).

Y1   S. Yasumi,   J. Phys. Soc. Japan $\underline{12}$, 493 (1957).

Y2   P. F. Yergin and B. P. Fabricand,   Phys. Rev. $\underline{104}$, 1334 (1956).

ADDENDUM TO THE BIBLIOGRAPHY

A22   B. S. Aidarkin, G. V. Gorshkov, A. G. Grammakov, V. S. Zhadin, and A. G. Kolchina, Trudy. Radievogo Inst. im V. G. Khlopina 5, 89 (1957).

A23   D. H. F. Atkins and A. A. Smales, "Activation Analysis", in H. J. Emeleus and G. Sharpe, eds., Advances in Inorganic Chemistry and Radiochemistry, Academic Press, New York, 1959, Vol. I, p. 350.

B54   T. E. Banks, R. Tupper, E. M. A. White, and A. Wormall, Intern. J. Appl. Radiation Isotopes 4, 221 (1959).

B55   G. L. Bate, J. R. Huizenga, and H. A. Potratz, Geochim. et Cosmochim. Acta. 16, 88 (1959).

B56   L. C. Bate and G. W. Leddicotte, USAEC Report No. TID-7568, Part III, 1958, p. 43.

B57   D. B. Beard, R. G. Johnson, and W. G. Bradshaw, Nucleonics 17, No. 7, 90 (1959).

B58   A. A. Benson, Second Intern. Conf. on the Peaceful Uses of Atomic Energy, Geneva, 1958, Paper A/Conf. 15/P/858.

B59   W. W. Beyer, J. N. Lewis, and G. L. Stukenbroeker, USAEC Report No. TID-7568, Part III, 1958, p. 158.

B60   R. L. Blanchard, G. W. Leddicotte, and D. W. Moeller, Second Intern. Conf. on the Peaceful Uses of Atomic Energy, Geneva, 1958, Paper A/Conf. 15/P/790.

B61   R. Booth, W. P. Ball, and M. H. MacGregor, Phys. Rev. 112, 226 (1958).

B62   D. C. Borg, Second Intern. Conf. on the Peaceful Uses of Atomic Energy, Geneva, 1958, Paper A/Conf. 15/P/841.

B63   H. J. M. Bowen, Intern. J. Appl. Radiation Isotopes 4, 214 (1959).

B64   H. J. M. Bowen, Intern. J. Appl. Radiation Isotopes 5, 227 (1959).

B65   J. E. S. Bradley and O. Bradley, Mineral. Mag. 31, 165 (1956).

B66   W. A. Brooksbank, Jr., and G. W. Leddicotte, Anal. Chem. 30, 1785 (1958).

B67   G. M. Brownell, K. Bramadat, R. A. Knutson, and A. C. Turnock, Trans. Roy. Soc. Canada, Series III, Section 4, 19 (1957).

C39   R. F. Coleman, B. E. Hawker, L. P. O'Connor, and J. L. Perkin, Proc. Phys. Soc. (London) 73, 215 (1959).

C40   R. F. Coleman and J. L. Perkin, Analyst 84, 233 (1959).

C41   J. F. Cosgrove, R. P. Bastian, and G. H. Morrison, Anal. Chem. 30, 1872 (1958).

D16   R. Druyan, T. G. Mitchell, E. R. King, and R. P. Spencer, Radiology 71, 856 (1958).

E12   R. L. Ely, H. G. Richter, and J. A. Roll, private communication.

F17   I. Fineman, K. Ljunggren, H. G. Forsberg, and L. G. Erwall, Intern. J. Appl. Radiation Isotopes 5, 280 (1959).

F18   J. Fouarge, Ind. chim. belge 24, 143 (1959).

G28   J. Gaittet and P. Albert, Compt. rend. 247, 1861 (1958).

G29   D. Gibbons, Intern. J. Appl. Radiation Isotopes 4, 45 (1958).

G30   R. A. Gill, Brit. Atomic Energy Research Establishment Report No. AERE-C/R-2758 (1958).

H53   K. L. Hall and W. W. Meinke, J. Inorg. Nuclear Chem. 9, 193 (1959).

H54   R. J. Howerston, USAEC Report No. UCRL-5226, Part 1, Vol. I-III (1958).

J15   R. E. Jervis and W. D. Mackintosh, Second Intern. Conf. on the Peaceful Uses of Atomic Energy, Geneva, 1958, Paper A/Conf. 15/P/189.

K32   B. D. Kern, W. E. Thompson, and J. M. Ferguson,   Nuclear Phys. $\underline{10}$, 226 (1959).

K33   J. D. Knight, R. K. Smith, and B. Warren,   Phys. Rev. $\underline{112}$, 259 (1958).

K34   V. K. Kristyanov and G. I. Panov,   Zhur. Anal. Khim. $\underline{12}$, 362 (1957).

K35   Y. Kusaka,   Bull. Chem. Soc. Japan $\underline{31}$, 917 (1958).

L20   A. A. Lbov and I. I. Naumova,   Atomnaya Energ. $\underline{6}$, 468 (1959).

L21   G. W. Leddicotte, W. T. Mullins, L. C. Bate, J. F. Emery, R. E. Druchsel, and W. A. Brooksbank, Jr.,
Second Intern. Conf. on the Peaceful Uses of Atomic Energy, Geneva, 1958, Paper A/Conf. 15/P/927.

L22   G. Leliart, J. Hoste, and J. Eeckhaut,   Anal. Chim. Acta. $\underline{19}$, 100 (1958).

L23   J. M. A. Lenihan and H. Smith,   Second Intern. Conf. on the Peaceful Uses of Atomic Energy, Geneva, 1958,
Paper A/Conf. 15/P/69.

L24   B. Lindner and R. A. James,   Phys. Rev. $\underline{114}$, 322 (1959).

L25   W. S. Lyon and R. L. Macklin,   Phys. Rev. $\underline{114}$, 1619 (1959).

M50   R. L. Macklin,   Second Intern. Conf. on the Peaceful Uses of Atomic Energy, Geneva, 1958, Paper A/Conf. 15/P/671.

M51   M. Mazari, L. Velazquez, and F. Alba,   Rev. mex. ffs. $\underline{8}$, 1 (1959).

M52   W. W. Meinke,   Anal. Chem. $\underline{31}$, 792 (1959).

M53   E. Merz and W. Herr,   Second Intern. Conf. on the Peaceful Uses of Atomic Energy, Geneva, 1958,
Paper A/Conf. 15/P/984.

M54   C. E. Miller,   USAEC Report No. ORNL-2715 (1959).

M55   D. F. C. Morris and R. A. Killick,   Anal. Chim. Acta. $\underline{20}$, 587 (1959).

M56   J. H. Muller,   UNESCO Intern. Conf. on Radioisotopes in Scientific Research, Paris, 1957, Paper 205.

P17   A. S. Penfold and E. L. Garwin,   Phys. Rev. $\underline{114}$, 1139 (1959).

P18   K. H. Purser and E. W. Titterton,   Australian National University Report No. ANU/P-200 (1958).

R17   W. J. Ramler, J. Wing, D. J. Henderson, and J. R. Huizenga,   Phys. Rev. $\underline{114}$, 154 (1959).

R18   J. Rapaport and J. J. van Loef,   Phys. Rev. $\underline{114}$, 565 (1959).

R19   G. W. Reed,   "Activation Analysis Applied to Geochemical Problems", in P. H. Abelson, ed., Researches in
Geochemistry, John Wiley and Sons, New York, 1959.

R20   G. W. Reed, H. Hamaguchi, and A. Turkevich,   Geochim. et Cosmochim. Acta. $\underline{13}$, 248 (1958).

R21   G. W. Reed, K. Kigoshi, and A. Turkevich,   Second Intern. Conf. on the Peaceful Uses of Atomic Energy,
Geneva, 1958, Paper A/Conf. 15/P/953.

R22   R. Ricamo,   Nuovo cimenti $\underline{8}$, 383 (1951).

S69   L. Salmon,   Brit. Atomic Energy Research Establishment Report No. AERE-C/R-2377, Part I (1959).

S70   R. S. Scaland and R. W. Fink,   Nuclear Phys. $\underline{9}$, 334 (1958).

S71   A. A. Smales, D. Mapper, J. W. Morgan, R. K. Webster, and A. J. Wood,   Second Intern. Conf. on the Peaceful
Uses of Atomic Energy, Geneva, 1958, Paper A/Conf. 15/P/282.

S72   A. A. Smales, D. Mapper, and A. J. Wood,   Geochim. et Cosmochim. Acta. $\underline{13}$, 81 (1958).

S73   H. Smith,   Anal. Chem. $\underline{31}$, 1361 (1959).

S74   R. S. Stoenner and J. Zahringer,   Geochim. et Cosmochim. Acta. $\underline{15}$, 40 (1958).

W17   L. R. Wager, J. van R. Smit, and H. Irving,   Geochim. et Cosmochim. Acta. $\underline{13}$, 81 (1958).

W18   T. Westermark and I. Fineman,   Second Intern. Conf. on the Peaceful Uses of Atomic Energy, Geneva, 1958,
Paper A/Conf. 15/P/140.

W19   A. B. Whitehead and J. S. Foster,   Can. J. Phys. $\underline{76}$, 1276 (1958).

W20   J. W. Winchester, L. C. Bate, and G. W. Leddicotte,   USAEC Report No. CF-59-7-127 (1959).

W21   J. W. Winchester, R. E. Meyer, L. C. Bate, and G. W. Leddicotte,   USAEC Report No. CF-59-7-128 (1959).

W22   J. W. Winchester,   "Radioactivation Analysis in Inorganic Geochemistry", in F. A. Cotton, ed., Progress in Inorganic Chemistry, Vol. 2, Interscience Publishers, Inc., New York (in press).

W23   J. W. Winchester,   private communication (1959).

INDEX

A

Absolute assay technique, 4
Abundance, isotopic, 2
Accelerator,
    charged particle, 2, 11
    electron linear, 11
    linear, 2–3
Actinium, 186
Activation, definition of, 195
    foil, 14
Activation analysis,
    application of, 2, 3
    assay techniques for, 4
    charged particle, 3
    choice of technique for, 3, 5
    comparison with spectro-
        photometry, 2
    competing reactions in, 10
    definition of, 1
    discovery of, 2
    error in, 14–15
    experimental methods, 11–15
    feasibility of, 10
    general techniques, 3–7
    history, 2–3
    interfering reactions in,
        9–10
    ion exchange use in, 2
    low-level neutron sources
        for, 2
    product formation in, 5
    proton scattering for, 3
    requirements for, 8
    reviews on, 2–3
    sample treatment in, 3
    selection of reactions for,
        8–10
    sensitivity of, 8, 14
    sources of experimental
        methods for, 7–8
    theory of, 5–10
Activation gradient, 9, 12
Activation product, definition
    of, 195
    suitability of, 8
Aluminum,
    activation analysis of, 2
    antimony in, 124
    bismuth in, 184
    carbon in, 37
    chromium in, 70
    cobalt in, 76
    copper in, 80
    holmium in, 154
    iron in, 74

    lanthanum in, 136
    manganese in, 72
    mercury in, 178
    nickel in, 78
    nuclear data and methods,
        48–49
    oxygen in, 41
    palladium in, 114
    phosphorus in, 52
    praseodymium in, 140
    samarium in, 144
    sample container, 13
    scandium in, 64
    selenium in, 90
    silicon in, 50–51
    sodium in, 44–45
    tellurium in, 126
    thorium in, 188
    titanium in, 66
    uranium in, 190
    yttrium in, 100
    zinc in, 82
    zirconium in, 102
Analysis, nondestructive, 196
Antimony, nuclear data and
    methods, 124–125
Archeology, activation analy-
    sis use in, 2
Argon, nuclear data and
    methods, 58–59
Arsenic, nuclear data and
    methods, 88–89
Assay,
    absolute, 13–14
    comparative, 4
    post-irradiation, 14
    radiometric, 4
    reliability of, 4
Astatine, 186
Atomic numbers, 21
Automation, 1

B

Barium, nuclear data and
    methods, 134–135
Beam(s),
    contamination of, 9
    current, 6
    degradation of, 13
    dimensions of, 13
    energy of, 6
    external cyclotron, 13
    linear accelerator, 13
Beryllium,
    carbon in, 37

    nuclear data and methods,
        32–33
    oxygen in, 40–41
Beta emitters, data for, 7
Beta radiation, definition of,
    195
Betatrons, 11
Bibliography, 199–212
Biochemistry, radioactive
    techniques in, 2
Biological material,
    arsenic in, 88
    barium in, 134
    boron in, 34
    gallium in, 84
    gold in, 176
    manganese in, 72
    molybdenum in, 106
    strontium in, 98
Biological systems, activa-
    tion analysis of, 2
Bismuth, nuclear data and
    methods, 184–185
Blood,
    bromine in, 92
    calcium in, 62
    copper in, 80
    iodine in, 128
    magnesium in, 46
    potassium in, 60
    sodium in, 44
Bone,
    barium in, 134
    strontium in, 98
Boron, nuclear data and
    methods, 34–35
Bremsstrahlung, 12
    definition of, 195
Bromine, nuclear data and
    methods, 92–93

C

Cadmium, nuclear data and
    methods, 118–119
Calcium, nuclear data and
    methods, 62–63
Capsule, irradiation, 8, 13
    cooling of, 4
Carbon, nuclear data and
    methods, 36–37
Carrier, definition of, 195
Cerium, nuclear data and
    methods, 138–139
Cesium, nuclear data and
    methods, 132–133

Charcoal, homogeneity, deter-
      mination, 3
Charged particle(s),
   activation analysis, 3, 4
   definition of, 195
   induced reaction, theory
      of, 6
   irradiations, 13
   reaction, data for, 7
   sources of, 11-12
Chlorine, nuclear data and
      methods, 56-57
Chromium, nuclear data and
      methods, 70-71
Cobalt, nuclear data and
      methods, 76-77
Comparator assay technique, 4
Comparator sample, 13-14
Concentration, chemical, 13
Constituents, see Element
Contaminant,
   reagent, 15
   surface, 15
Copper, nuclear data and
      methods, 80-81
Counting,
   beta, 4
   gamma, 4
Cross-section,
   data, 7
   definition of, 195
Cyclotron, 11, 12
   target preparation, 13

D

Data, evaluation of, 14-15
Decay rate, 5
Decay schemes, data, 7
Decontamination, radio-
      chemical, 15
Definitions, 195-196
Deuterium, analysis of, 12
Deuteron,
   definition, 195
   as reactant, 5
Disintegration rate, 5
   absolute, 4
   minimum detectable, 6
   standard, 17
Dosimeters, 14
Dysprosium,
   in yttrium, 2
   nuclear data and methods,
      152

E

Electron capture, definition
      of, 195
Electrophorograms, phos-
      phorus determination in,
      52
Element(s),
   atomic numbers of, 21
   matrix, 1, 4, 6, 8-9, 14, 195,
      198
   trace, 1, 4, 5-6, 8, 14, 17, 196
Encapsulation, sample, 12-14
Energy degradation, 6
Erbium,
   lutecium in, 160
   nuclear data and methods,
      154
   thulium in, 156
   ytterbium in, 158
Error, sources of, 4, 14-15
Europium,
   in gadolinium, 2
   nuclear data and methods,
      146
Excitation function, definition
      of, 195

F

Film, silver determination
      in exposed, 2, 116
Fluorine, nuclear data and
      methods, 42-43
Flux,
   gradient, 15
   intensity, 10
   perturbation, 195
Francium, 186

G

Gadolinium,
   europium in, 2
   nuclear data and methods,
      148-149
Gallium,
   in iron, 2
   nuclear data and methods,
      84-85
Gamma radiation, definition
      of, 195
Gamma spectrometry, 4, 7, 14
Geochemistry, activation analy-
      sis in, 2

Germanium,
   antimony in, 124
   arsenic in, 88
   bismuth in, 184
   copper in, 80
   iron in, 74
   nickel in, 78
   nuclear data and methods,
      86-87
   sodium in, 44
   tin in, 122
   zinc in, 82
Glass,
   fluorine in, 43
   sodium in, 45
Glossary, 195-196
Gold, 13
   nuclear data and methods,
      176-177
Graphite, vanadium in, 68

H

Hafnium, nuclear data and
      methods, 162
Half-lifes, data, 7
Helium, nuclear data and
      methods, 28-29
Holmium, nuclear data and
      methods, 154
Holmium oxide, dysprosium
      in, 152
Hydrogen, nuclear data and
      methods, 28-29

I

Indium, nuclear data and
      methods, 120-121
Iodine, nuclear data and
      methods, 128-129
   phosphorus in, 52
Iridium, nuclear data and
      methods, 172
Iron,
   activation analysis of, 2
   arsenic in, 88
   bismuth in, 184
   cobalt in, 76
   copper in, 80
   gallium in, 2
   holmium in, 154
   manganese in, 72
   mercury in, 178
   nickel in, 78
   nuclear data and methods,
      74-75

Iron (continued)
palladium in, 114
phosphorus in, 52
praseodymium in, 140
samarium in, 144
scandium in, 64
selenium in, 90
tellurium in, 126
yttrium in, 100
Irradiation, 14
charged particle, 13
cost of, 3
facilities, 3, 11-12
intensity of, 4
length of, 4
limiting factors for, 14
neutron, 12-13
optimum conditions, 4, 14
photon, 13-14
Isomer, definition, 195
Isomeric transition, definition
of, 195
Isotope, definition of, 195

K

Krypton, nuclear data, 94

L

Lanthanum,
cerium in, 138
nuclear data and methods,
136-137
Lead, nuclear data and
methods, 182-183
Linear accelerator, 11-12
Lithium,
nuclear data and methods,
30-31
sodium in, 44
Lutecium, nuclear data and
methods, 160-161

M

Magnesium,
arsenic in, 88
calcium in, 62
chromium in, 70
copper in, 80
iron in, 74
nuclear data and methods,
46-47
phosphorus in, 52

potassium in, 60
strontium in, 98
sulfur in, 54
Manganese, nuclear data and
methods, 72-73
Matrix element, see Element
Mercury, nuclear data and
methods, 178
Metallurgy, radioactivity
techniques in, 2
Metals,
antimony in, 124
cesium in, 132
chromium in, 70
cobalt in, 76
impurity determination
in, 3
strontium in, 98
Meteorites,
age determination of, 58, 60
bismuth in, 184
cesium in, 132
gallium in, 84
gold in, 176
lead in, 182
palladium in, 114
thallium in, 180
thorium in, 188
Methods,
assay, 4
irradiation, 11-12
Minerals,
cesium in, 132
dating by activation analysis, 2
indium in, 120
lithium in, 30
potassium in, 60
thorium in, 188
Molybdenum, nuclear data and
methods, 106-107
Monitors,
beam, 4
flux, 4
Monitor sample, 13-14
Monitoring, methods of, 14

N

Naphthas, bromine in, 92
Neodymium, nuclear data and
methods, 142-143
Neon, nuclear data and
methods, 42-43
Neptunium, nuclear data, 192

Neutron(s),
activation analysis
methods, 3-4. 24
definition of various,
195-196
fast, 9, 195
irradiation, sample preparation for, 12
monoenergetic, 6
as reactant, 5, 17
reactor spectrum, 16
resonance, 195
review papaers on, 1-2
sources of, 11
spectroscopy, 2
thermal activation, 7
Nickel, nuclear data and
methods, 78-79
Niobium,
nuclear data and methods,
104-105
tantalum in, 164
Nitrogen, nuclear data and
methods, 38-39
Nuclear data, sources of, 7
Nuclear emulsions, 2
Nuclear particle, definition of,
196
Nuclear reactions, examples
of, 196-197
Nuclides,
data sources for, 7
definition of, 196
radioactive, data for, 7
target, 196

O

Ores,
beryllium in, 33
selenium in, 90
Osmium, nuclear data and
methods, 170
Oxide films, oxygen in, 41
Oxygen, nuclear data and
methods, 40-41

P

Palladium, nuclear data and
methods, 114-115
Paper chromatograms,
bromine in, 92
chlorine in, 56-57

Particle,
    alpha, 5-6, 195
    charged, 6, 16
    nuclear, 196
    size, determination of, 3
Petroleum,
    copper in, 80
    nickel in, 78
Phosphorus,
    in silicon, 9-10
    nuclear data and methods,
        52-53
Photon(s), 6
    activation method, 3
    definition of, 196
    irradiation, 13
    as reactant, 5
    reactions, analysis
        methods, 25
    sources of, 11-12
Plants, barium in, 134
Plastics, fluorine in,
    42-43
Platinum, nuclear data and
    methods, 174-175
Plutonium, nuclear data,
    192-193
Polonium, 186
Potassium, nuclear data and
    methods, 60-61
Potassium iodide, thallium in,
    180
Potassium minerals, age de-
    termination, 58
Praseodymium, nuclear data
    and methods, 140-141
Preparation,
    chemical, 13
    physical, 12-13
    sample, 12-13
Procedure,
    analytical, 14
    radiochemical, 14
Promethium, nuclear data, 142
Protactinium, nuclear data,
    188
Proton,
    definition of, 196
    as reactant, 5
Purification, 4

Q

Quality control, 1
Quartz, sample container, 13

R

Radiation,
    beta, 195
    gamma, 195
Radium, nuclear data, 186
Radon, 186
Reaction(s),
    charged particle, 18-19
    competing, 196
    definition of various, 196
    interfering, 9-10, 196
    neutron, 250
    nuclear, 196-197
    photon, 18
    primary, 9, 196
    second order, 9, 14, 196
    secondary, 9-10, 14, 196
Reactor, 11
Reactor technology, activation
    analysis in, 2
Resonance,
    integral, definition of, 196
    parameters, 7
Rhenium, nuclear data and
    methods, 168
Rhodium, nuclear data and
    methods, 112-113
Rubidium, nuclear data and
    methods, 96-97
Ruthenium, nuclear data and
    methods, 110-111

S

Samarium, nuclear data and
    methods, 144
Sample(s),
    comparator, 13-14
    contamination in, 15
    definition of, 196
    liquid, 12-13
    preparation of, 12-14
    size of, 13
    treatment of, 3-4
Scandium, nuclear data and
    methods, 64-65
Selenium, nuclear data and
    methods, 90-91
Self-shielding,
    definition of, 196
    effects, 9
Sensitivity,
    calculation of, 6
    definition of, 196
    estimates of, 8

requirements, 14
    standard analytical, 17
Separation, chemical, 14
Silicate rocks,
    aluminum in, 48
    silicon in, 50
Silicates, niobium in, 105
Silicon,
    aluminum in, 48
    antimony in, 124
    arsenic in, 88
    bismuth in, 184
    calcium in, 62
    chromium in, 70
    cobalt in, 76
    copper in, 80
    gallium in, 84
    gold in, 176
    indium in, 120
    iron in, 74
    magnesium in, 46
    manganese in, 72
    mercury in, 178
    molybdenum in, 106
    nickel in, 78
    nuclear data and methods,
        50-51
    phosphorus in, 9-10, 52
    platinum in, 174
    potassium in, 60
    scandium in, 64
    sodium in, 44
    tantalum in, 164
    thallium in, 180
    tin in, 122
    tungsten in, 166
    vanadium in, 68
    zinc in, 82
    zirconium in, 102
Silver, nuclear data and
    methods, 116-117
Sodium,
    nuclear data and methods,
        44-45
    use in deuterium analysis,
        12
Sodium-potassium alloys,
    cesium in, 132
    rubidium in, 96
Soils, barium in, 134
Steel,
    carbon in, 37
    vanadium in, 68
Strontium, 17
    nuclear data and methods,
        98-99

218

Sulfur, nuclear data and
    methods, 54–55
Surfaces,
    analysis, 3
    etching of, 13

T

Tables, key to, 16–19
Tantalum, nuclear data and
    methods, 164–165
Target nuclide, definition of,
    196
Technetium, nuclear data and
    methods, 108
Technique, see Methods
Tellurium, nuclear data and
    methods, 126–127
Terbium, nuclear data and
    methods, 150
Thallium, nuclear data and
    methods, 180–181
Thermal conductivity, 13
Thorium, nuclear data and
    methods, 188–189
Threshold, 24
Thulium, nuclear data and
    methods, 156–157
Tin, nuclear data and
    methods, 122–123
Titanium,
    chlorine in, 56
    copper in, 80

manganese in, 72
nickel in, 78
nuclear data and methods,
    66–67
tungsten in, 166
vanadium in, 68
Trace elements,
    analysis schemes for, 14
    definition of, 196
Transistor, 1
Treatment, pre-irradiation,
    12–13
Triton,
    definition of, 196
    as reactant, 5
Tungsten,
    arsenic in, 88
    copper in, 80
    iron in, 74
    molybdenum in, 106
    nuclear data and methods,
        166

U

Uranium, nuclear data and
    methods, 190–191
Urine, sodium in, 45

V

Vanadium, nuclear data and
    methods, 68–69

W

Water,
    argon in, 58
    arsenic in, 88
    cesium in, 132
    gold in, 176
    magnesium in, 46
    rubidium in, 96
    silicon in, 50
    uranium in, 190

X

Xenon, nuclear data, 130

Y

Ytterbium, nuclear data and
    methods, 158
Yttrium,
    dysprosium in, 2
    nuclear data and methods,
        100–101

Z

Zinc, nuclear data and
    methods, 82–83
Zirconium,
    hafnium in, 1, 162
    nuclear data and methods,
        102–103
    silicon in, 50
Zirconium oxide, antimony in,
    124